REVIEWS IN ENGINEERING GEOLOGY
VOLUME V

GEOLOGY UNDER CITIES

Edited by
ROBERT F. LEGGET

The Geological Society of America
Boulder, Colorado 80301
1982

© 1982 by The Geological Society of America, Inc.
All rights reserved.

Published by the Geological Society of America, Inc.
3300 Penrose Place, P. O. Box 9140, Boulder, Colorado 80301
Printed in U.S.A.

Library of Congress Cataloging in Publication Data
Main entry under title:

Geology under cities.

    (Reviews in engineering geology ; v. 5)
    Includes bibliographies.
    1. Urban geology—Addresses, essays, lectures.
I. Legget, Robert Ferguson. II. Geological Society of
America. III. Series.
TA705.R4 vol. 5 [QE39.5.U7] 624.1′51s [557.3] 82-20991
ISBN 0-8137-4105-X

Contents

Foreword

Digby J. McLaren; President, The Geological Society of America

The Geological Society of America held its annual meeting for 1978 in Toronto, Canada, jointly with the Geological Association of Canada. One of the several symposia featured at that meeting was organized by the Engineering Geology Division of the Society, dealing with *Geology under Cities*. The opening paper dealt, appropriately, with the geology beneath the streets of Toronto. Since I was then the Director-General of the Geological Survey of Canada, the host country, it seemed appropriate to those responsible for the symposium that, in this capacity, I should say a few words by way of introduction. This I was pleased to do. The symposium was well received.

This volume contains revised and enlarged versions of seven of the papers presented at that Toronto meeting, together with two additional papers to give even better coverage of the major cities of North America. I now find myself in the position of President of the Society. The Editor has asked if, again, I would contribute a Foreword. I am glad to do so, since this is, in some ways, a unique volume, containing the first general treatment of its subject yet published by the Society.

Neglect of the geology that lies beneath the roads and streets of our cities is, as the Editor points out in his introduction, a strange gap in the steady development of the science during the last one hundred years. The ground is there, and details of its geology are obtainable (through excavations and other operations of man)—in many cases more easily than in open country. And yet it has been left, in general, for geotechnical engineers to realize the full significance of urban geology, as it may so rightly be called. Today, as this volume shows so well, there is an awakening appreciation of what collaboration between geologists and engineers can achieve in this field.

There were, naturally, individual exceptions to this broad statement about neglect. Let me mention just one—a message from a former member of the staff of the Geological Survey of Canada, Dr. H. M. Ami, a man of broad and varied interests, basically a paleontologist. He presented a paper to the Royal Society of Canada at its meeting in May 1900 on "The Geology of the Principal Cities in Eastern Canada" and had this to say by way of introduction:

What the drill has to penetrate in any one of our larger centres of activity in Canada, before reaching the old Archaean or original crust of the Earth in this portion of the North American continent covered by the areas under discussion, is a question not only of interest but also of economic value.[1]

Urban geology in Canada might have advanced far if these words had been heeded at the time.

The other side of the coin is well shown by the story of how Hans Cloos solved the riddle of the Rhine Graben by observations that he made in April 1929 during the construction of a short tunnel through the Lorettoberg in the city of Freiburg. This is related in his notable volume *Conversation with the Earth*.[2] The dual contributions possible from study of urban geology, the scientific and the practical, are well illustrated in this volume.

There is much to be done, therefore, in tapping the geological potential that the study of urban geology presents. If all the cities of North America, and the major towns as well, had as good a record of their underground as have the cities considered in the papers that follow, the science of geology would be enhanced and the practice of engineering geology greatly assisted. I hope, therefore, that this volume will act as a catalyst in awakening renewed interest in this neglected branch of applied geology, to the advantage of geotechnique but more particularly for the benefit of the science of geology.

---

[1]Ami, H. M., "On the Geology of the Princial Cities in Eastern Canada," *Proceedings and Transactions of the Royal Society of Canada*, Second Series, Volume VI, p. 125–173, Ottawa, 1900.

[2]Cloos, H., *Conversations with the Earth* (trans. E. B. Garside), London: Routledge & Kegan Paul Ltd., 1954.

Introduction

"Nature to be commanded" is not only the first part of a justly famous aphorism of Francis Bacon (1526–1626), the pointed ending being "must be obeyed," but it has been adopted as the title of one of the most remarkable of all the publications of the U.S. Geological Survey. If anyone should pick up this volume and wonder why the Geological Society of America is concerned with the geology that underlies cities, one glance at USGS Professional Paper No. 950 (G. D. Robinson and A. M. Spieker, editors) will set all such doubts at rest. Large in page size (so that it cannot be "tucked away" in a filing cabinet), the paper is vividly illustrated in brilliant colors. Through examples chosen from six very different areas, it shows clearly how geology controls all the development work of man. The title is well chosen since, if nature is to be controlled, as it must be in the orderly development of towns and cities, it must be obeyed in a manner that an accurate knowledge of the local geology alone makes possible.

This message from Francis Bacon is known and appreciated by the members of the Engineering Geology Division of the Society. Officers of the Division, in keeping with this imperative, decided to highlight the importance of geology under cities at the Society's annual meeting in Toronto in 1978. As Dr. McLaren has kindly indicated in his Foreword, the symposium on this subject was well received; this volume is one result. It is a pleasure to record appreciation to all the authors of the papers which follow, two of them specially prepared to supplement revised and enlarged versions of seven of the papers presented orally at Toronto. Their ready cooperation and all the work that their papers represent are appreciated. The assistance of the necessarily anonymous reviewers, whose suggestions were so generally adopted to the benefit of all the papers in this volume, was also valued.

A paper on the unusual geology under Mexico City was to be included, if only to balance the Canadian contributions from the north, but this did not prove possible. It is a matter of real regret that, despite the wide coverage given by the nine papers, no city on the west coast is included. This is not due to any anti-western bias on the part of the Engineering Geology Division, but to the fact that two western papers that were to be included were not available due to circumstances far beyond any editorial influence. Fortunately, some other excellent publications admirably fill this gap. As examples, let me mention the 119-page USGS Bulletin by D. E. Trimble on the geology of Portland, Oregon, and the surrounding district[1]; the well-known USGS maps showing the engineering geology of the Oakland and San Francisco areas[2]; and the comprehensive 1966 report on *Engineering Geology in Southern California,* edited by Lung and Proctor, and still a valuable reference[3].

Selection of the eight cities featured in the oral presentations at the Toronto meeting was not an easy task. This volume may therefore be regarded as an introduction only to a vast subject. Fortunately, the Association of Engineering Geologists has adopted a definite policy of encouraging the preparation of papers similar to those in this volume for publication as a regular feature in its Bulletin. Gradually, therefore, a corpus of information will be developed regarding the geology underlying a number of North American cities, each one unique in some respect so that comparative study will ultimately be of special value.

What has just been said might give the impression that this attention to *urban geology* (as the subject may so rightly be called) is something entirely new. A mere glance at some of the references accompanying the papers that follow will show that this is not the case at all. Dr. McLaren quotes from a paper published in Canada on this subject in 1900. Almost thirty years before that (in 1872), a well-known English Anglican priest, the Reverend Charles Kingsley, gave a series of lectures to young men on the subject of *Town Geology* under the auspices of the Chester Natural History Society, publishing them, with the same title, in 1873[4]. It was Kingsley who, in these lectures, described geology as "the people's science"—which it really is!

One brief quotation from this book of a century ago, even though in the rolling Victorian prose of the time, warrants inclusion, since it is so relevant to the subject matter of this book:

It does seem to me strange, to use the mildest word, that people whose destiny it is to live, even for a few short years, on this planet which we call the earth, and who do not at all intend to live on it as hermits. . . should in general be so careless about the constitution of the same planet, and of the laws and facts in which depend, not merely their comfort and their wealth, but their health and their very lives, and the health and the lives of their children and descendants.

Even before Kingsley's time, a few individuals had developed similar interests. In 1862, for example, Professor Eduard Suess published in Vienna a 300-page treatment of the geology, as it was then known, under his famous city. Just after Kingsley, Angelo Heilprin of the Academy of Natural Sciences of Philadelphia published in 1885 a well-illustrated volume on the *Rocks of Philadelphia*. There were probably other pioneers in this field in the nineteenth century. It is to be noted, however, that these were all individual activities, the work of men of vision who had seen the need for attention to the geology beneath their own cities—and this before the start of the major underground facilities that today are an essential part of all modern cities. It was not until the turn into the twentieth century that any corporate activity in relation to urban geology appears to have been undertaken.

An early (1905) Bulletin of the U.S. Geological Survey delineated *The Configuration of the Rock Floor of Greater New York,* an activity later followed up by municipal engineers of New York. The first paper in the first volume of the *Journal of the Boston Society of Civil Engineers* (1914) dealt with *Boston Foundations* and marked the start of the remarkable cooperative work in that city between engineers and geologists which is so well synthesized in the paper on Boston in this volume. In 1937, an interesting record of foundations in New Orleans was published, a WPA project. In Canada, a committee of the Engineering Institute in Winnipeg published, also in 1937, a useful review of foundation conditions in that prairie city—a pioneer venture that is now being actively developed by Professor Baracos of the University of Manitoba.

It was not until after the Second World War that activity in this field could be resumed with what results the papers which follow well demonstrate. Before introducing these, however, it must be observed that there are still all too many cities and towns that have no geologic records available. What is even more remarkable is that almost no municipal governments have yet undertaken the assembly of records of their geology as a civic responsibility. Almost

all cases known to me represent the work of interested individuals or voluntary groups of geologists and engineers, in addition to some notable examples carried out by either federal or state geological surveys.

This is difficult to understand, since records of urban geology would be of direct benefit and of invaluable assistance in the carrying out of civic public works. Correspondingly, the works carried out by municipalities include, as but one example, most of the tunnels beneath cities (for water and sewer purposes), works that yield unique geologic information that is thus directly available to the city at no cost. But before indicating what can be done in this direction, attention may be directed to the records that this volume contains.

The order in which to present the papers seemed, at first, an invidious editorial problem since, quite naturally, the papers differ from one another so markedly. Authors were given wide latitude as to treatment of their subjects and the length of their papers. It is now interesting to see how the lengths of the papers reflect, in general and with no editorial input whatever, the relative complexity of the geology underlying each city. Some papers start with engineering problems and then show how geology affects them. Others start with descriptions of the local geology and then proceed to show how this affects engineering works. In every case, however, the papers make vividly clear the benefit to the science of geology of the information revealed by the carrying out of engineering works within cities, when this is acutely observed and correlated with existing information. A prime objective of this volume is to direct attention to and illustrate the potential of this largely untapped wealth of information on urban geology, to the permanent benefit of the science.

Against this background, how then should the papers be arranged? The problem solved itself when once it was realized that the geology underlying the nation's capital city should have pride of place. When the other eight cities were arranged in alphabetical order, taking no account of the U.S.–Canadian border, it was found that an orderly and logical sequence was automatically provided, with the right paper at the end.

Washington D.C., therefore, comes first, the geology beneath which has recently been a matter of wide public interest in view of the construction of the new subway. The geology is complex, but it has had the benefit of many years of study by members of the staff of the US Geological Survey, notably by N. H. Darton, for over fifty years; the authors are members of the Survey staff.

Boston, Massachusetts, occupies a special place in any review of urban geology, since it now has available published records of test borings within the city going back well over 65 years. The paper presents a summary of the author's work in the Boston area for many years, being another contribution from the US Geological Survey; attention may be directed to another summary by the author—Bulletin No. 1476 of the Survey entitled *The Geology and Early History of the Boston Area of Massachusetts, a Bicentennial Approach,* published (appropriately) in 1976.

Chicago, Illinois, is now using its deep underground in a manner unequalled in any other city known to me; fortunately, construction of the deep drainage tunnels is assisted by the favorable local geology which has been studied for many years by members of the staff of the Illinois Geological Survey.

Edmonton, Alberta, is another city distinguished by cooperation between geologists and geotechnical engineers, now for many years past. Its geology is not as complex as that under some of the other cities featured, but underground construction work in the central city area has often been complicated by the presence of old coal workings of the early settlers. An admirable *Atlas* of these workings is a unique feature of local geological records.

Kansas City, Missouri, has won worldwide recognition in recent years for the use now being made of mined-out space in its underground for a variety of purposes (notably for cold-storage plants). It is not surprising, therefore, to find this featured at the outset of the fifth paper, the favorable and relatively straightforward local geology explaining how this has been possible. There are problems in the use of any underground space, and one problem in Kansas City is due to the properties of a local shale having involved research work of wide significance.

New Orleans, Louisiana, presents a unique geological picture insofar as its location at the mouth of the Mississippi River has given the city not only recent soils as the main foundation beds, but also a water table close to the surface. The combination of these features is at once geologically interesting but also challenging to foundation designers and constructors. The authors make this clear in their wide-ranging review of an underground condition shared by very few cities of the world.

New York, New York, has probably had more engineering works carried out in its underground than most other cities. Fortunately, the geology thus revealed has usually been recorded, and this has enabled the author (a resident of New York until, recently, he joined the US Geological Survey) to prepare a detailed and wide-ranging picture of the complex geology beneath the city—so very different from the popular idea of uniform Manhattan schist everywhere close to the surface.

Toronto, Ontario, in contrast, has a relatively simple geological structure beneath its streets,—glacial deposits overlying almost horizontal Ordovician shale. In recent years, this has been extensively studied because underground construction, especially in the downtown area, has proliferated. This has enabled the author (with the Ontario Geological Survey) to prepare his concise description, just such a summary account as I hoped to find (but did not)

when the first section of Toronto's subway system was started well over thirty years ago.

Twin Cities, Minnesota. The brevity of this final paper is deceptive since it describes, accurately but succinctly, what is believed to be the most extensive and significant study of urban geology yet carried out in North America, and this for the large area covered by the twin cities of Saint Paul and Minneapolis. It is unfortunate that publishing restrictions make it impossible to illustrate, even by a small specimen, the fine colored maps prepared with computer aid by utilizing some of the subsurface information for the area previously "locked up" in carefully filed records of test borings. As the best alternative, procurement of a set of the maps described is strongly commended, not only for their intrinsic interest, but also so that they may be used, as occasion permits, to demonstrate what every city and large town can and should do.

The prime objective of the papers now assembled in this volume is to start to fill the very serious gap that exists in the literature of North American geology by describing the geology under some of the major cities of the continent. It is strange indeed that, despite such early individual efforts as have already been briefly mentioned, there has been so little attention given in North America to the geology beneath city streets—almost as if it did not exist! The volume is a modest start at correcting this situation.

The task of preparing such accounts of urban geology is becoming, on the one hand, increasingly difficult with each succeeding year and yet, on the other hand, there is a steadily increasing volume of relevant information waiting to be tapped, if the interest to do this can only be aroused. Information on the geology under cities can be obtained by an initial study of the regional geology, supplemented by examination of such outcrops within municipal boundaries as still remain in view. The number of these is decreasing as development proceeds.

On the other hand, as development does proceed, new structures are being built, and these usually involve excavation. Every new hole that is dug or tunnel that is bored yields—for a very short time only—new exposures of the geological structures that have to be penetrated. The engineering records of such exposures will always be available somewhere when construction is complete; they can be made the more valuable, and the science can be enriched, if they are prepared with geological assistance. Records will also exist, in ever increasing number, for every town and city, of the test borings now almost mandatory at every urban building site prior to the completion of designs.

All nine papers in this volume illustrate, incidental to their main purpose, the use of such records available from engineering works. They demonstrate in this way the complete interdependence of geology and geotechnical engineering if knowledge of the geology beneath city streets is to be expanded, on the one hand, and if subsurface engineering work is to be safely and economically conducted, on the other.

The situation is so obvious, once thought is given to it, that such a statement as the foregoing would be almost a banality if it were not that the situation is, in general, so little recognized. It is the hope of all concerned with this volume that it may assist in correcting this widespread neglect, to the benefit of the science of geology and the practice of civil engineering.

To this end, may it be suggested, with all due respect, that: (1) In every city or town some arrangement should exist for the examination by geologists of every new exposure, in excavations or in tunnels, a task ideally suited to the geological departments of local universities; (2) all geotechnical engineers should be aware of the geological significance of their work, especially within towns and cities, both in preliminary site studies and in recording exposures in tunnels and excavations, and should do what they can to see that local geologists are aware of it; and (3) both geologists and engineers who appreciate the importance of urban geology should do all they can to ensure that their own municipality accepts responsibility for developing and maintaining the necessary information bank, as a vital local service that could easily be self-supporting.

It remains for me only to ask how an editor is expected to deal with the final paragraph in the introduction to the last paper in the volume, a far-too-generous statement that the author firmly but graciously insists be left in. Attention must be called to it, if only to indicate that the editor knows that it is there, and so that he may record his indebtedness to Dr. Walton for the encouragement given by such a statement in a field in which we both share so close and lively an interest. More than this, however, is the hope that will be shared by authors and editor alike—that this volume will itself prove to be of far more effect in encouraging active interest in the *Geology under Cities* than the writings of any one individual can ever be.

Ottawa Canada   Robert F. Legget
May 1982

REFERENCES:

1. Trimble, D. E., "Geology of Portland, Oregon, and adjacent areas," U.S. Geological Survey Bulletin, no. 1119, 1963.
2. Schlocker, J., Bonilla, M. G., and Radbruch, D. H., "Geology of the San Francisco North Quadrangle, California," Map I-272, U.S. Geological Survey, 1958; and Radbruch, D. H., "Areal and Engineering Geology of the Dakland West Quadrangle," Map I-239, U.S. Geological Survey, 1957.
3. Lung, R., and Proctor, R., eds., "Engineering Geology in Southern California," Association of Engineering Geologists, Glendale, California, 1966.
4. Kingsley, Charles, "Town Geology," London: Daldy, Isbister & Company, 1877.

Geological Society of America
Reviews in Engineering Geology, Volume V
1982

The geology beneath Washington, D.C.—The foundations of a nation's capital

John C. Reed, Jr.
U.S. Geological Survey
Denver Federal Center
Denver, Colorado 80225

Stephen F. Obermeier
U.S. Geological Survey
Reston, Virginia 22092

ABSTRACT

Washington, D.C., is the first and largest planned city in the United States. The city lies along the Fall Line at the boundary between the Atlantic Coastal Plain and the Piedmont Plateau and at the head of navigation on the estuary of the Potomac River. This site combines the engineering complexities of two vastly different geologic terranes with the other complications introduced by the terraces and channels of a major river-estuary system.

The western part of the city and most of the suburbs to the west and north are on the Piedmont Plateau, an upland underlain by complexly deformed metasedimentary and metaigneous rocks of late Precambrian or early Paleozoic age. These crystalline rocks are mantled by soil, saprolite, and weathered rock to depths of as much as 50 m, which adds both to their geologic inscrutability and to the problems of excavation and design of structures.

The Atlantic Coastal Plain is underlain by unmetamorphosed and little deformed fluvial and marine strata of Cretaceous through Miocene age. These deposits form a prism that thickens southeastward from a wedge edge at the Fall Line to as much as 450 m in the southeastern part of the metropolitan area. Unconformities, facies changes, and variations in physical properties with age and depth of burial add spice to the life of the engineering geologist dealing with these strata.

Terrace deposits ranging in age from Miocene(?) to Holocene bevel across the contact between the Coastal Plain deposits and the crystalline rocks of the Piedmont. The oldest deposits underlie a broad, deeply dissected upland that stands at an elevation of 80 to 90 m southeast of the Fall Line; isolated outliers cap hills and interfluves at elevations of as much as 150 m northwest of the Fall Line. Lower and younger terraces flank the major drainages and occur at various levels down to the modern flood plains. Much of the central city is built on low terraces of Sangamon or Wisconsin age. These younger terraces locally fill and conceal deep bedrock channels cut by the ancestral Potomac during low stands of sea level during the Pleistocene. The terrace deposits show conspicuous differences in degree of weathering and soil development, depending on their age and physiographic position. Estuarine and marsh deposits flank the tidal reaches of the Potomac and Anacostia Rivers, and considerable parts of the central city are built on artificial fill over these deposits.

Considerable experience in underground excavation has been gained in the last decade during construction of METRO, a regional rapid transit rail system. Tunneling techniques have been developed for both crystalline rocks and Coastal Plain deposits, but cut and cover methods are generally used in the young materials, which are generally weakest. Foundation and slope stability problems are widespread in some geologic units in the metropolitan area and are locally serious. They affect structures ranging from single family dwellings to the Washington Monument.

INTRODUCTION

The locations of all great cities are controlled directly, or indirectly, by local geology. Generally, it is impossible to point to a single set of decisions that determines the location of a city and to isolate the geologic factors that influence those decisions. However, for Washington, the geologic influences are relatively easy to analyze, because that city is the first and largest so-called planned community in the United States. Its general location was selected by Congress (in 1790), its site was established by Presidential proclamation (by George Washington, March 30, 1791), its boundaries were surveyed under the direction of a Presidential commission (by Andrew Ellicott), and its plan was prepared by a government contractor (Charles Pierre L'Enfant). In spite of these inauspicious beginnings, it has survived to become one of the great cities of the world.

The general location of the capital was chosen by Congress on the basis of convenience of access to all parts of the country, as well as on political grounds.[1] It directed (1 Stat. L. 130):

"That a district of territory, not exceeding ten miles square, to be located as hereafter direct on the river Potomac, at some place between the mouths of the Eastern Branch [the present Anacostia River] and Connogochegue [Conococheague Creek] be, and the same is hereby selected accepted as the permanent seat of government of the United States"

but left the selection of the final site to the President.

Although George Washington left no record of his thinking in the selection of the site for the federal district, it seems likely that one major consideration was to include as much of the tidewater parts of the Potomac and Anacostia Rivers as possible; there is no evidence that he ever seriously considered a site above tidewater. A second consideration of importance to Washington as an ex-surveyor was to have the boundaries run in principal compass directions. These criteria are best fulfilled by placing one boundary at Little Falls (the head of tidewater on the Potomac) and orienting the square with its diagonals, rather than its sides, running north-south and east-west. Thus, the original federal district was established as a 16 kilometer (10 mile)

square, with its sides oriented northeast-southwest and northwest-southeast, and its southern tip at Jones Point on the west bank of the Potomac. The Virginia part of this original square was retroceded to the State in 1846, and it now comprises Arlington County and part of the City of Alexandria; the remainder is the present District of Columbia.

The rapids at Little Falls, which so strongly influenced the decision on the boundaries of the federal district, mark the place where the Potomac River crosses the Fall Line, the boundary between the Piedmont Plateau to the northwest and the Atlantic Coastal Plain to the southeast. It is this line that marks the head of navigation for ocean-going vessels on all the major rivers on the eastern seaboard south of the Hudson. Because the easiest crossings of the major rivers are in the vicinity of the Fall Line, the first major highways and many of the principal cities of the Atlantic seaboard were established along it. Considerations of accessibility and defense practically preordained a Fall Line site for the national capital, because such a choice combined easy access to both land and sea, and it was at the head of a long, navigable, but easily defended estuary.[2]

The central part of the site finally selected consisted of a large natural amphitheatre, flanked by step-like terraces (Carr, 1950) and floored by a terrace remnant, cradled between the Potomac on the southwest and the Anacostia (Eastern Branch) on the east, and surrounded, as L'Enfant noted in his diary, by ". . . a saucer-shaped rim of hills, well suited for defense" (Bryan, 1914).

The position of the Fall Line, the length and configuration of the protected estuary, the terrace remnants, and even the encircling gravel-capped hills are all the results of a long and complicated geologic history. Just as geology helped influence the choice of the site of the national capital, it has influenced the growth and development of the city for 180 years. During early stages of development, the proximity of building materials played an important role in determination of architectural styles and building types (Withington, 1967; U.S. Geological Survey, 1975). Stone was quarried locally from crystalline rocks and strongly

---

[1] A detailed account of the deliberations on choice of a location for the national capital is contained in Bryan (1914).

[2] This reasoning was sound as far as it went, but was proven inadequate by the British, who marched overland from Annapolis to capture the city during the War of 1812.

cemented sedimentary rocks in the Coastal Plain sequence. Bricks were made from clay taken from Coastal Plain sediments, which also yielded bountiful supplies of sand and gravel.

Development in lowland areas along the Potomac and Anacostia Rivers and their tributaries has been restricted because flooding is an ever-present hazard. Highly destructive floods are rare, and parts of the floodplains are submerged so infrequently that they invite development, and subsequent disaster.

Today, the need for detailed knowledge of the geology and geologic history has become greater than ever in planning for the future—for the need of the three and a half million people who will live in the metropolitan area by the year 2000. To serve a part of that need, this paper focuses on the geologic setting of the Washington metropolitan area and a discussion on how the geologic setting relates to present-day engineering problems.

PHYSIOGRAPHIC AND GEOLOGIC SETTING

The Fall Line site guaranteed that the city of Washington would have a diverse and complex geologic underpinning, combining, as it does, the stratigraphic and structural complexities of two vastly different geologic terranes with surficial complications introduced by the terraces and channels of a major river-estuary system. The Fall Line is nearly coincident with the physiographic boundary between the rolling, hilly topography of the Piedmont Plateau and the lower, flatter, but still deeply dissected topography of the Atlantic Coastal Plain. The Fall Line is also a major geologic boundary (Figure 1). The Piedmont is underlain by a complicated terrane of metasedimentary and metaigneous rocks of Proterozoic and early Paleozoic ages. These rocks were variously metamorphosed and deformed during the early and middle Paleozoic. The Atlantic Coastal Plain is underlain by unmetamorphosed and nearly undeformed Cretaceous and Tertiary fluvial and marine strata that rest unconformably on the crystalline rocks of the Piedmont. These sedimentary deposits form a southeastward thickening wedge that attains a thickness of more than 450 m in the southeastern part of the metropolitan area. Both the Coastal Plain deposits and the crystalline rocks of the Piedmont are overlapped by fluvial deposits of Miocene(?) and post-Miocene age. These deposits record a complicated history of downcutting, infilling, and adjustment of the Potomac River and its tributaries since deposition of the youngest marine beds in the Coastal Plain sequence in Miocene time. The oldest and highest fluvial deposits underlie the dissected remnants of a plateau whose upper surface slopes southeastward from altitudes of more than 150 m on ridges near the Fall Line to altitudes of about 60 m in Maryland east of the Anacostia River, where fluvial deposits cap the conspicuous flat interfluves. Below

the level of this old surface, younger fluvial deposits cap a series of lower terraces. The upper terraces tend to be broad remnants that are only generally related to the present drainage. Materials on these upper terraces are conspicuously weathered, soil profiles are mature, and the terrace deposits rest on considerable thicknesses (commonly 10 m or more) of saprolite, evidently developed since deposition. The younger terraces are mostly of Pleistocene age and, thus, are more closely related to the present drainage. The effects of weathering and soil development are less pronounced, and the underlying bedrock is fresh or only slightly weathered.

Most of the larger streams in the Coastal Plain are flanked by broad floodplains underlain by alluvial materials. The flats bordering the tidewater reaches of the Potomac and Anacostia Rivers, however, are underlain by estuarine deposits accumulated during the post-glacial sea level rise. These deposits also conceal earlier river channels, some of great depth. The shorelines of both the Potomac and Anacostia have been considerably altered in post-colonial times by extensive filling and reclamation of tidal marshes. Most of the Mall west of the Washington Monument, all of East Potomac Park and Hains Point, and much of National Airport are on land reclaimed from tidal marshes (Figure 2).

CRYSTALLINE ROCKS

General Description

The crystalline rocks in the metropolitan area are part of one of the most complex and poorly understood metamorphic terranes on the continent. They consist of several sequences of indurated, flysch-like sedimentary rocks that contain sheets and pods of ultramafic rocks and pods, dikes, and plutons of intermediate and felsic rocks of various types. The metasedimentary rocks include phyllite, pelitic schist, and rhythmically-bedded metagraywacke, but the most common rock in the subsurface in most of the inner city is medium- to coarse-grained, massive to well-foliated gneiss having a superficially granitic aspect. The gneiss contains pebbles, cobbles, boulders, and slabs of a wide variety of rocks, including schist, metagraywacke, mafic and ultramafic rocks, granite, felsic volcanic rocks, and vein quartz. The sedimentary origin of this rock, previously mapped as granite, granite gneiss or migmatite, was first recognized by Cloos and Cooke (1953) and later confirmed by Coulter and Carroll (1964) and Hopson (1964). The gneiss has been referred to as boulder gneiss (Southwick and Fisher, 1967), diamictite (Higgins and Fisher, 1971; Fleming, 1978), melange (Drake and Morgan, 1980), and Sykesville Formation (Cloos and Cooke, 1953; Drake

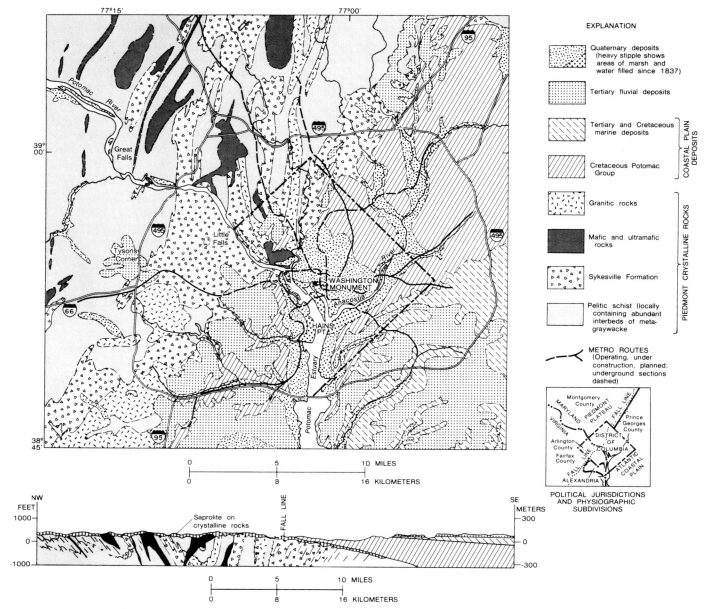

Figure 1. Generalized geologic map of the Washington area. Compiled from Darton and Keith (1901), Darton (1947), Cloos and Cooke (1953), Froelich (1975d), Hack (1977), Froelich and Hack (1975), Johnston (1964), and Drake and others (1979). Line of section is approximately from northwestern to southeastern corner of map. General structure of the crystalline rocks in the section is sketched diagrammatically without vertical exaggeration. Thickness and attitude of younger deposits are shown in the sections with vertical exaggeration indicated.

and others, 1979; Crowley, 1976). We follow this latter usage.

The mafic and ultramafic rocks include greenstone and greenschist, amphibolite, and metagabbro, as well as serpentinite and talc schist derived from peridotite and pyroxenite. Some of the bodies are clearly intrusive, but many are elongate pods and slabs that are probably huge, exotic melange blocks (Drake and Morgan, 1980).

The intermediate and felsic igneous rocks range from tonalite to granite. The largest bodies include the Kensington pluton in Maryland and the central District of Columbia, the Georgetown complex in the southwestern District of Columbia, and the Occoquan batholith in Virginia. The rocks in all of these larger bodies are foliated and show evidence of shearing and metamorphism, but igneous textures and structures are locally preserved.

Figure 2. View northeast across the Potomac River and downtown Washington. F, artificial fill; T_1, T_2, T_3, T_4, Pleistocene fluvial terraces; C, Cretaceous deposits; R, crystalline rocks. The long projection of artificial fill east of the Washington Monument marks the former course of Tiber Creek. The R at the extreme left marks the approximate site of Braddock Rock, the first outcrop of crystalline rock on the northern bank of the Potomac and the place where British troops under General Braddock landed in 1755 on their way to Fort Duquesne. They were accompanied by Col. George Washington (Carr, 1950). Photograph by Air Photographics, Inc., August, 1968, from files of the U.S. Geological Survey.

The metamorphic grade of the pelitic rocks increases southeastward from chlorite-sericite in the northwest part of the area of Figure 1 to kyanite or staurolite and locally to sillimanite near Great Falls. The rocks to the east are generally of garnet grade, but staurolite grade rocks are found locally in the District of Columbia (Fleming, 1978). The western border of the large mass of Sykesville west of Little Falls is a zone of intense shearing and retrograde metamorphism that marks a major structural discontinuity (Drake and Morgan, 1980). In this zone and in many local zones elsewhere, the medium- and high-grade rocks have been retrograded to chlorite-sericite phyllonites, and the older structures have been obliterated or reoriented by shearing. Pods and veins of quartz are common in the Piedmont rocks. Some are 15 m or more thick and can be traced for more than a kilometer (Reed and Reed, 1969). Some quartz veins clearly follow post-metamorphic shear zones, but quartz bodies of several ages may be present.

The age of the Piedmont rocks in the Washington area has been a matter of debate (and sometimes heated dispute) for at least two generations. Recent work suggests that most of the rocks are of very late Proterozoic or early Paleozoic age. The latest interpretation (Drake and Morgan, 1981) suggests that they comprise several detached sheets that originally lay some distance to the southeast and that were emplaced in their present position partly by large-scale slumping or sliding and partly as rigid or semi-rigid thrust sheets. The formation of the sedimentary gneiss of the Sykesville Formation was apparently related to one or more such episodes of detachment and massive slumping during the advance of one of these sheets. Isotopic dates from near Great Falls (Reed, Marvin, and Mangum, 1970; Muth, Arth, and Reed, 1979) suggest that the climax of deformation and regional metamorphism of the Piedmont rocks in that area was slightly before 470 million years ago (Middle Ordovician), but that shearing and retrogressive metamorphism (possibly associated with emplacement of the thrust sheets) may have continued until about 360 million years ago (Late Devonian).

Physical Properties and Structure

Measurements by Meuser and others (1969, 1972) show that the unconfined compressive strengths of most of the fresh, massive, crystalline rocks such as the Sykesville Formation are medium to high (500 to 1,800 kgf/cm²). Unaltered mafic rocks and vein quartz may have strengths approaching 2,000 kgf/cm², whereas, more foliated pelitic schists generally are in the range of 250 to 1,000 kgf/cm². Intensely sheared and altered ultramafic rocks and altered rocks along shear zones have strengths less than 250 kgf/cm²; a few are as low as 35 kgf/cm², and clay seams in shear zones are as weak as 5 kgf/cm²

Structural inhomogeneities are more critical than the compressive strength of the rock itself for most engineering purposes. The structural elements of principal concern include schistosity (foliation), joints, and shear zones. In addition, mechanical inhomogeneities due to the presence of large cobbles and boulders of diverse rock types juxtaposed in the gneiss of the Sykesville Formation pose special problems. Because of the complex depositional, structural, and metamorphic history, no simple sketch of the structural pattern of the Piedmont terrane is adequate for more than the most general planning purposes. It is essential that detailed investigations of the type described by Cording and Mahar (1974) and Bock (1974) be carried out in connection with the design and construction of any major structure involving excavation in the crystalline rocks. Most of the rocks in the Piedmont have undergone multiple deformations that have produced superimposed structures of several generations (Figure 3), and, because of limited natural exposures, detailed structural studies (Reed and Jolly, 1963; Fisher, 1970) have been confined to a few areas, chiefly along the Potomac River.

The general north or northeast trend of the outcrop belts of the major lithologic units (Figure 1) is parallel or subparallel to axes of major late-stage folds having amplitudes of hundreds or thousands of meters. The strike of the principal schistosity is also generally parallel to the trend of the outcrop belts. Although many outcrops show several interpenetrating foliations, the principal schistosity is commonly approximately parallel to the axial planes of the major folds that control the outcrop patterns. The dip of the principal schistosity is locally consistent but is regionally highly variable. Near the Fall Line, dips are generally 40° to 80° west or northwest (Figure 1). They steepen gradually to near vertical 5-10 km west of the Fall Line, and in the northwestern part of the area they are 30° to 70° southeast. In the micaceous rocks in the northwestern part of the area, parting surfaces parallel to schistosity are spaced only a few millimeters apart and are more or less continuous for many meters, forming easily opened planes of separation. In the higher grade metamorphic rocks to the southeast, especially in more massive rocks such as the gneiss of the Sykesville Formation, the parting surfaces are spaced a centimeter or more apart and are continuous for only a few centimeters, so that they form less significant mechanical discontinuities. Bedding is rarely discernible in the gneiss of the Sykesville Formation and is only locally conspicuous in the pelitic schist units, generally in areas where the schist is interlayered with metagraywacke, as along the Potomac River near Great Falls.

The most conspicuous lineations in the Piedmont rocks in the northwestern part of the area of Figure 1 are axes of minor folds, bedding-cleavage intersections, and mineral streaking, all of which tend to lie parallel to the major late stage fold axes and to have gentle to moderate

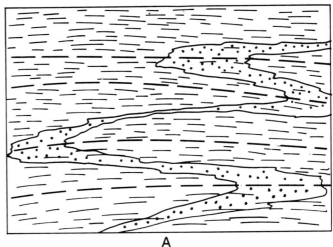

A

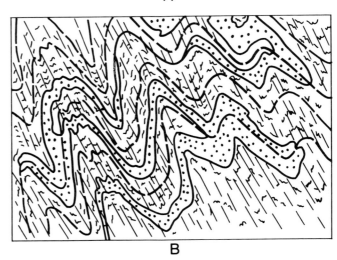

B

Figure 3. Idealized sketches showing superposition of two generations of folds with styles typical of the crystalline rocks of the Washington area. Diagrams can be read either as maps or cross-sections and have long dimensions ranging from a few centimeters to several kilometers. Drawings based on exposures near Great Falls described by Reed and Jolly (1963) and Reed, Sigafoos, and Fisher (1980). A. Early tight folds deform layers of approximately uniform original thickness. Fold limbs are nearly parallel to axial planes (indicated by heavy dashed lines). Schistosity produced by growth of metamorphic minerals, chiefly micas, has formed parallel to fold axial planes. The original layer has been thinned on the fold limbs by shearing and flowage of material into the fold noses. B. More open folds of a second generation deform early tight folds. Schistosity parallel to axial planes of second generation folds has overprinted and largely obliterated the earlier schistosity. Folds of the general style of the second-generation folds control much of the map pattern of the metasedimentary rocks in Figure 1, and schistosity related to them is the principal regional schistosity in most of the Piedmont rocks in the area.

northeast or southwest plunges (Cloos and Cooke, 1953; Cloos, 1964). In the southeastern part of the area, where schistosity dips west or northwest, the most conspicuous lineations are marked by aligned mineral grains and aggregates and elongated pebbles and cobbles that generally plunge moderately to steeply northwest, down the dip of the schistosity.

All of the crystalline rocks are jointed, and the orientation, spacing, tightness, and fillings of joints are critically important, because joints are the most common cause of zones of weakness in otherwise sound rock. In spite of their importance in design and construction of surface and underground structures, there has been no systematic study of the regional distribution and character of joints in the crystalline rocks of the metropolitan area. Cloos (1964) listed several common joint orientations in the crystalline rocks of Montgomery County: (1) perpendicular to fold axes, (2) perpendicular to mineral lineations other than fold axes, (3) parallel to foliation, schistosity, or bedding, and (4) diagonal to linear or planar structures. Fan-shaped joint arrays and sheared zones containing weak materials occur in the hinge areas of folds in bedded rocks.

Most joints in unweathered rock are tight, even at shallow depth, and walls are in contact at many small asperities and undulations. Most are unmineralized, but some are filled with quartz, calcite, or chlorite. Some are slickensided, but there is no indication of significant residual stress, at least at depths less than 100 m.

Cording and Mahar (1974) reported that three or four major sets of joints are common, one set parallel to schistosity, one set striking parallel to schistosity but dipping in the opposite direction, and one or two sets striking at high angles to schistosity. In addition to those they list, sheeting joints parallel to the ground surface are common, especially in massive rocks. Because several sets of joints are generally present in a given area, they facilitate breakage of most rocks into complex polyhedral blocks less than a meter to several meters in diameter.

Although the orientations of schistosity, fold axes, and mineral lineations shown on geologic maps provide some clues as to the expected orientations of major joint sets, only a few generalizations can be drawn as to the spacing and character of the joints. Typically, joints are more widely spaced and more continuous in massive rocks (intrusive rocks and gneiss of the Sykesville Formation). In the massive rocks, especially in the Sykesville, the best developed joints are those parallel to the regional schistosity. They are commonly continuous for distances of tens of meters and are spaced at rather regular intervals ranging from several meters to as much as twenty meters. In the pelitic schists, joints perpendicular to fold axes tend to be best developed. They are generally spaced at intervals of a few meters and are less continuous.

In addition to joints, the crystalline rocks are locally cut by shear zones along which the rock has been variously crushed, silicified, pyritized, chloritized, or argillized. Along some of these zones, feldspars and micas are altered and softened to the consistency of a weak soil for distances of as much as 0.6 m. The shear zones presumably mark faults, but they generally cannot be traced beyond the limits of exceptional natural outcrops or artificial excavations. Most do not have displacements large enough to offset major lithologic units and are therefore not detectable by routine geologic mapping. Reed and Reed (1969) were able to map several kilometers of shear zones associated with gold mineralization in old surface and underground workings near Great Falls. There, the shears and associated quartz veins form an anastomosing pattern with principal orientations N 5° to 15° W and vertical dips, N 0° to 15° E and vertical to steep westerly dips, and N 20° W and dips 60° to 85° W. This general pattern may be typical of unmineralized sets of shear zones elsewhere in the Piedmont.

Shear zones parallel to schistosity (foliation shear zones of Deere, 1971) have been found in many places in the subway excavations. They are mica-rich zones with abundant slickensides and seams of weak, clay-rich gouge, so soft it can be easily penetrated with the thumb. The zones are commonly 0.1 to 2 m wide and are continuous for tens or hundreds of meters. They are commonly in swarms as much as 20 m wide. Swarms are typically spaced 100 to 300 m apart and tend to be most closely spaced in highly foliated rocks. Swarms of foliation shears are common at contacts of contrasting rock types. Good examples are exposed in natural outcrops along the Potomac River below Chain Bridge (about 1 km southeast of Little Falls, Figure 1). Shear zones striking parallel to schistosity but dipping in the opposite direction (conjugate shear zones of Deere, 1971) are much less common but have been seen.

Most shear zones in the crystalline rocks do not affect overlying deposits, but a few can be traced up into faults that offset Coastal Plain strata and fluvial gravels. These faults are discussed briefly in the section on young faults.

Weathered Mantle

Distribution and Character

Chemical weathering has produced a thick regolith of weathered rock, saprolite, and residual soil on most of the Piedmont rocks. In a typical profile (Figure 4), unweathered rock grades upward into weathered rock in which the feldspars and mafic minerals are partly altered, and this material changes upward into saprolite, a clay-rich, soil-like residuum that preserves the original structure and volume of the parent rock but has few of the original minerals and as little as half the density. The saprolite, in turn, grades into the B and A soil horizons. Fresh rock is gener-

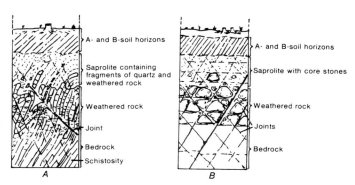

Figure 4. Typical profiles of the weathered mantle on crystalline rocks. A, foliated metasedimentary rocks; B, massive igneous rocks.

ally exposed only in recently incised stream valleys, where the rate of downcutting has exceeded the rate of weathering and saprolite formation, estimated to be about 10 m per million years.

The combined thickness of weathered materials is commonly 10 to 15 m, but locally it is as much as 50 m. In general, the weathered mantle is thickest on the interfluves and thin or absent in valleys. The contacts between saprolite and weathered rock and between weathered and unweathered rock are generally gradational and irregular. However, the base of the weathered zone can be approximately mapped in many areas (Froelich, 1975c; Froelich and Heironimus, 1977a; 1977b) on the basis of water well, bore hole, and outcrop data and minor breaks in slope associated with springs and seeps produced where unweathered rock forms a barrier to downward percolation of water. Many minor streams in the Piedmont tend to flow near the base of the weathered zone. Typically, the base of the weathered zone is much more irregular in bedded or schistose rocks than in the more massive rocks (Figure 4). The weathered mantle is generally thickest on rocks of felsic or intermediate composition, somewhat thinner on mafic rocks, and very thin or absent on ultramafic rocks such as serpentinite (Froelich, 1975b). It is generally thicker and better developed on medium-grained, biotite-bearing pelitic schists than on finer grained sericite-chlorite phyllites. Quartz pods and veins are preserved more or less intact in the weathered mantle, and the larger quartz bodies produce jumbles of residual boulders that commonly cap hills and ridges.

Saprolite is present beneath the basal Cretaceous beds of the Coastal Plain, and detailed contact relations indicated that in some places it may have formed prior to deposition of the overlying strata (Reinhardt and Cleaves, 1978). Elsewhere, it has been shown to have developed long after deposition and erosion of Cretaceous strata (Pavich and Obermeier, 1977). Saprolite also occurs beneath the Miocene(?) and post-Miocene fluvial deposits, where it generally seems to have formed after deposition of the overlying material, because well-rounded pebbles and cobbles of local rock types in the gravels are themselves thoroughly saprolitized. Detailed geochemical studies suggest that saprolite is forming under present conditions at rates comparable to those that have prevailed since the Pliocene.

Physical and engineering properties

Weathering products of different bedrock types are highly variable in strength, compressibility, and other physical and engineering properties. This variability arises partly from differences in the mineralogy of the parent rock and partly from differences in degree of weathering. Most felsic or intermediate rocks weather to sandy, kaolinitic soils; pelitic schists weather to silty, kaolinitic soils; mafic rocks weather to montmorillonite-rich, silty soils; and most weathering products of ultramafic rocks are removed by solution (Leo, Pavich, and Obermeier, 1977; Cleaves, 1974). Only quartz is unaltered in the weathering profile.

Although saprolite and weathered rock generally grade almost imperceptibly into one another, it is useful for many applications to describe zones in the weathering profile that have significantly different properties. A generalized descriptive system for the Washington area is shown in Table 1. For some applications, such as locating relatively firm rock on which caissons for heavy buildings are to be set, or for distinguishing materials through which boring machines can be used for tunnel excavations, more specific, quantitative criteria, such as the Standard Penetration Test (SPT) (American Society for Testing and Materials, 1978) are required. However, for many purposes, this simplified system has proven useful.

In the classification in Table 1, the saprolite zone is defined as having less than 10 percent core stones (stones so hard that they can only be broken with a hammer). Much of the remainder of the saprolite zone is so weak that it would be categorized as soil by an engineer. The most highly weathered saprolite in the upper part of the profile commonly contains as much as ten percent clay; the clay content may be even higher on mafic rocks. Saprolite becomes coarser with depth, as the clay fraction diminishes and the sand fraction increases. Original jointing is preserved in this zone, and there may be more fractures than at depth. Joints in saprolite at or near the surface are, commonly strongly cemented with iron or manganese oxides. In highly micaceous rocks having many parting planes, however, there are no cementations along most partings. In saprolite developed on mafic rocks, the joints are commonly coated with soft clay, apparently washed in from above. Clay coatings are also rather common on joints in saprolite beneath Coastal Plain deposits. Coatings of weak material on steeply dipping joints can seriously impair the stability of excavations.

TABLE 1. DESCRIPTION OF A WEATHERING PROFILE FOR IGNEOUS AND METAMORPHIC ROCKS*

ZONE		DESCRIPTION[†]	RQD[§]	NX CORE RECOVERY %	RELATIVE PERMEABILITY	RELATIVE STRENGTH	COMMON THICKNESS (m)
Residual Soil	A-horizon	-topsoil, roots, organic material; zone of leaching and eluviation; may be porous	n.a.**	0	medium to high	very low	0.2
	B-horizon	-characteristically clay-enriched; also accumulations of Fe, Al, and SI	n.a.**	0	low	commonly low; medium if very dry	0.3
	Saprolite	-relicit rock structures retained; clay-bearing silt or clay-bearing sand grading to sand at depth: commonly micaceous; feldspars and mafic minerals altered to clays; less than 10% core stones; joints strongly cemented with oxides in many places	0 or n.a.**	generally 0 to 10	medium	low to medium[††]	1 to 15
Weathered Rock	Transition from residual soil to partly weathered rock	-highly variable, soil-like to rock-like; fines commonly fine- to coarse-grained sand (gruss). 10 to 95% core stones; feldspars and mafic minerals altered in part	variable, generally 0 to 50	variable generally 10 to 90	high; water losses common during drilling	medium to low[††]	1 to 15
	Partly weathered rock	-rock-like, soft to hard rock; joints stained to altered; some alteration of feldspars and micas	generally 50 to 75	generally less than 90	medium to high	medium to high[††]	0.3 to 3
Unweathered Rock		-iron stains only as traces along joints; no weathering of feldspars and micas; no sheared zones	more than 75; Commonly 90	generally 100	low to medium	very high[††]	

*Modified from Deere and Patton, 1971.

[†]The descriptions provide the only reliable means of distinguishing the zones.

[§]Rock Quality Designation, described in Deere and others (1967).

**Not applicable.

[††]Considering only intact rock with no adversely oriented geologic structures.

Very silty micaceous saprolite commonly has the property of slaking soon after exposure. When first exposed in an excavation, the saprolite may be so strong that it can only be chipped with a shovel, but within a day or so, it may be so weakened that it can be dug easily by hand.

Very low density saprolite on all rock types is quite compressible, especially silty, montmorillonite-bearing, micaceous saprolite. In general, quartz-rich saprolite is less subject to deformation, but it is still easily deformed and may cause significant settlement of even small buildings. Except where frost-action and roots have partly destroyed the rock-like structure, saprolite typically behaves as an overconsolidated soil in the consolidometer test, a standard method for analyzing one-dimensional vertical compression of soils (Terzaghi and Peck, 1948). Below a threshold stress greater than present overburden stress, it deforms at a smaller rate than under loads exceeding the threshold. The preconsolidation stress in saprolite is less than in clays of the overlying Coastal Plain sediments at some places (Pavich and Obermeier, 1977).

The unconsolidated, undrained (UU) shear strength of saprolite and of colluvium derived from most Piedmont rocks generally is about 0.5 kgf/cm^2 where the material is affected by seasonal moisture changes and where the water table approaches the ground surface at the toe of the slopes. Saprolite buried beneath colluvium is commonly very weak for a depth of 1 to 2 m beneath the contact. The UU shear strength of saprolite generally increases with depth to about 1 kgf/cm^2 at 1.7 m and 1.2 to 1.5 kgf/cm^2 at 3 to 5 m. Saprolite beneath sediments in upland areas is weaker and more compressible than the overlying sediments at many places.

UU strength envelopes of saprolite are commonly strongly curbed at confining pressures greater than the overburden weight and approach being flat at high confining pressures, probably because of the positive pore pressure developed during shearing. However, UU strength envelopes from nearby samples can have slopes of 20 to 30 degrees even at high confining pressures, because of differences in moisture content or texture. Thus, caution should be exercised before accepting the premise that saprolite invariably behaves as a strong frictional material. UU test data are normally considered good approximations of the *in situ* undrained shear strength for some types of problems, such as bearing-capacity design.

Material in the weathered-rock zone ranges from soil-like to rock-like in very short lateral and vertical distances. The texture of the soil-like part is commonly fine to coarse sand. Joints are only very weakly cemented or stained. Cementing material, such as calcite, that may be present in joints in underlying unweathered material is commonly leached from this zone. Physical properties range so widely that for some purposes the weathered rock zone is further subdivided into an upper transition zone and a lower, partly weathered rock zone, in which the material is predominantly rock-like.

In weathered rock, shear strength along joints is almost always the strength of concern for stability calculations. Based on observations of the minimum angle at which rock slides have taken place along the Potomac River gorge, the minimum friction angle along joints is about 30 degrees. At some places, though, rock in thin foliation shear zones and dikes in the weathered rock zone has decomposed to a much weaker material, and, undoubtedly, it has an angle of internal friction much less than 30 degrees, probably approaching 15 degrees.

Deformation caused by building loads in weathered rock is predominantly by joint closure, except where there are thin sheared zones or weathered dikes.

COASTAL PLAIN DEPOSITS

General description

The Coastal Plain deposits of the Washington area are part of a wedge of strata that thickens southeastward from a feather edge along the Fall Line to more than 450 m in the southeastern part of the metropolitan area (Figure 1). The base of the sequence dips southeastward at about 20 m/km, but the stratigraphically higher units farther to the southeast dip 4 m/km or less. The regional dip in the lower beds is considerably steeper than the initial dip and must be due to regional tilting, although initial dips of as much as 15 degrees are found locally in some of the fluvial units. The Coastal Plain strata are essentially undeformed, except for the regional tilting and for a few flexures and small faults.

Local and regional unconformities are common in the Coastal Plain succession. The most prominent regional unconformity is at the base of the Cretaceous sequence. Another major regional overlap is present at the base of the Miocene (Darton, 1951). Most of the Mesozoic and Cenozoic units overlie older beds on erosional disconformi-

ties. As most unconformities are overlain by porous basal gravels and sands, they are commonly the loci of ground-water flow and of conspicuous discontinuities of physical properties. Mechanical properties such as shear strength and compressibility are generally related to age. Older sediments typically have a much stiffer consistency (Table 2), are more compact than younger sediments, and are jointed at some places. Marine units are much more uniform vertically and laterally than fluviatile and estuarine units.

Where faults cut the sediments, fault splays and many open joints are commonly found near the main fault. All these are zones of weakness through much stronger material. Poorly cemented or uncemented joints are widespread and rather commonplace in many of the older sediments, especially in clay-rich members.

Stratigraphic units and physical properties

Cretaceous Potomac Group

The Potomac Group of Early and Late Cretaceous age comprises the basal three-quarters or more of the Coastal Plain sequence in the area of Figure 1. The unit

Table 2

QUALITATIVE AND QUANTITATIVE EXPRESSIONS FOR CONSISTENCY OF
FINE-GRAINED SOILS AND COMPACTNESS OF COARSE-GRAINED SOILS

Fine-grained soils

Consistency	Field Test	UCS[1] (kgf/cm^2)	SPT[2] (blows per ft)
Very soft	Easily penetrated several inches by fist	<1.0	<2
Soft	Easily penetrated several inches by thumb	1.0-2.0	2-4
Medium	Penetrated several inches by thumb with moderate effort	2.0-4.0	4-8
Stiff	Readily indented by thumb but penetrated only with great effort	4.0-8.0	8-15
Very stiff	Readily indented by thumb nail	8.0-16.0	15-30
Hard	Indented by thumb nail with difficulty	>16.0	>30

Coarse-grained soils

Compactness	SPT[2] (blows per ft)
Very loose	<4
Loose	4-10
Medium compact	10-30
Compact	30-50
Very compact	>50

[1] Unconfined compressive strength
[2] Standard penetration test resistance

thickens gradually from a feather edge on the west at the Fall Line to more than 300 m at the southeastern part of the area, where it includes beds formerly mapped as the Raritan and Magothy Formations (Hack, 1977). It is largely composed of complexly interbedded clay, silty clay, and silt, but it also contains pockets, lenses, and layers of sand and gravel, minor ironstone layers and nodules, and a few beds of lignite. These deposits are of fluvial and estuarine origin; the clay represents mainly overbank deposits, and the sands represent channel fill and point-bar facies (Drake and others, 1979). Although the unit is quite variable both vertically and laterally, some beds of predominantly silty clay or sand can be traced laterally for long distances.

A major regional facies change in the Potomac Group has been documented by Force and Moncure (1978). They have demonstrated that north and east of the Potomac River the sands are predominantly quartzose and the interbedded clays are mainly kaolinitic and illitic, whereas, to the south and west the sands are feldspathic and clays are montmorillonitic.

The basal part of the Potomac Group is predominantly light gray to white fluvial sand and gravel containing some lenticular bodies of silt and clay. The gravel is generally poorly sorted and contains mostly quartz and quartzite pebbles and cobbles in a coarse sand matrix. Crossbedded sand containing minor amounts of pebbly gravel occurs as lenses and extensive layers, and thin silt and clay beds and hard concretionary ironstone layers are common. The ironstone layers, which are more common near the ground surface, are well indurated and are as much as 2 m thick. In some places, they can be continuous laterally for 50 to 100 m. The sands are predominantly arkosic and clay-rich south and west of the Potomac River, where they have a low permeability, but some very porous permeable lenses of medium- to coarse-grained channel-fill sands are continuous for long distances (Johnston and Froelich, 1977) and make good aquifers. The arkosic and clayey sands are generally quite firm and are difficult to excavate with hand tools. North and east of the river, the clean, mainly quartzose sands are generally friable but locally are cemented by silica into extensive ledges a meter or more thick. Unweathered sands of both facies are typically compact to very compact, but weathered feldspathic sands can be much weaker and are subject to significant deformations under building foundations.

Silty and sandy clay, interbedded with minor amounts of fine sand and gravelly sand, typically make up the upper part of the Potomac Group. The clay is mainly mottled purplish red, green, or gray and is locally carbonaceous or lignite-bearing. Massive clays as much as 30 m thick are widely distributed. The clays north and east of the Potomac River are generally of low plasticity and contain chiefly kaolinite and illite. They have been used to make bricks and tile. Siderite deposits are associated with these clay bodies

in some places. South and west of the river, clays are predominantly montmorillonite and related mixed-layer clays. These clays are highly plastic and locally have abundant slickensided joints. They have moderate to high shrink-swell characteristics and are generally poorly drained.

Natural landslides are common in clay-rich sediments of both facies, but they are more abundant where the clay is montmorillonite-bearing. Where unweathered, the clays and silts in both facies are very stiff to hard, and they are difficult to excavate with light power equipment. Throughgoing, high-angle, and subhorizontal joints are common in the thick, massive clays of the montmorillonitic facies, but joints are unusual in the feldspathic sands (Langer and Obermeier, 1978). Sheared zones containing multiple joints are widespread but probably are not commonplace throughout the Potomac Group in the area of Figure 1. No studies of joints in the Potomac Group north of the river have been published, although joints certainly must exist at other places. Residual shear strength angle of internal friction can be as low as 8 to 10 degrees in the highly plastic clays along the sheared zones.

Both clays and feldspathic, clay-rich sands have commonly been weathered and softened to depths of 5 m or more in the upland areas, even where unconformably overlain by other deposits. The depth of weathering and softening is generally less on slopes than on stable flatlands, because of removal of the weakened material by landsliding, creep, and erosion.

Cretaceous and Tertiary marine deposits

The upper part of the Coastal Plain sequence includes the Magothy Formation and Monmouth Group of Late Cretaceous age, the Brightseat Formation of Paleocene age, the Aquia Formation of Paleocene age, the Nanjemoy Formation of Eocene age, and the Chesapeake Group of Miocene to Pleistocene age. These units consist chiefly of drab clays and fine calcareous sands of shallow marine origin. The basal units of the sequence (the Monmouth Group in outcrop and the Magothy Formation farther southeast in the subsurface) are separated from the underlying Potomac Group of Early and Late Cretaceous age by a regional disconformity. The individual formations range in thickness from a feather edge on the northwest to as much as 15 m on the southeast; the aggregate thickness of the sequence generally does not exceed 50 m. The predominant lithology is clayey and silty sand, but thin beds of silty, micaceous, and glauconitic sand and green, gray, and black silty clay are common. The clay is locally moderately plastic. There are also some beds of shelly marl and occasional beds of gravel. In contrast to the terrace deposits, alluvium, and Potomac Group, these marine strata are generally thin bedded (0.3 to 5 m) and have only minor lateral variation, so their engineering properties are predictable with some confidence if the local section is known.

A very permeable gravel bed about 0.7 m thick occurs at many places at the base of the sequence. Some sandy beds contain indurated ironstone concretions and cemented layers. The sand and gravel layers are typically medium-compact to compact, except locally on uplands, where they have been reworked into sand dunes as much as 8 m thick.

Clays and clay-rich silts have a stiff consistency at most places; locally, they are softer because of weathering. The clays are chiefly kaolinite and illite. In some of the more plastic clay strata (especially the Marlboro Clay beneath the Nanjemoy Formation), there are many high-angle, silt-filled joints. Natural landslides are commonplace at or near outcrops of this formation; it is probable that the joints are partially responsible for this plethora of landslide activity. Well-developed, open, high-angle joints are also present in some of the clayey sands in the marine sequence.

UPPER TERTIARY FLUVIAL DEPOSITS

Gravel and sand deposits of late Miocene(?) and Pliocene age cap remnants of formerly extensive plateau surfaces along and southeast of the Fall Line (Figure 1). A large outlier of similar deposits caps high ridges at Tysons Corner, Virginia, 10 km northwest of the Fall Line. These deposits commonly grade upward from interbedded sand and gravel at the base to poorly bedded silt loam in the upper part (Hack, 1955), but there is pronounced lateral variation. Some of the granular deposits are loose, and the clays generally have a medium to stiff consistency. The principal clay minerals are illite and kaolinite. Thin, iron-cemented layers occur throughout the deposits, commonly, with a thicker layer at the base. The thickness of the deposits averages about 10 m.

The pebbles in the gravel are typically 5 cm or less in diameter and are predominantly vein quartz, chert, and quartzite. The chert and quartzite pebbles are mostly rotten and easily crumbled. The Tertiary fluvial deposits are generally yellow-orange to red-brown and show well developed A and B soil horizons, commonly with a hardpan layer developed near the surface in the finer grained materials (Hack, 1955; 1977). Where the fluvial deposits rest on crystalline rocks, saprolite is developed to depths of as much as 20 m below the base of the fluvial materials.

QUATERNARY DEPOSITS

The Quaternary deposits include low-level river terrace deposits, alluvium along modern streams, estuarine deposits, and, for convenience, artificial fill.

The terrace deposits consist of gravel, sand, silt, and clay capping terraces at various elevations, ranging from a few meters to as much as 35 m above sea level (Figure 5).

Relatively compact gravel and sand in a clay or silt matrix make up the bulk of these deposits. Lenses of medium to stiff silt and clay, and peaty beds as much as 5 m thick, are locally intercalated with the sand and gravel. Illite and kaolinite are the major clay components. The terrace deposits are generally less than 10 m thick, but locally are as much as 50 m where they fill old channels cut during low stands of Pleistocene sea level (Figure 5; Darton, 1950; Froelich, Johnston, and Langer, 1978).

Most of the terrace deposits consist of upward-fining sequences that pass from gravel and coarse sand at the base to fine sand, silt, and clay in the upper parts; some terraces have multiple sequences of this type. The lower, younger terraces tend to have the greatest proportion of fine-grained materials, but they also contain some of the coarsest material. The gravels in the Quaternary terrace deposits tend to be coarser than those in the Tertiary deposits and to contain a wider variety of rock types, including boulders, cobbles, and pebbles of locally derived crystalline rocks and diabase, sandstone, quartzite, and metamorphosed volcanic rocks derived from areas to the west. Very large ice-rafted boulders (Wentworth, 1928), some as large as 2 m in diameter, locally occur in the gravel part of the lower terrace sequences. The distribution of these oversize boulders is irregular and unpredictable, but they are especially common where the terrace deposits fill deep bedrock channels.

Fine-grained materials in the Quaternary terrace deposits tend to be buff, gray, or brown, except where stained by circulating ground water. Soil development is less distinct on these terraces than on the Tertiary deposits. Chert and quartzite pebbles are unweathered, although pebbles and cobbles of crystalline rocks are saprolitized in all but the youngest terraces. Saprolite is developed to depths of as much as 10 m beneath some of the higher terrace deposits, but crystalline rocks beneath younger terrace deposits are only locally weathered. The degree of weathering and the extent of saprolite development suggest that the highest terraces are of late Tertiary or early Pleistocene age. Pollen and spores recovered from a peat deposit near Dupont Circle in downtown Washington, in which fossil cypress stumps were found in growth positions (Wentworth, 1924), suggest that the broad terrace on which much of the central city is built (T_2 of Figure 2) is of Sangamon age (Thompson, 1972). Pollen profiles indicate that the slightly lower terrace flanking the Mall (T_1 of Figure 2) is of early Wisconsin age (Knox, 1969).

Alluvium, consisting of sand, silt, clay, organic materials, and minor amounts of gravel, underlies channels and floodplains of modern streams. These deposits are fairly well bedded and moderately well sorted; commonly, they show the same upward-fining sequence as the terrace deposits. Along streams draining Piedmont rocks the alluvium is comonly quartzose and micaceous and contains fragments of weathered crystalline rocks and abundant vein

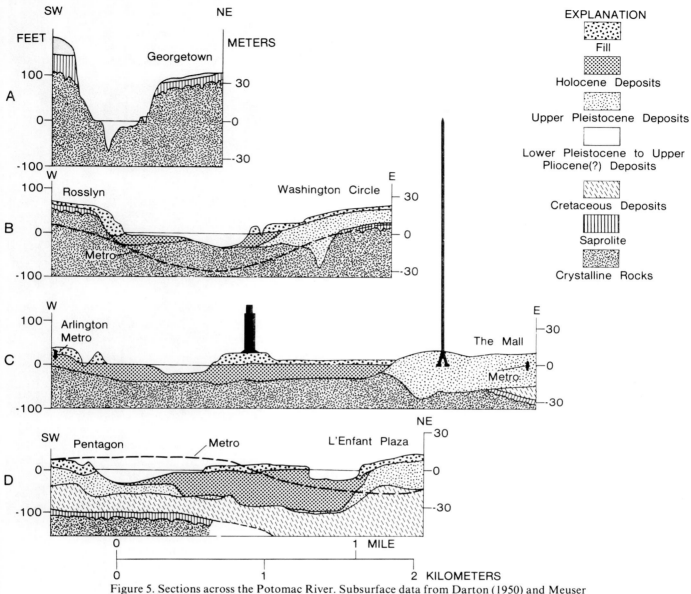

Figure 5. Sections across the Potomac River. Subsurface data from Darton (1950) and Meuser and others (1967, 1970, 1975). A. Approximately 5 km southeast of Little Falls at the site of the proposed Three Sisters Bridge. B. Along the upper (northern) METRO crossing near Key Bridge. C. Along Memorial Bridge and the centerline of the Mall. Outlines of the Lincoln Memorial and Washington Monument show vertical exaggeration, which is the same for all sections. D. Along the lower (southern) METRO crossing near Rochambeau (14th Street) Bridge.

quartz. Along streams in the Coastal Plain the alluvium contains pebbles of quartz and quartzite but few fragments of crystalline rocks. Thickness of the alluvium is highly variable. It is locally as much as 10 m, but probably averages about 3 m. Vertical and lateral variations are common, and the fine-grained materials are generally soft. Sands are commonly loose.

Swamp, tidal-marsh, and estuarine deposits composed chiefly of silty carbonaceous muds and oozes underlie the Potomac estuary and the flanking flats below Memorial Bridge. Deposits on some of the flats must have accumulated within the last five or six thousand years when sea level was 8 to 11 m higher than at present. In many areas, these deposits are intermixed with artificial fill derived from dredging the channels of the Potomac and Anacostia Rivers.

Figure 6. Reverse fault offsetting terrace deposits above Rock Creek, just east of Calvert Street Bridge. Terrace deposits rest on saprolitized gneiss (Sykesville Formation?) and show typical basal gravel member overlain by loam. Photographed in 1901 by N. H. Darton. From the files of the U.S. Geological Survey. View is toward the north.

YOUNG FAULTS

Although most of the Coastal Plain and younger deposits are undeformed, several high-angle reverse faults displace the older terrace deposits by as much as 2 m (Figure 6; Darton, 1950; Froelich, 1978; Jacobeen, 1972). A system of steeply dipping reverse faults having a cumulative vertical displacement on the order of 100 to 150 m has been described along the Fall Line about 30 km south of Washington (Mixon and Newell, 1977), and the faults in the Washington area are apparently part of a similar system that may control the general position of the Fall Line. Whether these faults are young enough to pose any seismic hazard is still a matter of speculation, but they clearly are of engineering significance in both surface and subsurface excavations.

GROUND WATER

Long before the coming of the white man to the confluence of the "Potowmack" and the "Eastern Branch" (Anacostia) Rivers, the Indians utilized the abundant pure water from the many springs and brooks. Captain John Smith described the region in 1629 as follows: "The country is not mountainous, nor yet low, but such pleasant plaine hills, and fertile valleys, one prettily crossing another, and watered so conveniently with fresh brooks and springs, no lesse commodious, than delightsome" (Johnston, 1964).

These springs, mainly in the Piedmont, supplemented with water from shallow-dug wells, were the major sources of water for the Washington area prior to the Civil War. In 1863, the aqueduct from Great Falls was completed, and since that time the city has been supplied almost exclusively

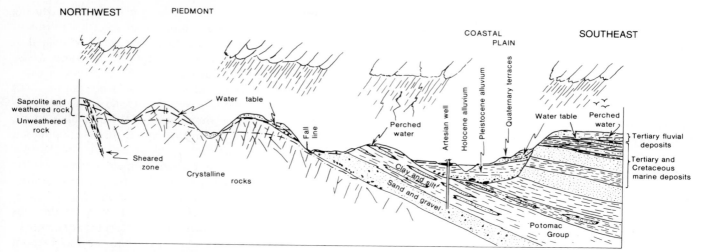

Figure 7. Diagrammatic sketch showing typical ground water conditions in the Washington area. Based on Mack (1966), Hack (1977), Richardson (1976a, b), Nutter (1974), Nutter and Otton (1969), Drake and others (1979), Johnston and Larson (1979), Froelich, Johnston, and Langer (1978), and Meuser and others (1967, 1969, 1970, 1972, and 1975).

with water from the Potomac River. Suburban areas are supplied from smaller streams, including the Patuxent River in Montgomery County, Maryland, and Occoquan Creek in Fairfax County, Virginia, or from deep wells.

Ground water is abundant in both crystalline rocks and in sediments (Johnston, 1964; Papadopulos and others, 1974). Shallow ground water is often an important factor for land development and construction. It is a valuable asset for domestic and commercial purposes, but it can adversely affect stability of slopes and contribute to serious problems in tunneling and other construction activities.

The average annual precipitation in the Washington area is about 100 cm, rather evenly distributed throughout the year. Local precipitation is the main source of ground water in the Piedmont. The water table is essentially a subdued reflection of the local topography, and the flow system is unconfined (Figure 7). The water table generally lies above unweathered rock, and differences in permeability among colluvium, saprolite, and weathered and unweathered rock are subordinate to topography in controlling the location of the water table. Local variations in permeability are generally not large enough to cause extensive perched water tables or confined flow, although clay-rich colluvium draped over the slope can impede flow at the bases of slopes in some places, and joints and sheared zones that cut through unweathered rock locally cause confined flow.

Although the position of the water table in the Piedmont is controlled primarily by topography, there are major permeability differences within the regolith. Regolith permeability is generally related systematically to the weathering profile. Permeability of the clay-rich B-horizon of the soil zone is much less than that of saprolite imme-

diately beneath. Because the clay content of the saprolite zone and cementation of joints decrease with depth, permeability generally increases with depth. Greatest permeability in the regolith generally occurs in the weathered rock zone, where joints are open, parting planes are numerous, and saprolite contains little or no clay. Permeability of unweathered rock is generally an order of magnitude less than that of the overlying regolith. Joints in fresh rock are normally tight, and intergranular porosity is very low. However, most quartz dikes are intensely jointed or shattered and are quite commonly permeable. Foliation shear zones in unweathered rock are also typically much more permeable than the surrounding rock. Even though there are large differences in relative permeabilities throughout the weathering profile, the absolute permeability of weathered, unweathered, and shattered or sheared zones is generally low, being approximately equivalent to that of silt or very fine sand.

The ground water setting in the Coastal Plain contrasts sharply with that of the Piedmont (Figure 7). Confined or artesian conditions are commonplace in the Coastal Plain, especially in the Potomac Group, where they occur even at shallow depth. Confined-flow conditions are present, but not commonplace, in the Cretaceous-Tertiary marine deposits. Younger deposits are generally so discontinuous laterally that artesian and confined conditions do not exist. The outcrop belts of porous and permeable units along the Fall Line are the principal recharge areas for the artesian aquifers of the Coastal Plain.

Both the Potomac Group and the Cretaceous-Tertiary marine deposits are capped at many places with the Tertiary fluvial deposits. These Tertiary deposits commonly have permeable sand and gravel in their basal parts, but the impermeable hardpan near the surface prevents infiltration in many areas. Where infiltration does occur, water is commonly perched above more impermeable underlying sediments. Localized perched water and small areas of confined ground water are also commonplace in the Potomac Group in upland areas. These local sources of water are especially unpredictable because the rocks contain discontinuous sand lenses separated by impermeable clays and have many open joints and fractures.

Water emanating from myriad small and discontinuous sources causes seeps along and near the base of many slopes in upland areas on the Coastal Plain. On flat interfluves, the ground surface is commonly very wet or has standing water during the spring, either due to the hardpan of the fluvial deposits or to shallow, clay-bearing sediments of the Potomac Group.

Holocene alluvial deposits occupy broad swales and lowlands in the Coastal Plain, and the ground water table is commonly within a few meters of the surface, especially on alluvium near major streams. Infiltration from these streams probably contributes significantly to ground water recharge.

ENGINEERING CHARACTERISTICS

The geotechnical engineering characteristics of the various geologic materials in the Washington area have a significant influence on regional and site-specific planning (Froelich, Garnaas and Van Driel, 1978). Some of the ways in which the different geologic materials affect underground excavation, stability of foundations, slope stability, and road construction are outlined below. More detailed information is in reports by Hack (1977); Froelich and Hack (1975); Froelich, Hack, and Otton (1980); Froelich (1975a, 1975d); Langer (1978); Obermeier (1979); Smith, 1955; and in the reports prepared for METRO by Meuser and others (1967, 1969, 1970, 1972, and 1975).

Subsurface excavation

Most of the practical experience with subsurface excavation in the Washington area has been in connection with construction for METRO, a regional rapid transit rail system for Washington and the metropolitan area, which began in the early 1970's. The system will have approximately 160 km of route when completed (Figure 1), and it will be mostly underground in the inner city and mostly above ground in the residential suburbs. Construction of the underground parts is largely complete, and part of the system is operational.

Much of the following discussion focuses on problems related to excavations for METRO in rock and weathered materials, because much was learned about tunneling through Piedmont rocks that is transferrable to other large

cities in the eastern United States. A major problem during early construction was development of criteria for evaluating properties of weathered rocks that could be related to excavation processes and tunnel support. Previously developed methods were inadequate because of a lack of experience in tunneling through the foliated crystalline rocks using modern excavation systems. Criteria finally developed were based on a combination of the SPT blow count, RQD value, percent core recovery, and visual examination and description of weathering. Because much of the running line is underground, construction costs and geometric constraints require that passenger stations also be underground. Underground stations are commonly large chambers in crystalline rock (Figure 8), kept as shallow as possible to enable passenger movement from the surface to the train. The first large chamber excavated was Dupont Circle Station. At the time of construction, it was the largest underground chamber excavated with such a thin rock roof (about 6 m of unweathered rock at some places) in the Piedmont of the eastern United States. This thin roof, coupled with the large size of the chamber (approximately 20 m wide by 13 m high), adversely oriented foliation shear zones through the roof, very low residual stress in the rock, and relatively high compressibility of the rock mass, made it imperative that great care be taken during excavation. The chamber was excavated in multiple drifts, using the conventional drill-and-blast method. Structural support was by rock bolts, shotcrete, and steel ribs. Detailed information about rock properties and excavation technology for this and other chambers is in Cording, Mahar, and Brierley (1977); information about running lines is in Cording and Mahar (1974) and Daugherty, Ware, and Gould (1976). Their major suggestions for constructing similar shallow rock chambers are as follows:

1. A continuous cover of unweathered rock over the chamber is very desirable, though a very limited amount of weathered rock extending to or even below the crown is acceptable.

2. Less structural support is required, and fewer excavation problems are encountered, with increasing depth into the rock, provided weathering and jointing of the rock are also diminished, and there are no adversely oriented shear zones; the more massive, less jointed rocks are preferable.

3. The smallest forces on support systems (rock bolts, shotcrete, and steel ribs) take place after there are small displacements in the rock, immediately or very shortly after the excavation is opened. (This is in contrast with squeezing ground conditions in some parts of the United States, where large displacements must occur, possibly over prolonged time periods, before forces on support systems reach a minimum value.) Minimum forces on support systems take place at slightly larger than elastic deformations into the ex-

Figure 8. Partly completed METRO station excavated in rock, showing the shotcrete-covered steel ribs and the architectural shell.

cavation, commonly only a few millimeters. Any delay in support emplacement can result in rock loosening and overbreak and may cause increased load on the support system and possible surface settlement.

4. In high-quality crystalline rocks at many other places in the United States, rock bolts alone provide full support of a rock arch. In the sheared, blocky, and seamy rock in Washington, however, rock bolts are not long enough or of high enough capacity to provide sole

support to the thin rock arch, but they can be used in combination with shotcrete to support a partially excavated heading. A more substantial structural support is then required after the arch is opened to its full width. Standard practice in rock tunneling with steel supports is to place steel ribs at a spacing that provides full support of the initial rock loads, but in the Washington area a combination of shotcrete and light-steel ribs, installed as the heading is fully excavated, is more economical and helps minimize rock movements. The shotcrete-steel rib combination also serves as the permanent structural support for the station arch. Shotcrete thickness is commonly 20 to 30 cm (Figure 8).

5. Adversely oriented joints, foliation shear zones, and weathered rock should be located long before full excavation of the heading to design the structural support system properly and to plan the instrumentation (primarily extensometers) layout for monitoring movements during excavation.

6. Drill-and-blast excavation should be eliminated as much as possible to prevent loosening of the rock, the number of drifts should be minimized, and the chambers should be kept as small as possible.

7. Foliation shear zones can be continuous and quite planar for large distances, permitting large wedges of rock to creep, slide, or fall into the excavation. An especially troublesome condition can arise where a foliation shear zone is intersected by a conjugate foliation shear zone. Joints generally have enough asperites in contact and are sufficiently wavy to prevent large blocks from loosening, but 1 to 2 m wide blocks can fall with little or no warning. Cores should be examined carefully to determine the character of the critically oriented joint surfaces.

The large stations, such as the Dupont Circle Station, were very expensive to build, so to reduce costs the size of the excavated chambers for other METRO stations was decreased greatly. This cost reduction was made possible because of relaxation of architectural constraints and major improvement in excavation technology. Large stations were originally planned to be in harmony with the monumental architecture of the Nation's capital, but later, smaller, and less ostentatious stations were accepted. Improved excavation technology resulted from development of a tunnel-boring machine (TBM) that could excavate very hard rocks, including quartz bodies, much less expensively than drill-and-blast methods. For later excavated stations, the TBM's excavated two parallel bores for the running lines, and at station locations those bores were subsequently enlarged into a station vault. This procedure reduced the number of drifts and the amount of drilling and blasting for excavations.

Tunnels for METRO running lines in all materials are generally excavated as parallel bores approximately 6 m in diameter, separated by a pillar about one tunnel diameter in thickness. Two smaller tunnels are excavated, rather than a large one, because they cost less and cause less surface settlement.

Running lines excavated as tunnels are located, where possible, in strong sediments of the Potomac Group or in unweathered or only slightly weathered crystalline rock. The TBM does not operate well in highly weathered rock or in saprolite because the weak material disintegrates and clogs the cutter head, and because it is difficult to get around the TBM to support the weak material near the face of the tunnel. Another problem in weathered rock and in large, adversely oriented, foliation shear zones is that the standard pillar width of about 6 m may be inadequate. Failure of the pillar may be caused by shearing along clay-coated joints in the shear zone or by compression of the weak mass. At places, the pillar was widened to as much as 20 m to compensate for these weak zones. Where running lines must go through highly weathered bedrock, cut-and-cover excavation is preferable.

Tunneling has also been found to be very undesirable where both sediments and bedrock are at the same face (mixed face tunneling). Excavation there is very slow and expensive, and cut-and-cover procedures are used whenever possible.

Earth (soil) tunnels are excavated in the sediments with a shield and are generally kept as deep as possible to reduce surface settlement. The minimum soil cover is about one tunnel diameter. Although catastrophic failure is possible where the tunnel depth is so great that the strength of the soil is less than depth-induced stresses (Heuer, 1976), this problem has not been encountered in METRO construction because the running lines are quite shallow.

It has been found preferable to drive METRO earth tunnels through Potomac Group clay-rich sediments rather than through terrace deposits. No tunnels have been driven in alluvium. The younger materials, especially alluvium, are weak and very permeable and are wet at many places, making them subject to squeezing and running into the excavation, and expensive to dewater near streams. Although the Potomac Group is beneath the water table at most places, the clay-rich parts have a very low permeability and normally stand unsupported for a long time. Tunneling in the fissured clays of the montmorillonite facies is complicated by the tendency for blocks as large as 1 m across to slide or fall into the excavation.

The tunnel crown in the Potomac Group was set 4 to 5 m beneath the overlying deposits wherever possible, because the Potomac is commonly overlain unconformably by very permeable, water-bearing sands. The contact is generally very undulating, making it difficult to locate without a large number of borings. Sands overlying clay materials of the Potomac have run into METRO tunnels on several occasions, causing serious support problems and large surface settlements.

Cut-and-cover excavated running lines in soil are normally more economical than mined tunnels where the base of the excavation is less than 12 to 15 m below the surface. At greater depths, the open excavations are generally more costly because of the large volume of material excavated and greatly increased support requirements. Cut-and-cover excavations are typically much less expensive than mined tunnels where both soil and rock must be excavated from the tunnel. Cut-and-cover methods are used in excavations for stations wherever soil extends to or below the crown, because the soil has been deemed too weak for the large cavities. Mined tunnels are avoided as much as possible in highly weathered rock, and stations are never built where there would be too much poor material. Where weathered rock is thin and there is a rock cover at the crown, it has generally been preferable to mine the tunnel, especially where complicated and expensive support systems requiring vertical walls would be necessary in cut-and-cover excavations.

Water-related problems are a major concern in excavating cut-and-cover trenches and in tunneling in Coastal Plain materials. Problems such as flooding, running soils, or heaving at the base of excavation can have disastrous consequences, and, to avoid these problems, expensive dewatering is necessary, using well points at many places. Terrace deposits containing large boulders in permeable sand and gravel layers present a special problem in cut-and-cover excavations, especially near large streams. Sheet piles driven into the boulder-bearing layers have buckled and split, permitting large volumes of water to rush into the excavation. On one occasion, part of the completed METRO line was flooded, and much of the system was endangered. Clean sands in many Coastal Plain units have required grouting prior to excavation to prevent them from running or caving into the tunnel.

Water-related problems in Piedmont rocks are infrequent and not as serious. Water encountered in excavation can usually be controlled with sump pumps. Many tunnels in unweathered rock are nearly dry, except near foliation shear zones.

Foundations for structures

Alluvium in many low lying areas has a 5 to 10 m thick covering of rubble, trash, or other fill, which masks the underlying very soft and weak swamp and estuarine deposits. Even lightly loaded spread footings founded on these materials are prone to large settlements. Medium to large structures are normally supported on deep foundation systems, such as piles or caissons. Alluvium and fill are generally so thin that these systems easily reach firm bearing materials such as bedrock or compact sediments, but problems can still be encountered, because the soft sediments spread laterally under even vary small loads, and because boulders in the buried terrace deposits can prevent piles from penetrating to design depth.

The Washington Monument is supported with a large spread footing on alluvium (Darton, 1950). It is also one of the earliest cases in the United States of underpinning an inadequate foundation beneath a large structure (Gillette, 1933). Construction was started in 1848, and the monument was carried to a height of 47 m. Construction stopped in 1854 due to lack of funds and was not resumed until 1880. During this interval, the structure settled significantly and tilted northward due to compression of an unrecognized northward-thickening clay bed (Figure 9). When construction resumed, underpinning was inserted to increase the foundation from a 24 m square at the base to a 38 m square, and bring the axis back into plumb. The 169 m high monument was completed in 1884 and settled another 15 cm during the next 50 years, although vertically and at a much slower rate.

Most terrace deposits and marine units in the Coastal Plain section are much firmer than alluvium or estuarine deposits, so that shallow foundation systems can be used for many medium-size structures. Unweathered Potomac Group sediments are so strong that caissons are commonly used for medium- and large-size buildings.

Medium-size and larger buildings on saprolite commonly require deep foundation systems. Weak saprolite is highly compressible, and, especially where mica-rich, may

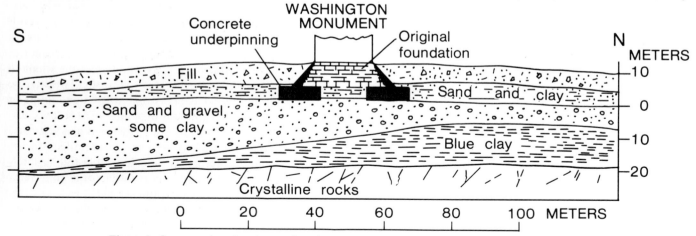

Figure 9. Cross section showing geology beneath the Washington Monument. Modified from Gillette (1933) and Darton (1950).

also be subject to large time-dependent deformations. Many large buildings must be supported on caissons, but very weak saprolite is locally so deep that other systems are more economical. At Tysons Corner, Virginia, for example, saprolite with SPT blow counts less than 10 per foot extends to depths of at least 15 m, and thicker saprolite is known in many other places in the Piedmont. Alternatives to caissons in these areas include a mat foundation or long piles. Cast-in-place concrete piles are commonly used where weak saprolite is underlaid by material having SPT blow counts of 30 or more per feet within 10 to 15 m of the base of the building.

Caissons are commonly founded on saprolite or weathered rock having SPT blow counts greater than 200 per foot, where the relatively strong material is not extremely deep. Caisson excavations in saprolite should be filled with concrete as soon as possible, because of the tendency of saprolite to swell and weaken, possibly causing large settlements. The highly stressed region at the base of the caisson should be carefully examined to ensure there are no weak weathered zones or foliation shear zones or faults.

At many places, hard pieces of quartz or unweathered rock as small as 2 to 5 cm in diameter make it very difficult to obtain samples of saprolite that are suitable for laboratory testing to determine compressibility and shear strength properties. In the past, SPT data have been widely used for design of foundations, but this method is still not very satisfactory, because the hard pieces make the blow counts unrealistically high. In recent years, consultants have begun using other field methods, such as the cone penetrometer or the Menard pressuremeter (Martin, 1977). Very weak zones can be detected better with the penetrometer than with the SPT method because of the continuous record of resistance as a function of depth; very weak samples critical for design are then collected for laboratory testing. The pressuremeter, which measures horizontal compressibility, has the advantage of being little affected by small, hard pieces in a softer matrix, and it has been used for design of some buildings in the Washington area. Local experience with the pressurmeter has been chiefly in areas of steeply dipping schistosity. It may be difficult to apply these results where schistosity has low or moderate dips, because compressibility parallel to schistosity may be quite different than that normal to it.

Slope stability

Excavated construction period slopes are normally kept as steep as possible, with no bracing at many places. Tertiary and Cretaceous marine sediments, Potomac Group sediments, and all crystalline rocks have very high angle, uncemented, through-going joints, faults, or sheared zones that are apt to fail in inadequately supported excavations. Failure to recognize these zones has periodically resulted in injury or death of construction workers.

A serious problem in the area is long-term failure of slopes in the clay-rich Potomac Group, especially in the montmorillonitic facies. Naturally occurring and construction-related landslides are normally not large, but they are widespread and rather commonplace and have caused much destruction and damage. Slumping due to swelling and weakening of clays often takes place as much as 10 years after excavating a slope as low as 10 degrees. The slumps normally occur after an intense rainstorm or when melted snow and prolonged rains have saturated the ground.

Design of permanent slopes in Potomac Group clays is necessarily complicated and rather uncertain, unless extremely conservative design parameters are used. Where unweathered, the clays are highly overconsolidated and very stiff, but they are susceptible to shrinking and swelling. These properties alone pose difficult problems for geotechnical design. In addition, subhorizontal weak weathered zones, faults, and joints; highly variable strength properties; localized artesian ground water in sand lenses; and water in joints and faults add to the complexity. Both previously failed and unfailed slopes on highly fractured, highly plastic, clays should be designed using residual (drained) shear strength parameters, even though many first-time (initial) failure landslides probably take place in undrained or partly drained shear. Slopes on silts containing little clay and slopes on clay-bearing sand can be safely designed using normally consolidated, drained peak shear strength parameters measured on remolded samples (i.e., the "fully softened" strength). Selection of realistic parameters for low- to moderate-plasticity clays and for weakly fractured, highly plastic clay is often controversial. Values between residual and fully softened parameters are normally used. Because of the difficulty of ensuring that all weak or water bearing zones have been found during exploration, quite conservative values are generally appropriate. All previously failed slopes should be designed using residual parameters along the pre-existing surface of rupture.

Although not nearly as widespread as clays in the Potomac Group, the Marlboro Clay has numerous small to medium size landslides wherever it crops out. This marine clay, about 10 m thick, has many high-angle open joints or fractures and is remarkably uniform laterally for large distances. It is predominantly of low to medium plasticity and has some extensive silt laminations. No detailed studies have been made of factors causing first-time failure landslides. It seems likely that an important factor is high water pressure in the joints, fractures, and silt partings.

Evidence of very slow creep on steep slopes of colluvium and saprolite is common throughout the Piedmont; some creep occurs even on slopes as low as 18 to 20 degrees. Trees are bowed at the base, steep foliation in the uppermost saprolite is bent downhill at many places, and colluvial debris has accumulated at the base of slopes. The depth of distorted saprolite does not normally exceed 1 m, and much of the weakening and resultant movement probably is frost-related. Even though the steep slopes offer beautiful settings, few houses have been built there because of the traditional preference for ranch and colonial style homes and the expense of construction on shallow bedrock. Damage to structures such as retaining walls on steep slopes can probably be eliminated by ensuring that the base is in firm saprolite or shallow bedrock and by properly taking account of creep-induced forces during design.

Cliffs as much as 12 m high in the weakly lithified Quaternary sediments are being cut by wave action along the Potomac estuary. Undercut banks cause destabilization of nearly vertical slopes, which recurrently fail and topple to form a jumbled mass at the toe of the cliff. A poignant narrative of the often futile efforts of man to stabilize shorelines throughout the Chesapeak Bay area and its tributaries (such as the Potomac River) appears in the recent bestselling novel *Chesapeake,* by James Michener.

Road construction

Geologic conditions do not present major constraints to road construction in the Washington area, although conditions in some geologic units pose special problems. Weak organic materials in alluvium and estuarine deposits under a thin layer of fill have caused settlement of as much as 1 m long along the George Washington Parkway on the Virginia side of the Potomac River opposite the Washington Monument (Figure 1). Resurfacing is needed periodically to relevel this part of the highway. At places throughout the alluvial lowlands, the soils are so wet and organic they must be removed and replaced with better quality materials to prevent the recurrence of problems such as those encountered on the Parkway.

The principal problems in the Coastal Plain are caused by the highly plastic clays of the Potomac Group, whose swelling and weakening commonly cause distressed pavements and misaligned curbs. The problem of weakening can be made less severe by mixing lime with the clay during construction, which changes the clay into a much stronger, non-swelling material.

In the Piedmont the micaceous silts that are so commonplace are difficult to compact and are especially troublesome to the performance of low- and medium-grade flexible pavements. Mica in silts makes them prone to shoving and shearing during compaction. Even where compacted properly, these silts deform greatly under traffic loadings, especially when they are soaked. They are so susceptible to frost softening and heaving that low to medium grade roads can be severely distressed during winter, even though Washington winters are normally mild. The prob-

lem is so aggravated on roads with poor base drainage that pavements disintegrate completely under moderate traffic loading during periods of thawing. The only techniques to ensure satisfactory performance of these types of soils are to provide very good base drainage or to stabilize the soil with cement. Some highways have been built in recent years by mixing cement into the soil, making a monolithic, rocklike base that will not disintegrate and weaken during freezing.

Throughout the Washington area, seeps in layered sediments and at contacts between permeable soil and bedrock are responsible for widespread and severe frost-related damage to pavements, even on major highways. Standard base courses are commonly inadequate to remove seeping water, which causes problems such as pumping, subgrade weakening, and frost softening. Many of these problems can be eliminated by proper drainage systems.

CONCLUDING REMARKS

In the preceding pages we have attempted to show the influence that the local geology has had on the growth and development of the city of Washington and to point out some of the geologic factors that ought to be considered in land-use planning and in the siting, design, and construction of engineering works. As the city moves into its third century, the necessities of economy and energy conservation, coupled with aspirations for an improved urban environment and quality of life, will place ever greater stress on the available space, particularly in the central city. As this demand for space increases, incentives to utilize underground space effectively will inevitably increase. In addition to the METRO system, underground space is already utilized for sewers, utilities, water-distribution systems, parking facilities, and certain critical security installations. The possibility of underground storage of natural gas in existing geologic structures in nearby parts of Prince Georges County, Maryland, has been investigated (Jacobeen, 1972) but did not prove to be practical. An underground pump-storage facility is in the final stages of design in northern Montgomery County, Maryland. The use of underground space as a heat sump for air-conditioning systems is increasing, raising special technical, legal, and environmental problems.

In a metropolitan area where geologic knowledge is so critical to orderly and effective utilization of available space and where geologic relations are so complex and poorly exposed, it is essential that a close symbiotic relationship be developed between the geologic and engineering communities. The best available geologic information in many parts of the area, especially in the central city, is developed during engineering design and construction, and it is essential that maximum use of that information be made as it becomes available. This utilization requires the careful and methodical collection of data on a day-to-day, week-to-week, and year-to-year basis and its integration into a constantly evolving and improving understanding of the geologic underpinning of the city. N. H. Darton of the U.S. Geological Survey carried on such an effort on a spare-time basis for nearly half a century, between 1890 and 1940. Since then, other Geological Survey projects under the leadership of H. W. Coulter, C. F. Withington, J. T. Hack, and A. J. Froelich have made enormous contributions to the knowledge of the geology beneath Washington and its suburbs. However, the missions of a federal survey make it difficult for the U.S. Geological Survey to fill the necessary role in the regular long-term collection and synthesis of detailed engineering geologic information throughout the metropolitan area. In view of the critical need for such an effort, it is surprising that no county or municipality in the area, as yet, has an engineering geologist on its staff. Hopefully, this obvious step cannot be long in coming!

ACKNOWLEDGMENTS

We thank Rachel M. Barker, William E. Davies, Charles A. Baskerville, Milan J. Pavich, Avery A. Drake, and John T. Hack, all of whom read parts or all of earlier versions of this manuscript, pointed out myriad errors, and made valuable comments and suggestions. We owe special thanks to Albert J. Froelich for his very careful and complete review of several earlier drafts. His generous contributions have resulted in very major improvements in the organization and content of the paper! Charles F. Withington read the final version of the manuscript and suggested several improvements.

REFERENCES CITED

American Society for Testing and Materials, 1978, Standard method for penetration test and split-barrel sampling of soils—Designation 1586–67 (reapproved 1974), *in* 1978 Annual Book of ASTM Standards, Part 19: Philadelphia, p. 235–237.

Bock, C. G., 1974, Rosslyn station, Virginia: Geology, excavation and support of a large, near surface, hard rock chamber: Proceedings of 1974 Rapid Excavation and Tunneling Conference, San Francisco, v. 2, p. 1373–1391.

Bryan, W. B., 1914, A history of the National Capital, v. 1, 1790–1814: New York, Macmillan Co., 667 p.

Carr, M. S., 1950, The District of Columbia—its rocks and their geologic history: U.S. Geological Survey Bulletin 967, 59 p.

Cleaves, E. T., 1974, Chemical weathering and landforms in a portion of Baltimore County, Maryland: Baltimore, Maryland, Johns Hopkins University Ph.D. thesis, 104 p.

Cloos, Ernst, 1964, Structural geology of Howard and Montgomery Counties, *in* Geology of Howard and Montgomery Counties: Maryland Geological Survey County Report, p. 216–259.

Cloos, Ernst, and Cooke, C. W., 1953, Geologic map of Montgomery County and the District of Columbia: Maryland Department of Geology, Mines, and Water Resources, scale 1:62,500.

Cording, E. J., and Mahar, J. W., 1974, The effect of natural geologic discontinuities on behavior of rock in tunnels, *in* Pattison, H. C., and D'Appolonia, Elio, eds., Rapid Excavation and Tunneling Confernce, San Francisco, California, June 24–27, 1974, Proceedings, v. 1: New York, American Institute of Mining, Metallurgical, and Petroleum Engineers, Inc., p. 107–138.

Cording, E. J., Mahar, J. W., and Brierley, G. S., 1977, Observations for shallow chambers in rock, *in* Kovari, K., ed., Field measurements in rock mechanics—Proceedings of the International Symposium, Zurich, April 4–6, 1977, v. 2: Rotterdam, A. A. Balkema, p. 485–508.

Coulter, H. W., and Carroll, G. V., 1964, Selected geologic localities in the Washington area: Washington Academy of Science Journal, v. 54, no. 5, p. 153–159.

Crowley, W. P., 1976, The geology of the crystalline rocks near Baltimore and its bearing on the evolution of the eastern Maryland Piedmont: Maryland Geological Survey Report of Investigations 27, 40 p.

Darton, N. H., 1947, Sedimentary formations of Washington, D.C., and vicinity: U.S. Geological Survey mineral-resource map, scale 1:31,680.

—— 1950, Configuration of the bedrock surface of the District of Columbia and vicinity: U.S. Geological Survey Professional Paper 217, 42 p.

—— 1951, Structural relations of Cretaceous and Tertiary formations in part of Maryland and Virginia: Geological Society of America Bulletin, v. 62, p. 745–780.

Darton, N. H., and Keith, Arthur, 1901, Washington, D.C.-Md.-Va.: U.S. Geological Survey Geologic Atlas of the United States, Folio 70, scale 1:62,500.

Daugherty, C. W., Ware, K. R., and Gould, J. P., 1976, Selection of the vertical alignment of rapid transit tunnels, *in* Robbins, R. J., and Conlon, R. J., eds., Rapid Excavation and Tunneling Conference, Las Vegas, Nevada, June 14-17, 1976, Proceedings: New York, American Institute of Mining, Metallurgical, and Petroleum Engineers, Inc., p. 311–331.

Deere, D. U., 1971, The foliation shear zone—an adverse engineering geologic feature of metamorphic rocks: Boston Society of Civil Engineering Journal, v. 60, no. 4, p. 163–176.

Deere, D. U., Hendron, A. J., Jr., Patton, F. D., and Cording, E. J., 1967, Design of surface and near-surface construction in rock, Chapter 11 *in* Fairhurst, Charles, ed., Failure and breakage of rock: Proceedings of the Eighth Symposium of Rock Mechanics held at the University of Minnesota, September 15-17, 1966: New York, American Institute of Mining, Metallurgical and Petroleum Engineers, Inc., p. 237–302.

Deere, D. U., and Patton, F. D., 1971, Slope stability in residual soils: Pan American Conference on Soil Mechanics and Foundation Engineering, 4th, San Juan, Puerto Rico, June 1971, Proceedings, v. 1, p. 87–170.

Drake, A. A., and Morgan, B. A., 1981, The Piney Branch Complex—a metamorphosed fragment of the central Appalachian ophiolite in northern Virginia: American Journal of Science, v. 281, p. 484–508.

Drake, A. A., Nelson, E. A., Force, L. M., Froelich, A. J., and Lyttle, P. T., 1979, Preliminary geologic map of Fairfax County, Virginia (Sheet 1) and Map showing selected geologic data (Sheet 2): U.S. Geological Survey Open-File Report 79-398, 2 pl., scale 1;48,000.

Fisher, G. W., 1970, The metamorphosed sedimentary rocks along the Potomac River near Washington, D.C. *in* Fisher, G. W., Pettijohn, F. J., Reed, J. C., Jr., and Weaver, K. N., eds., Studies of Appalachian geology—central and southern: New York, Wiley-Interscience, p. 294–315.

Fleming, Anthony, 1978, The geology of the crystalline rocks of west-central Washington, D.C.: Beloit, Wisconsin, Beloit College M.S. thesis, 77 p.

Force, L. M., and Moncure, G. K., 1978, Origin of two clay-mineral facies of the Potomac Group (Cretaceous) in the Middle Atlantic States: U.S. Geological Survey Journal of Research, v. 6, no. 2, p. 203–214.

Froelich, A. J., 1975a, Surface materials map of Montgomery County,

Maryland: U.S. Geological Survey Miscellaneous Investigations Series Map I-920-A, scale 1:62,500.

——1975b, Thickness of overburden map of Montgomery County, Maryland: U.S. Geological Survey Miscellaneous Investigations Series Map I-920-B, scale 1:62,500.

——1975c, Contour map of the base of saprolite, Montgomery County, Maryland: U.S. Geological Survey Miscellaneous Investigations Series Map I-920-C, scale 1:62,500.

——1975d, Bedrock map of Montgomery County, Maryland: U.S. Geological Survey Miscellaneous Investigations Series Map I-920-D, scale 1:62,500.

——1978, Map showing planar and linear features of Fairfax County, Virginia: U.S. Geological Survey Open-File Report 78-443, 1 pl., scale 1:48,000.

Froelich, A. J., Garnaas, A. D., and Van Driel, J. N., 1978, Franconia area, Fairfax County, Virginia: Planning a new community in an urban setting: Lehigh *in* Nature to be commanded, U.S. Geological Survey Professinal Paper 950, p. 69–89.

Froelich, A. J., and Hack, J. T., 1975, Preliminary geologic map, District of Columbia: U.S. Geological Survey Open-File Report 75-537, 8 p., 1 pl., scale 1:24,000.

Froelich, A. J., Hack, J. T., and Otton, E. G., 1980, Geologic and hydrologic reports for land-use planning in the Baltimore-Washington urban area: U.S. Geological Survey Circular 806, 26 p.

Froelich, A. J., and Heironimus, T. L., 1977a, Map showing contours on the base of saprolite, Fairfax County, Virginia: U.S. Geological Survey Open-File Report 77-710, scale 1:48,000.

——1977b, Thickness of overburden map of Fairfax County, Virginia: U.S. Geological Survey Open-File Report 77-797, scale 1,48,000.

Froelich, A. J., Johnston, R. H., and Langer, W. H., 1978, Preliminary report on the ancestral Potomac River deposits in Fairfax County, Virginia, and their potential hydrogeologic significance: U.S. Geological Survey Open-File Report 78-544, 37 p.

Gillette, D. H., 1933, Washington Monument facts brought up to date: Engineering News-Record, v. 110, no. 16, p. 501–502.

Hack, J. T., 1955, Geology of the Brandywine area and origin of the upland of southern Maryland: U.S. Geological Survey Professional Paper 267-A, 41 p.

——1977, Geologic map for land-use planning, Prince Georges County, Maryland: U.S. Geological Survey Miscellaneous Investigations Series Map I-10004, scale 1:62,500.

Heuer, R. E., 1976, Catastrophic ground loss in soft ground tunnels, *in* Robbins, R. J., and Conlon, R. J., eds., Rapid Excavation and Tunneling Conference, Las Vegas, Nevada, June 14-17, 1976, Proceedings: New York, American Institute of Mining, Metallurgical, and Petroleum Engineers, Inc., p. 278–295.

Higgins, M. W., and Fisher, G. W., 1971, A further revision of the stratigraphic nomenclature of the Wissahickon Formation in Maryland: Geological Society of America Bulletin, v. 82, p. 769-774.

Hopson, C. A., 1964, The crystalline rocks of Howard and Montgomery Counties: *in* The geology of Howard and Montgomery Counties, Maryland Geological Survey, p. 27–215.

Jacobeen, F. H., Jr., 1972, Seismic evidence for high-angle reverse faulting in the Coastal Plain of Prince Georges and Charles Counties, Maryland: Maryland Geological Survey Information Circular 13, 21 p.

Johnston, P. M., 1964, Geology and ground water resources of Washington, D.C., and vicinity: U.S. Geological Survey Water Supply Paper 1776, 97 p.

Johnston, R. H., and Froelich, A. J., 1977, Map showing lithofacies and inferred subsurface distribution of channel-fill aquifers: U.S. Geological Survey Open-File Report 77-287, 8 p.

Johnston, R. H., and Larson, J. D., 1979, Principal sources of ground water in Fairfax County, Virginia: U.S. Geological Survey Open-File Report 79-211.

Knox, A. S., 1969, Glacial age marsh, Lafayette Park, Washington, D.C.:

Science, v. 165, p. 795–797.

Langer, W. H., 1978, Surface materials map of Fairfax County, Virginia: U.S. Geological Survey Open-File Report 78-78, 9 p., 7 figs., 1 pl., scale 1:48,000.

Langer, W. H., and Obermeier, S. F., 1978, Relationship of landslides to fractures in Potomac Group deposits, Fairfax County, Virginia: U.S. Geological Survey Open-File Report 78-779, 37 p.

Leo, G. W., Pavich, M. J., and Obermeier, S. F., 1977, Mineralogical, chemical, and physical properties of the regolith overlying crystalline rocks, Fairfax County, Virginia, a preliminary report: U.S. Geological Survey Open-File Report 77-644, 14 p.

Mack, F. K., 1966, Ground water in Prince Georges County: Maryland Geological Survey Bulletin 29, 101 p.

Martin, R. E., 1977, Estimating foundation settlements in residual soils: American Society of Civil Engineering Proceedings, Journal of Geotechnical Engineering Division, v. 103, no. GT3, p. 197–212.

Meuser, Rutledge, Wentworth, and Johnston, General Soil Consultants, 1967, Final report-subsurface investigation, Pentagon route (COO2 to COO7), Vol. II, Washington Metropolitan Area Transit Authority: U.S. Department of Commerce, National Technical Information Service, PB 179-654.

——1969, Preliminary subsurface investigation for Washington Metropolitan Area Rapid Transit Adopted Regional System 1968, revised 1969: U.S. Department of Commerce, National Technical Information Service, PB 186-066.

——1970, Final report-subsurface investigation, L'Enfant-Pentagon route (LOO1 and L002), Washington Metropolitan Area Transit Authority: U.S. Department of Commerce, National Technical Information Service, PB 216-972.

——1972, Final report-subsurface investigation, Rockville route (A009 to A013), Washington Metropolitan Area Transit Authority: U.S. Department of Commerce, National Technical Information Service, PB 216-642.

——1975, Final report-subsurface investigation, Branch route (F004 to F008), Washington Metropolitan Area Transit Authority: U.S. Department of Commerce, National Technical Information Service, PB 249-773.

Mixon, R. B., and Newell, W. L., 1977, Stafford fault system—Structures documenting Cretaceous and Tertiary deformation along the Fall Line in northeastern Virginia: Geology, v. 5, p. 437–440.

Muth, K. G., Arth, J. G., and Reed, J. C., Jr., 1979, A minimum age for high-grade metamorphism and granite intrusion in the Piedmont of the Potomac River Gorge near Washington, D.C.: Geology, v. 7, p. 349–350.

Nutter, L. J., 1974, Well yields in the bedrock aquifers of Maryland: Maryland Geological Survey Information Circular 16, 24 p.

Nutter, L. J., and Otton, E. G., 1969, Ground water occurrence in the Maryland Piedmont: Maryland Geological Survey Report of Investigations 10, 56 p.

Obermeier, S. F., 1979, Engineering geology of soils and weathered rocks of Fairfax County, Virginia: U.S. Geological Survey Open-File Report 79-1221, 59 p., 4 pls.

Papadopulos, S. S., Bennett, R. R., Mack, F. K., and Trescott, P. C., 1974, Water from the Coastal Plain aquifers in the Washington, D.C., metropolitan area: U.S. Geological Survey Circular 697, 11 p.

Pavich, J. J., and Obermeier, S. F., 1977, Post-Miocene weathering beneath the Atlantic Coastal Plain: Geological Society of America Abstracts with Programs, v. 9, no. 2, p. 174.

Reed, J. C., Jr., and Jolly, J., 1963, Crystalline rocks of the Potomac River Gorge near Washington, D.C.: U.S. Geological Survey Professional Paper 414-H, 16 p.

Reed, J. C., Jr., Marvin, R. F., and Mangum, J. H., 1970, K-Ar ages of lamprophyre dikes near Great Falls, Maryland-Virginia: U.S. Geological Survey Professional Paper 700-C, p. C145-C149.

Reed, J. C., Jr., and Reed, J. C., 1969, Gold veins near Great Falls,

Maryland: U.S. Geological Survey Bulletin 1286, 22 p.

Reed, J. C., Jr., Sigafoos, R. S., and Fisher, G. W., 1980, The river and the rocks—The geologic story of Great Falls and the Potomac River gorge: U.S. Geological Survey Bulletin 1471, 75 p.

Reinhardt, Juergen, and Cleaves, E. T., 1978, Load structures at the sediment-saprolite boundary, Fall Line, Maryland: Geological Society of America Bulletin, v. 89, p. 307–313.

Richardson, C. A., 1976a, Availability of ground water in Prince Georges County, Maryland: U.S. Geological Survey Open-File Report 76-197, 9 p.

——1976b, Availability of ground water in Montgomery County, Maryland: U.S. Geological Survey Open-File Report 76-882, 13 p.

Smith, Horace, 1976, Soil survey of District of Columbia: Soil Conservation Service, U.S. Department of Agriculture, 194 p.

Southwick, D. L., and Fisher, G. W., 1967, Revision of stratigraphic nomenclature of the Glenarm Series in Maryland: Maryland Geological Survey Report of Investigations 6, 19 p.

Terzaghi, Karl, and Peck, R. B., 1948, Soil mechanics in engineering practice: New York, John Wiley and Sons, Inc., p. 56–67.

Thompson, D. E., 1972, Paleoecology of the Pamlico Formation, Saint Mary's County, Maryland: Rutgers University, Ph.D. thesis, 178 p.

U.S. Geological Survey, 1975, Building stones of our Nation's Capital: U.S. Geological Survey, Washington, D.C., 44 p.

Wentworth, C. K., 1924, The fossil swamp deposit at the Walker Hotel suite, Connecticut Avenue and DeSales Street, Washington, D.C.: Journal of the Washington Academy of Sciences, v. 14, p. 1–11.

——1928, Striated cobbles in the southern states: Geological Society of America Bulletin, v. 39, p. 941–953.

Withington, C. F., 1967, Geology—its role in the development and planning of metropolitan Washington: Journal of the Washington Academy of Sciences, v. 57, p. 189–199.

MANUSCRIPT RECEIVED BY THE SOCIETY MAY 24, 1982
MANUSCRIPT ACCEPTED JUNE 1, 1982

Geological Society of America
Reviews in Engineering Geology, Volume V
1982

Bedrock and Quaternary geology of the Boston area, Massachusetts

Clifford A. Kaye
U.S. Geological Survey
150 Causeway Street
Boston, Massachusetts 02114

ABSTRACT

Boston lies near the geographic center of the Boston Basin, a roughly triangular area of sedimentary and volcanic rocks of late Precambrian and Cambrian age that is surrounded by older, contemporary, and younger granites and related rocks. The basin rocks are mostly argillites, sandstones, and conglomerates interlayered with rhyolitic and spilitic volcanics and volcaniclastic sediments. The rocks are deformed into large east-west folds and are much broken by faults of several orientations. Dikes and sills abound. Deep alteration of rock to a soft clayey aggregate is widespread. The irregular bedrock surface is the result of differential glacial erosion of rocks of varying hardness, and under most of the central Boston area, bedrock is buried by thick drift. The stratigraphy of the drift is complex and includes four stratigraphically distinct tills and outwash units, representing several advances and retreats of glacial ice. These are provisionally interpreted to consist of two glacial stades of the early Wisconsinan and two of the late Wisconsinan, including a readvance that overrode much of the Boston area about 12,000 years B.P. The effects of the geology on local engineering practices are briefly described.

INTRODUCTION

Boston, like all things, began small—a coastal settlement of about 1,000 people who came over together in 1630 from southern England (Kaye, 1976a). It prospered almost immediately, attaining the status of the leading town, if not city, of New England before the century was out. Why, one may ask, did this small community grow while so many villages and towns were destined to remain small forever? The question can, of course, be asked of any city, but it is particularly relevant to Boston, because few cities show better the interrelationship of geology and man.

The influence of geology on Boston was threefold. First, the site was on one of the largest well-protected harbors of the New England coast. This submerged coastal lowland was the combined expression of the presence of relatively soft, erodible bedrock; a long history of erosion by the several continental glaciers that passed over it during the Pleistocene; and the work of ocean waves and currents

that built two protective sand spits at the lowland's mouth, thereby, transforming a bay into a harbor. Secondly, the site of the settlement was hydrologically favored by abundant shallow ground water and flowing springs (Lathrop, 1800). Lastly, the town site was isolated and well protected from surprise attack, owing to the fact that it was built on a small peninsula with a very narrow and, therefore, easily defended connection to the mainland. Moreover, rising from the peninsula was a central hill, well-suited for a lookout and for a signal tower (Beacon Hill or Trimountain, as it was originally called). The peninsula had a complex glacial origin that will be discussed in more detail later (Figure 1).

In addition to the obvious influence of topography and its underlying geology on the young city, there were local deposits of construction materials in abundance. In the first two centuries, the city was built mainly of bricks made

Figure 1. Boston. View to east across Boston Peninsula: Charles River and Beacon Hill, covered with small 19th century houses, in foreground; Boston Common and the Public Garden on right; Boston Harbor, Logan Airport, Winthrop, Deer Island, and Massachusetts Bay in background. (Photograph courtesy of Aerial Photos International, Inc., Boston.)

locally from glaciomarine clays. In the 19th century, building stone was quarried nearby, and deposits of glacial outwash, sand, and gravel were extensively exploited for use as fill in the enlargement of the city through the reclamation of salt marshes and tide flats (Kaye, 1976a).

AREA OF CONCERN

The following discussion will concentrate on the old city of Boston and parts of Brookline and Cambridge, referred to here as the central Boston area, which comprises approximately the northern half of the Boston South quadrangle (U.S. Geological Survey, 7.5-minute topographic map series). This area includes the peninsula of the original city, the area of the Back Bay adjoining Roxbury (now incorporated into the City of Boston), and Brookline and Cambridge (Figure 2). This is the area where major engineering construction has been concentrated during the last four decades and, therefore, the area that has yielded the most new geologic information. Thousands of logs of foundation borings from these many projects have been collected (Boston Society of Civil Engineers, 1961, 1969, 1970, 1971) and about 150 foundation excavations have been visited and studied in detail by the author.

In the central Boston area, bedrock is mostly buried deeply, and the overlying unconsolidated deposits are largely glacial and estuarine in origin. The following discussion will cover both bedrock and surficial geology but will emphasize the latter because these deposits have been studied more intensively and because their impact on man is more direct.

TOPOGRAPHY

The surface of the central Boston area is mostly low lying, rarely exceeding an altitude of 15 m. Exceptions to this are: several drumlins that reach altitudes of 60 m; a somewhat fragmented moraine (Beacon Hill) that reaches an altitude of 30 m; and a high-standing bedrock area on the southwest that also reaches an altitude of about 30 m. The area is crossed from west to east by the Charles River, which joins the Mystic River to form the Inner Harbor. Until the 19th century, most of the low-lying area was tideland consisting of extensive salt marshes and mud flats, through which the Charles River meandered. During the late 19th century, in an effort to enlarge the city, which was badly restricted to the small confines of the Boston Peninsula, most of this wetland was filled to an altitude of 2 m. This new-made land included all of the Back Bay (the name originally given to the tidal flat that lay west of the peninsula and south of the Charles River), and the tidal flats in Cambridge, on the northern side of the Charles River, later to be the site of the Massachusetts Institute of Technology (Whitehill, 1968; Aldrich, 1970; Kaye, 1976a).

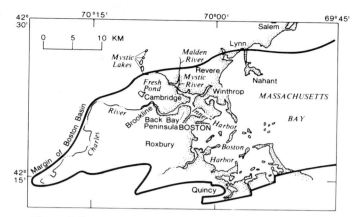

Figure 2. Boston area and the outline of the Boston Basin.

BEDROCK

Boston Basin

Boston is located near the center of the Boston Basin, a wedge-shaped, down-faulted body of sedimentary and volcanic rock that is flanked on the north, south, and west by various granitic rocks (Emerson, 1917; LaForge, 1932; Billings, 1929, 1976; Kaye, 1979). Onshore, the basin is widest along the coast, where it measures about 24 km, north to south; offshore, it extends to the east under Massachusetts Bay, where it appears to widen still more. On the west, the basin tapers to a point about 29 km west-southwest of Boston (Figure 2).

The age of the sedimentary rocks making up the Boston Basin was long a matter of debate. By the second half of the last century, early Cambrian and middle Cambrian fossils were known from the Weymouth-Braintree area and Nahant (Figure 2)—two widely-spaced localities along the margins of the basin. The rest of the basin appeared barren of fossils. At first, the entire basin was thought to be Cambrian, but, later, the view became established that the basin was Carboniferous, or perhaps Devonian-Carboniferous, and was an analogue—although an unfossiliferous one—of the nearby Norfolk and Narragansett Basins. The Cambrian rocks were thought to represent fault blocks of older terrane. However, recent mapping by the writer (Kaye, 1980b), radiometric dating of rhyolite at the base of the basin section (Kaye and Zartman, 1980), and the finding of microfossils in argillite (Lenk and others, 1982) have shown that the unfossiliferous rocks lie stratigraphically beneath the Cambrian and that the entire basin ranges in age from very late Precambrian (Proterozoic Z) to middle or late Cambrian. In terms of plate tectonics, the Boston Basin is part of the Avalonian plate; and, indeed, it bears a family resemblance to the rocks of the Avalon Peninsula of eastern Newfoundland (King, 1980).

The rocks of the Boston Basin appear to have been

deposited in a basin, or basins, that were undergoing active block-faulting. The sedimentary rocks, therefore, consist of detritus eroded from surrounding highlands and fault-scarps and deposited as interfingering lithofacies. Conglomerate, sandstone, argillite, and volcaniclastic sediment grade or interfinger into each other, laterally and vertically. Thin limestones interbedded with argillite and sandstone are locally abundant. There is at least one well-developed redbed zone (at the base of the Cambrian), but this, too, grades laterally into normal gray sediments.

Volcanic activity was widespread and occurred in at least six intervals during the Precambrian. Early eruptions were rhyolitic and later were spilitic and keratophyric. Volcanic rocks occur as flows, flow breccias, explosion breccias, pillow lavas, plugs, necks, and diatremes.

Bottom conditions were unstable in the depositional basins, for at many stratigraphic levels, the telltale evidence of submarine sliding and turbidity currents, including convoluted bedding, intraformational breccia, rhythmites, and large lenticular masses of coarse-grained diamictite ("tillite"), is present. Bottom slumps and slides were probably triggered by earthquakes originating from volcanic eruptions and block faulting.

The depositional Boston Basin was deformed by compression into a series of long, east-west to east-northeast–trending folds, overturned to the south and, as we see them today, plunging east. Because the oldest rocks crop out in the central part of the basin, the overall structural configuration is geanticlinal. This fold-fabric is fragmented by longitudinal faults of large displacement. Recent mapping by the author (Kaye, 1980b) indicates that there are at least 8 of these, most of which are 15 km or more in length. They break the basin into long, narrow fault blocks, each of which consists of a single fold, either an anticline, syncline, or homocline. In addition, the rocks are broken by a complex of later faults, most of which are transverse to the longitudinal faults. Besides faults with large to small displacement, there are shear zones with various cataclastic effects but relatively small displacement. The longitudinal faults are mostly high-angle reverse. Slickensides on fault surfaces show a strong strike-slip component to movement on many of the transverse faults. There is surprisingly little to no unconsolidated fault breccia or gouge lining many faults. One finds, however, in many faults, lithified cataclastic material (cataclasite, mylonite, etc.) which is difficult to recognize without petrographic study. Although the density of faults varies from place to place, such data as we have indicates an average fault-spacing throughout the area of about 150 m, measured in any direction.

The structural deformation of the Boston Basin probably is the result of two orogenies, one in the Ordovician and the other in the Permian, as well as some faulting and dike-intrusion in the Mesozoic. The longitudinal faults may represent reactivation of the Precambrian basin-range faults. This faulting and the major folding were possibly produced by plate-collision and subduction in the Ordovician, for it has been suggested (Skehan, 1973; Kaye, in press) that a major suture between the Avalonian plate and the North American plate lies just north of the Boston Basin. Transverse faulting and some folding are attributed to the widespread Appalachian (Permian) orogeny. In addition, there is excellent evidence that some faulting and shearing, as well as the intrusion of many basic dikes, occurred in the Triassic-Jurassic (Kaye, in press).

Central Boston Area

Figure 3 is a geologic map of the central Boston area. Because bedrock is deeply buried except for a few outcrops of conglomerate in the south, most of the information was obtained from rock cores taken in foundation borings and from observations made in the Boston Main Tunnel (Rahm, 1962) on the south, and the City Tunnel Extension (Billings and Tierney, 1964) to the northwest. The sedimentary rocks are divisible into three main facies: coarse grained (conglomerate and sandstone), fine grained (argillite), and a mixed facies consisting of maroon and green tuffaceous siltstone and sandstone. Traditionally (LaForge, 1932; Billings, 1976), these have been given formational names: Roxbury Conglomerate and its middle member, the Dorchester Member, and Cambridge Slate, in that order of the previously ascribed Paleozoic age.

The southern part of the map falls on the faulted northern flank of a large east-plunging anticline (Central Anticline of Billings, 1929; Roxbury Anticline of LaForge, 1932). Closure on this anticline is expressed by the southeast-trending contact of the conglomerate and the overlying tuffaceous beds. Cutting across the northern tip of Boston Peninsula is the east-northeast-trending axis of the large Charles River Syncline (Billings, 1929), with argillite cropping out in the trough of this long fold.

Dikes

Dikes and sills abound in all rocks, particularly in the argillites. From outcrop and tunnel observations, the average spacing of these intrusions on a horizontal plane is about 100 m. Thicknesses range from a fraction of a meter to more than 50 m. The dikes show a preferred orientation of east-west and north-south ~20° (Billings, 1976, Figure 12). Diabase is the most abundant rock type (Billings, 1976, Table 5), with fewer lamprophyre dikes. Most sills are of medium-gray, aphanitic trachyte (bostonite). These latter rocks resemble massive argillite in appearance and are easily overlooked in both outcrop and in tunnel mapping. Bostonite sills were particularly abundant in bedrock cores taken during exploratory boring for the Prudential Center and have been seen in cores from other major construction

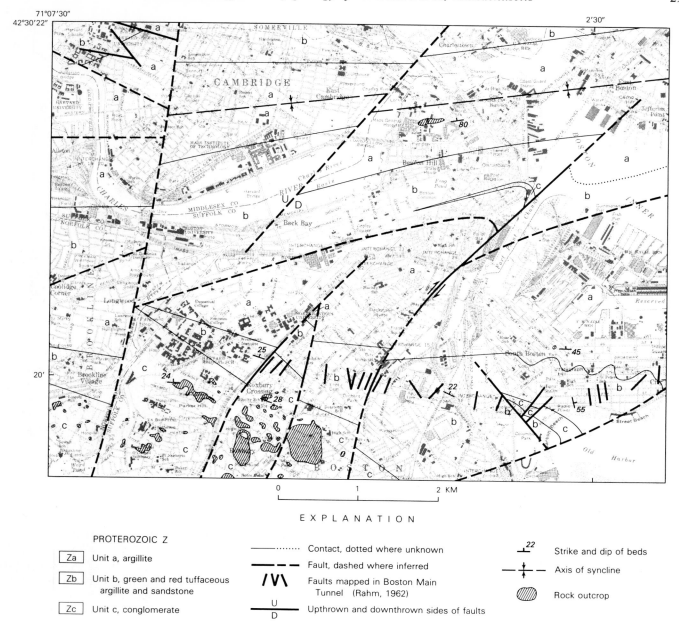

EXPLANATION

PROTEROZOIC Z

| Za | Unit a, argillite |

| Zb | Unit b, green and red tuffaceous argillite and sandstone |

| Zc | Unit c, conglomerate |

⸺ ········· Contact, dotted where unknown

⸺ ⸺ Fault, dashed where inferred

/ V \ Faults mapped in Boston Main Tunnel (Rahm, 1962)

U / D Upthrown and downthrown sides of faults

²²— Strike and dip of beds

— Axis of syncline

⬭ Rock outcrop

Figure 3. Bedrock geologic map of central Boston area (mapped by C. A. Kaye).

sites. The walls of many diabase dikes are commonly slickensided, and adjacent wall rocks show wide zones of drag—evidence that these dikes intruded earlier faults.

Dikes are not shown in Figure 3 for several good reasons: most are too thin to be plottable, but, more importantly, outcrops are too few and far between and faults are too numerous, and for the most part unknown, to allow a meaningful picture of their distribution to be drawn.

Soft-Rock Alteration

W. O. Crosby (Worcester, 1914, p. 225) called atten-

tion to the fact that under the new Cambridge site for Massachusetts Institute of Technology (MIT), the normal argillite was "rotted to a whitish and more or less plastic clay." Since then, this type of alteration has been found at many places in the Boston Basin. The alteration has been found in all types of sedimentary rock, including conglomerate. There are several excellent outcrops of altered conglomerate, but for the most part these softened rocks lie deeply buried. Thin-section study shows that the normal rock minerals, including quartz, have been variously replaced by sericite and kaolinite. This alteration seems to favor certain beds and stratigraphic zones but not exclu-

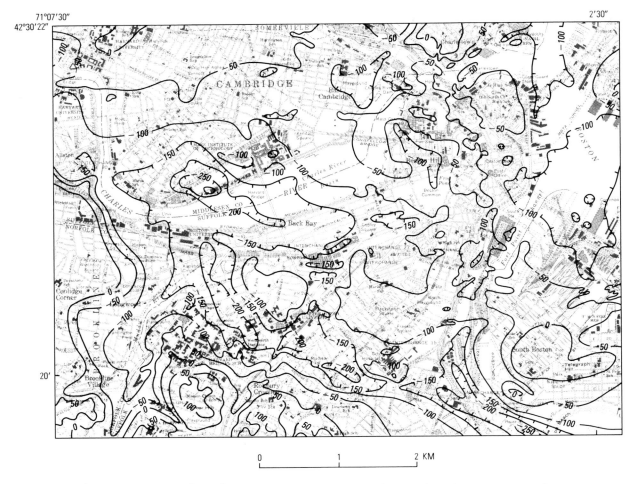

Figure 4. Bedrock surface of central Boston area. Contour interval is 50 ft (15 m). Datum is mean sea level.

sively so. It also seems to occur in close proximity to certain faults. The origin of soft-rock alteration is conjectural and may be the result of hydrothermal activity, but it may also represent the roots of lateritic weathering in Tertiary time (Kaye, 1967a).

Bedrock Surface

Figure 4 shows contours on the surface of bedrock of the central Boston area. Because more than 95 percent of this surface lie buried beneath Quaternary deposits, subsurface data (about 2,000 borings) provided the control.

The bedrock surface reflects rock erodibility; the deeper section under the Charles River and Back Bay is underlaid by softer rocks (argillite, siltstone, and sandstone), and the high-standing area along the southern margin marks the outcrop of massive conglomerate. In detail, the bedrock surface is highly irregular. Dikes stand up as knobs and ridges, major joints are deeply grooved, and closed depressions abound. The deep, somewhat interrupted and ramified trough that cuts diagonally across the

map from the northwest to the southeast has sometimes been called part of a buried, preglacial valley (Crosby, W. O., 1899; LaForge, 1932; Crosby, I. B., 1937, 1939; Chute, 1959; Upson and Spencer, 1964). Seismic refraction and subbottom seismic profiling under Dorchester Bay, along the trend of the depression to the east and southeast, failed to reveal its seaward continuation and showed, instead, that it turned south and terminated in a cul-de-sac. This trend follows the strike of bedrock and, in particular, the strike of soft ashy siltstones. It now seems more probable that the depression was produced by glacial erosion of more erodible rock strata.

PLEISTOCENE DEPOSITS

Glacial deposits overlie bedrock almost everywhere in the central Boston area, attaining a maximum thickness of 90 m in a few places under the Charles River Basin. These deposits include: till, sand, gravel, and silt and clay, most of which are glaciomarine in origin. Knowledge of these deposits is extensive and, to a degree, puzzling. Earlier workers recognized the occurrence of till over clay in the Boston area and speculated as to its meaning. Marbut and Woodworth (1896) concluded that the clay at Boston had been overridden by ice. For this reason, LaForge (1932, p. 80) suggested that the clay was pre-Wisconsinan. Judson (1949) advocated a late Wisconsinan readvance over the northwestern part of the Boston Basin. Chute (1959) substantiated this interpretation by new foundation borings in that area. However, the problems are not only the post-clay glacial readvance, which now seems well established, but also the existence of at least three older tills with intervening outwash deposits, including clay, and the existence of extensive faulting and deformation of these deposits in certain areas. The recognition that multiple tills represented multiple glacial events was delayed by the fact that the tills looked alike, possessing the same general colors and textures. Although the lithologies of the clasts do differ, these differences are subtle and were not evident before a close knowledge of the bedrock geology had been obtained. Some of the essential facts and interpretations yielded by the Boston data will be outlined below.

Directions of Glacial Flow

The direction of ice flow in the Boston Basin and adjoining uplands was studied by means of the orientation of striations and grooves on the bedrock surface, the orientation of the long axes of drumlins, the direction of transport of erratics in till, and the direction of thrusting and overturning of bedding in glacially deformed drift. These data range through 360° in azimuth. Analysis of this confusing message shows the existence not of an ever-shifting single ice current but of at least four separate and distinct ice currents of different ages. Three of these flowed fairly rectilinearly, but one (the last) was multicomponent and marked by strong lobation (Table 1).

Drumlins

Some of the drumlins fronting the harbor and the open waters of Massachusetts Bay are cliffed (Kaye, 1967b). These exposures yield invaluable data on the composition and internal structures of the drumlins and, in a few instances, on the striation direction on the bedrock surface lying immediately beneath.

The distribution of drumlins seems to be random in the Boston Basin, although on the map they are strongly clustered along east-west to east-northeast-trending lines that are parallel to the prevailing strike of bedrock. This distribution, however, is apparent and not real. The reason for this is that most drumlins lie directly on bedrock, and their crests, in consequence, follow the bedrock surface. Where the bedrock surface is well below sea level, drumlins are buried by glaciomarine clay and other later deposits. A second fact to note is that the Boston drumlins do not have

TABLE 1. SUGGESTED CORRELATION OF BOSTON WISCONSINAN SECTION WITH NOVA SCOTIAN, CANADIAN SAINT LAWRENCE, GREAT LAKES, AND ILLINOIS SECTIONS

Designation this paper	Direction of glacial flow	Dates in years before present (YBP) * = Radiocarbon date	Great Lakes and St. Lawrence Region Dreimanis and Goldthwait (1973) Terasmae and Dreimanis (1976)	Southwestern Nova Scotia Grant (1980, Table 2)	Illinois Willman and Frye (1970) Evenson and others (1976)	Chronostratigraphic age
Outwash IV		11,600*	North Bay Stade	Port Maitland Gravel	Great Lakean	Late
Till IV	Multiple lobation	11,800		(missing)		
Outwash III		12,200*	(missing)	Gilbert Cove Clay	Two Creekan	Wisconsinan
Till III	S. 31°±2° E.	14,000*	Missouri Stade	Beaver River Till	Woodfordian	
——— UNCONFORMITY ———			Plum Point Interstade	Cape Cove Gravel	Farmdalian	
Outwash II			Cherry Tree(?) Interstade			
			Port Talbot Interstade	Salmon River Sand		
Till II	S. 63°±18° E.		Guildord Stade			Early Wisconsinan
Outwash I			St. Pierre(?) Interstade	Red Head and Little Brook Tills	Altonian	
Till I	S. 23°±1° E		Guildord(?) Stade Nicolet(?) Stade			

bedrock cores, although a few of them overlie high points on the bedrock surface. The drumlins are mainly of exceptionally well-compacted, well-graded till, typically containing about 15 percent clay-size by weight. Boulders are sparse, and large boulders are generally found on the surface or in the upper 3-4 m. Many drumlins contain some sorted and stratified sediment. In cliff exposures, the ratio of sorted sediment to till rarely exceeds 0.2. Fresh cliff exposures, such as can be seen in the spring when the frozen face of a drumlin has thawed and sloughed off (Kaye, 1967b), exhibit a well-defined layering and internal structure. The layering consists of parallel partings, generally marked by very thin, silty zones. Layering generally conforms to the drumlin shape, imparting an anticlinal structure. In places, these layers are distorted and sheared as though the entire mass had undergone intense deformation.

The bedrock surface is exposed beneath four of the harbor drumlins. These data, when examined in conjunction with other types of flow data, indicate that the Boston drumlins are the product of at least two different ice currents and that the streamlined shapes of some of them was the work of glacial flow subsequent to their deposition. The best evidence of this is where till clasts are of rock types that had to have been transported from a direction strongly divergent to the long axis of the drumlin. The elongated drumlin shapes, coupled with the sheared anticlinal structure, point to some sort of lateral squeezing together of earlier drift by flowing ice.

Stratigraphy

Perhaps the most complete stratigraphic section of Pleistocene deposits in the Boston area underlies the old Boston Peninsula, particularly Beacon Hill and its surroundings. Fortunately, this is an area where many deep excavations in recent years exposed these deposits to close study. This is also an area of intense structural deformation that had to be understood before the deposits could be arranged in a reasonable stratigraphic order.

Four drifts are recognized, each consisting of a couplet—till overlaid by outwash. Table 1 summarizes some of the characteristics of these deposits. Till I overlies bedrock directly and is the principal drumlin till. It is a very compact, well-graded deposit, medium greenish gray to slightly bluish gray where unoxidized and of a characteristic light-buff color where oxidized. As much as 11 m of surface oxidation have been measured in some drumlins. The till is slightly plastic when moist and has some cohesion when dry. Striated argillite and other local Boston Basin rocks make up the majority of clasts. When freshly exposed in building excavations, this till tends to puddle underfoot, and vertical faces spall after several days' exposure to the air—perhaps an elastic response to residual stresses built up over a long history of glacial loading. Striations on underly-

ing bedrock and lithology of the clasts show that the direction of glacial flow responsible for this deposit was approximately S. 22° E.

The overlying outwash is varied, ranging from coarse gravel through interbedded sand and clay to well-bedded silty clay and silt. In the eastern part of Beacon Hill, a large foreset gravel delta more than 30 m high, buried by deformed beds, belongs to outwash I. These deposits may constitute the sorted sediment that is found sheared and sandwiched between till in drumlins.

Till II overlies outwash I in many excavations in the Boston Peninsula. It tends to be slightly more greenish in color and more bouldery than till I but, otherwise, has about the same physical properties. It also forms part of some, if not all, drumlins. From the directions of grooves and striations on bedrock, lithologies of clasts, and the direction of drumlin elongation, this till was deposited by ice flowing to the east-southeast, more precisely, in a course that shifted within the range S. 45° E. to S. 81° E.

Outwash II forms the most distinctive and easily recognized stratigraphic unit in Beacon Hill, mostly because it is generally oxidized and, in places, somewhat decomposed. It was shown as drift II in an early attempt to establish the stratigraphy from an excavation in Bostom Common at the northeastern foot of Beacon Hill (Kaye, 1961).

Where exposed, the outwash is almost entirely sand and gravel, although in Beacon Hill there are thin, interbedded silt layers and thin, lenticular beds of greenish till. In borings along the margins of the Back Bay, there are clay layers interbedded with the sand. Much of the sand is a light-greenish-yellow color and characteristically silty and highly compact. On Beacon Hill, the upper part of the sand is massive and complexly intercalated with fine to coarse gravels, rich in cracked, well-rounded pebbles of argillite. These gravels are commonly either "openwork," that is, lacking in interstitial sand, or the pore spaces between pebbles are filled with dense light-gray to nearly white silt which appears to be the same material as that which makes up altered soft argillite. This interstitial material probably represents pebbles of soft argillite, originally part of the gravel, that were somehow squeezed and crushed between pebbles of stronger rocks.

Outwash II generally shows the effects of prolonged weathering. Argillite pebbles are variously decomposed. Pebbles of the openwork gravel, and, particularly, the argillite pebbles, are coated with crusts of black manganese oxide, and some pebbles consist entirely of soft, black, pulverulent manganese oxide resembling peat balls.

For several years, the author considered this weathered outwash to be pre-Wisconsinan in age, in spite of the fact that its stratigraphic position was well up in the Beacon Hill section (Kaye, 1976b, c; 1979). The author explained its stratigraphic position as disordered, the result of glacial thrusting during the formation of the Beacon Hill moraine.

Careful reanalysis of the data has led to the conclusions that the outwash is probably in its correct stratigraphic position in Beacon Hill and that the weathering probably dates from the long interstadial that separated the early and late parts of the Wisconsinan Glaciation (Table 1).

Exposed in the eastern part of Beacon Hill, overlying outwash II, was a thin bluish- to greenish-gray till, rarely more than 3 m in thickness. This fragmentary till is certainly late Wisconsinan (Woodfordian) in age. It was missing in the Boston Common garage excavation and in many other excavations in the area, although it probably is present in parts of the Back Bay beneath the thick clay (outwash III). The small drumlinoidal hill that fronted the harbor in downtown Boston (Fort Hill), before it was leveled in the 19th century, may have consisted of this till (Kaye, 1976a; Whitehill, 1968).

In the central Boston area, outwash III consists mainly of clay—the clay that is informally referred to in the engineering literature as the Boston "blue clay," although its moist color is typically light greenish gray, more rarely, medium gray. This blanket of well-bedded clay, silt, and interbedded fine sand underlies much of Massachusetts Bay, Boston Harbor, the rivers, and surrounding lowlands that ramify from the harbor, including the Charles and Mystic Rivers, the Back Bay, and other former estuarine marshlands that are now landfills. Clay thicknesses as great as 75 m are known. Traced up the valley of the Charles River, clay and interbedded sand grade into littoral sand and, thence, into fluviatile outwash consisting of sand and gravel. The clay, therefore, represents the fine-grained (rock-flour) component of Woodfordian outwash, deposited in coastal marine waters. The deposit is thickest in Boston Harbor and the lower valley of the Charles River, thinning under Massachusetts Bay to the north, east, and south. The topographic trough provided by Boston Basin appears to have been a major drainageway for glacial meltwater coming from the west. Boston formed the apex of a large, submarine, clay delta of outwash origin.

Except for sparse foraminifera (Phleger, 1949), fossils are lacking in the clay of Boston. About 5-10 km to the northeast of Boston, however, in the Winthrop, Revere, Lynn, and Salem areas, the lower part of the clay contains an abundant, cool-water fauna, consisting of mollusks (dominated by *Yoldia sapotilla*), barnacles, starfish, ostracodes, and foraminifera. Four radiocarbon dates of the large barnacle, *Balanus hameri* (Ascanius), have yielded a mean age of 14,000 years B.P. (Kaye and Barghoorn, 1964). The absence of fossils at Boston probably reflects the low salinity and excessive turbidity of the water at the mouth of a major outwash river.

Knowledge of outwash III is based mainly on borings, geotechnical laboratory tests, and on hundreds of kilometers of subbottom seismic profiles of Boston Harbor and Massachusetts Bay. A typical subbottom profile shows that the clay possesses excellent stratification, with the sandy strata showing up as dark lines (Figure 5). The most striking characteristic of the bedding apparent on these profiles is that it conforms to the surface of the basement on which it was deposited, whether this was bedrock or drift, which imparts a folded appearance to the clay, with anticlines overlying basement highs and synclines overlying low areas on the basement surface. A second feature that is apparent on subbottom profile which cannot be deduced from other types of subsurface data, is that everywhere the surface of the clay has been eroded and, consequently, the sedimentary section is truncated. Because of this erosion of "folded" deposits, the youngest clay in the sedimentary section is confined to the centers of synclines, and the age of the clay at the surface of the deposit becomes progressively older as one moves towards the sides of the synclines (Figures 5, 6). The reverse relationship, of course, holds for anticlines, with the oldest beds being confined to the center of the fold.

On land, where subbottom seismic profiling is not available, a reasonable approximation of the folded configuration of the clay can be made by obtaining a good profile of the underlying surface. Figure 6, a geologic profile of the Back Bay, shows how this surface was used to deduce the structure of the overlying clay.

The clays are well-stratified and are rhythmically bedded. Rhythms occur on three scales. Clay stratification is not evident on fresh exposure because of the uniform coloration of the moist clay, but, on partial drying, alternate beds of finer and coarser-grained sediment can be seen—either alternate beds of clay and silt or silt and internally laminated fine sand. The average thickness of a layer is about 1 cm, although there is considerable variation here. The next larger rhythm averages about 50 cm in thickness and shows up well on seismic profiles, particularly those tuned to pick it up. This represents an alternation of more clayey and more sandy deposition within the cycles of the 1 cm layers. Finally, subbottom profiles reveal in the upper part of the clay section a well-defined, 3-5 m cycle consisting of strong sand zones separated by more clayey material.

In places, the clay of outwash III is structurally disturbed. In the Back Bay and parts of Boston Harbor, the upper 2-5 m may be broken, folded, and badly contorted. In subbottom profiles, this zone appears structureless; in undisturbed samples from borings, it is apparent only on partial drying out. Some subbottom profiles show thrust faulting limited to the upper part of the clay section. Others reveal small thrust faults only in the basal part of the clay. Several of the latter type were exposed in deep excavations in the Boston Peninsula and proved to be most puzzling. They were lined with about 1 cm of brecciated argillite bedrock, even where both walls of the faults were of clay.

Another type of clay deformation that shows up strikingly on seismic profiles consists of large, funnel-shaped downfolds that involve the entire thickness of clay and gen-

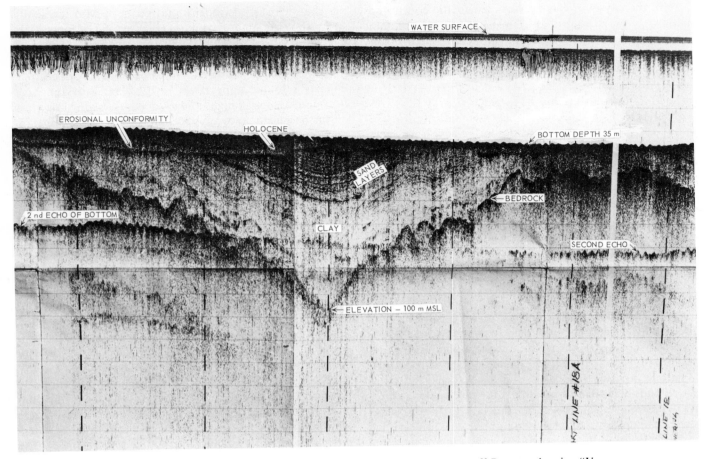

Figure 5. Subbottom seismic profile in western Massachusetts Bay, off Boston, showing "V-shaped" trough in bedrock filled with clay and, in upper part, interbedded sand (outwash III). Note conformable bedding, erosional unconformity, and overlying postglacial sand. Bottom of trough at about -95 m (mean sea level).

erally are 100-200 m across. These structures appear to represent collapse of the clay over isolated blocks of glacial ice, left behind from the wastage of the preceding glaciation (III) and weighted to the bottom of this late glacial Massachusetts Bay by englacial rock debris.

The top 1-3 m of the clay are generally oxidized, and this is true even where the top of the clay is currently below sea level. This last condition is attributed to subaerial exposure that took place subsequent to 12,600 years B.P., when relative sea level fell below present sea level (Kaye and Barghoorn, 1964).

As much as 10 m of till (till IV) overlie the clay in several places at the margins of the Back Bay (Kaye, 1961). Similar till occurs above the clay in Cambridge between Harvard Square and the Fresh Pond area. This till was deposited by a glacial readvance, called the Fresh Pond readvance by Chute (1959), which is now known to have consisted of three separate ice lobes rather than the single lobe that descended the valley of the Mystic Lakes to the Fresh Pond area suggested by that author. One of these

lobes was a large ice tongue that descended the Charles River Valley from the west; another lobe moved south, more or less, along the axis of the Malden River; and the third was the Mystic Lakes-Fresh Pond lobe. The margins of these ice tongues, which coalesced at several places, are marked by low morainic ridges (see below). The glacial source of the readvance is thought to have been residual glacial ice on the uplands surrounding the Boston Basin that had persisted after the general disappearance of Woodfordian ice from the region. The persistence of this coastal

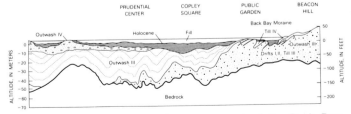

Figure 6. Geologic cross section across part of the Back Bay, extending southwest from Beacon Hill and showing Quaternary deposits. Vertical scale exaggeration 20X.

ice cap was probably due to the special climatic conditions along the coast that prevailed at the time—that is, a belt of abnormally high precipitation brought on by moist onshore, oceanic winds (Kaye, 1980a). The readvance accompanied a sharp climatic deterioration, of which there are indications in outwash IV, as detailed below.

Outwash IV consists of current-bedded, fine to coarse sand, gravelly sand, and, more rarely, fine to medium gravel. In most places, it is underlaid by clay (outwash III). Much of the city of Cambridge is underlaid by this outwash, where it forms a plain sloping gradually to the east. Deposits of outwash IV are found in discontinuous low-lying terraces on both sides of the lower Charles River. A large patch of outwash IV occupies the central part of the Back Bay (Figure 6).

Cold-climate features are conspicuous in outwash IV. For example, in the lower part of the outwash, there is an abundance of fragile, shaly chips, as much as 8 cm across, which were derived from argillite pebbles split along bedding or slaty cleavage by ice action. In addition, the upper 2-3 m of clay (outwash III), where it underlies outwash IV, have a prominent prismatic structure, the "cubical jointing" noticed by Marbut and Woodworth (1896, p. 991), and which the present author attributes to freezing and the formation of a network of thin ice partings—a process very similar to one active today during cold winters in the clays of Glacial Lake Hitchcock along the sides of the Connecticut River Valley. A slab of prismatic clay, about 1.5 m in length, found embedded in the lower part of outwash IV, must have been torn from the bed, or bank, of the outwash stream and transported and deposited as a coherent, frozen mass.

Large, remnant ice blocks occupied the Back Bay and the lowlands of the Charles River when outwash IV was being deposited in these areas. One of these blocks occupied the valley of the Charles River downstream from Harvard University; at least two others occupied the Back Bay.

Moraines

There are two morainic systems of different age in the central Boston area: Beacon Hill, the oldest (Kaye, 1976a, b, c), and the Fresh Pond, Back Bay, and Charles River moraines, which comprise a single system although formed by three ice tongues (Figure 7).

Knowledge of the geology of Beacon Hill is uneven. The interior, the eastern portion of the hill, and the lower slope on its northern and eastern sides are well known from deep excavations and borings, but the rest of the hill is known only from a single line of deep borings made at the turn of the century for the subway tunnel (Boston Society of Civil Engineers, 1961). Taken all together, however, the entire hill seems to have much the same structure and composition.

Beacon Hill consists mainly of a pileup of outwash I, till II, and outwash II over an undeformed core consisting of thick till I and a large foreset delta of coarse gravel (Figure 8). The deformed beds consist of clay, sand, gravel, and till which have been thrust, in part, over the core but which also seem to have been complexly deformed in a manner that is difficult to explain. Some beds have been folded. There are many high-angle faults. In places, on the lower flanks of the hill, there are large festoons of tight, overturned folds in clay and sand, which may have been formed by solifluction down the slope of the hill. Whether the Beacon Hill pileup represents an end moraine, a subglacial squeezing together (not unlike the squeezing actions probably responsible for drumlins), some other glacial or glaciotectonic process, or even a combination of several processes is not clear. The deformed deposits of Beacon Hill are unconformably overlaid, up to an altitude of 10 m, by undeformed beach sands of outwash III. The Beacon Hill moraine, or deformation, therefore, appears to have been associated with the early part of the late Wisconsinan and possibly was formed during the general advance of Woodfordian ice, perhaps by a local readvance.

The Fresh Pond, Charles River, and Back Bay moraines, on the other hand, were clearly built by the local readvance that deposited drift IV. The combined moraine varies considerably in composition, structure, and topographic prominence from place to place. The Back Bay lobe stopped against the lower slope of Beacon Hill. Excavations in lower Boston Common show the type of morainic push structures that were developed there. These consist of

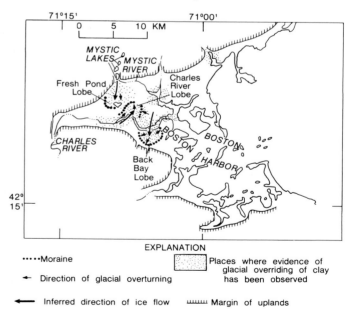

EXPLANATION

·····Moraine

→ Direction of glacial overturning

← Inferred direction of ice flow

▭ Places where evidence of glacial overriding of clay has been observed

⊔⊔⊔ Margin of uplands

Figure 7. Fresh Pond, Charles River, and Back Bay moraines and areas that have yielded evidence of glacial overriding of clay (outwash IV).

outwash II, outwash III, and till IV folded into three anti-clines, overturned to the northeast towards Beacon Hill (Kaye, 1961). Part of a push ridge is present in the low clay hill in the center of the Common ("Powder House Hill" of colonial times; Kaye, 1976a). Southward from Boston Common, along the western side of Boston Peninsula and including Boston Neck, is highly compact, deformed clay overlain in places by lenticular till. The neck itself is of deformed clay and is interpreted to be part of the moraine. On the western side of the Back Bay, morainic deformation is more intense. A chain of foundation excavations there exposed much the same type of thrusting, folding, and faulting as was seen in the Common garage excavation, except that here the structures are overturned to the west. Therefore, at the margins of the Back Bay, a semicircle of low ridges is seen, consisting of outwash III and older de-posits that have been centrifugally thrusted and folded. The shape of the entire Back Bay ice tongue is not known, but it probably involved a confluence of ice moving south from the Malden area and ice moving east along the Charles River trench.

Ice moving east along the Charles River trench also spread to the north, into the area that now centers around Harvard University. Its moraine, which includes Mount Auburn Cemetery, Harvard Observatory Hill, Shady Hill, and Dana Hill, consists largely of badly contorted clay that shows overturning outward to the north and northeast (Figure 4).

The Fresh Pond moraine, which was described by Chute (1959) encircles that pond on the west and southwest as a very low ridge. The ridge is lost at the southern margin of the lake, where it appears to lie buried by sandy outwash.

POSTGLACIAL DEPOSITS

These deposits include two contrasting types of sedi-ment. There are gray clays similar in appearance and in most physical properties to the clay of outwash III, and there are organic-rich estuarine sediments and salt-marsh peat. Both types of sediment unconformably overlie older deposits in the Boston Harbor estuary. Postglacial deposits are mostly less than 13 m in thickness, although thicknesses of 26 m are known. The top of these deposits generally falls below mean high water. In addition to these estuarine sed-iments, peaty, fresh-water, swamp deposits are found at all elevations.

The geology of postglacial deposits is keyed to sea-level changes. While the onset of postglacial time here was marked by climatic warming and the disappearance of gla-cial ice, an event that took place about 11,650 years B.P. according to the radiocarbon age of the base of postglacial organic sediments under the new John Hancock Tower, the depositional story of the postglacial clay started earlier,

when relative sea level[1] began falling about 13,000 years ago from its high of about altitude 16 m. This fall brought relative sea level down to an altitude of −23 m about 10,500 years ago. This negative sea-level movement was caused by the rate of crustal rise from glacial unloading exceeding the rate of eustatic sea-level rise from glacial melting (Kaye and Barghoorn, 1964).

The drop in relative sea level had an interesting effect on the clay of outwash III. As sea level fell, the clayey bottom was progressively exposed to wave-base erosion and, later, to subaerial erosion. Much of the clay blanket, particularly at higher elevations, was eroded entirely by this means. At the same time, clay that was stirred back into suspension by wave action moved downslope as turbidity currents, eventually coming to rest in closed depressions on the floor of Boston Harbor and Massachusetts Bay. There, it built up deposits that are readily recognized on subbot-tom seismic profiles because they are horizontally bedded, unlike the conformably bedded earlier clays. The contact between the two clays is generally sharply delineated as a result of the unconformity separating them.

The deposition of reworked outwash III clay appar-ently continued well into postglacial time. These clays are found widely: in the estuary systems of the lower Charles River, Mystic River, and Malden River and in the lowlands separating Charlestown from Somerville and East Cam-bridge, where they can be recognized by the presence of a layer of till IV or of outwash IV separating them from underlying clay III. Postglacial clay is particularly thick in the lowland separating Fresh Pond and Spy Pond in North Cambridge. Intensive study of this clay for the new subway excavation has shown it to be highly sensitive and to have a higher natural water content than the more consolidated older clays of outwash III.

As sea-level fell, the Back Bay emerged as a poorly drained meadowland, dotted with shallow ponds, with a low, drier terrace rising in the central section—a terrace that is now overlain, in part, by the Prudential Center and adjacent Massachusetts Avenue. Trees rapidly became es-tablished. The base of the postglacial organic deposits in the Back Bay, therefore, consists of pond deposits and woody peat ("Lower" peat of Johnson, 1942, 1949; Kaye and Barghoorn, 1964). About 8,500 years ago, after an in-terval of relative sea-level stability that lasted approxi-mately 2,000 years, sea level began a slow rise to its present position. The rich, riverside land of the Back Bay foun-dered slowly under the spreading estuary. Its forests were killed and buried beneath bay muds rich in marine life. These black silts, smelling of H_2S, are richly fossiliferous (Johnson, 1942, 1949; Kaye, 1976a). The salt marshes that flourish along the margins of the spreading Back Bay inter-

---

[1] *Relative* sea level, not to be confused with *eustatic* sea level. Relative sea level is the resultant of two independent movements: eustatic sea-level movement and crustal movement. See Kaye and Barghoorn (1964).

fingered with dark silts in a complex relationship, as revealed by excavations into these deposits.

IMPACT ON ENGINEERING

The Back Bay

The rapid development of the Back Bay in the late 19th century (Whitehill, 1968) focused engineering attention on the special foundation conditions found there: high water table; weak, compressible, organic-rich deposits; soft clay; and, here and there, a sand stratum between. In a few decades, the entire Back Bay was completely covered with large townhouses and churches, many of which are still standing. All these structures are supported by wooden piles, most of which were driven through the estuarine deposits to bear either on the sands of outwash IV (Figure 6) or on the oxidized crust of the clay, although a small percentage rested on friction piles driven into unoxidized clay (Aldrich, 1970). The coming to the Back Bay of larger and heavier buildings near the middle of this century pointed up the need for foundations other than shallow piles, particularly, in places where the outwash IV stratum was missing. Experience in the city had already shown the disruptive effects on neighboring buildings of driving dense arrays of long displacement piles into the clay. In addition, the new science of soil mechanics brought with it an understanding of the process of clay consolidation and how it could be computed in advance of construction (Kaye, 1950). Differential clay consolidation and uneven settlement of a building could be predicted, and it became clear that using the clay for bearing was unadvisable for these larger buildings. The floating foundation that exerted no load on the clay was one solution to the problem (Lincoln, 1978). This technique was first used in the Back Bay in the New England Mutual Life Insurance Company Building, on Boylston Street (Casagrande and Fadum, 1944). The foundation excavation was entirely confined to the fill and underlying estuarine deposits. The weight of soil excavated for the foundation was nicely balanced against the total weight of the building, less the buoyancy forces acting on the submerged basement, that is, that part of the basement falling below the water table. The basement structure itself was a water-tight box and acted in the manner of a ship's hull, while the building simulated the ship's superstructure.

A second solution to the problem of differential consolidation of the clay, particularly where the Outwash IV stratum is present, is the reinforced concrete mat. This foundation has the advantage of distributing building loads evenly and of resisting strain from differential ground settlement. However, for the support of very heavy structures, the practice of driving displacement piles through clay to bedrock has not disappeared. Both the 52-story Prudential Insurance Tower and the 61-story John Hancock Insurance Company Tower are supported by steel caissons and piles driven through the clay. In the case of the Prudential Tower, the supporting caissons are constructed of 76-cm diameter open-steel pipe, driven to depths ranging from 36 to 56 m through clay to underlying argillite. The soil column that filled a pipe was extruded by compressed air. A cylindrical hole into rock, approximately 6 m deep, was then churn drilled through the empty pipe, after which a steel "H" beam was placed down the center of the hole and the entire opening was then filled with concrete. The Prudential Tower was located in the center of a large cleared space and the disruptive effect on the neighborhood of the caisson driving was minimal.

The forest of nineteenth-century spruce piles under the Back Bay has created a conservation problem. The piles decay rapidly on drying out and are, therefore, vulnerable to a lowering of the water table. In order to insure against this, particularly during construction, water withdrawn with the dewatering of excavations is used to recharge the water table outside the perimeter of a site. This was done on a large scale for the extensive excavation for the Prudential Center. The effects of this program on the water table outside the site were monitored by a series of observation wells (Ball, 1962).

Boston Peninsula

The heterogeneity of soils and the structural complexities that occur in the Boston Peninsula (Figure 8) have resulted in a variety of foundation types. Piles have been used in thick clay, spread footings, and reinforced concrete mats on sand, gravel, and till. Recent construction has favored mat foundations for high-rise buildings, but one building, the Boston Company Building, is partially supported by large concrete caissons on soft bedrock (Johnson, 1972).

Most of the clay in Beacon Hill belongs to outwash I and differs from the younger clay (outwash III) in being stiffer and structurally deformed. As an example of a problem arising from this deformation, the foundation of the Leverett Saltonstall State Office Building on Cambridge Street can be cited. Here, piles were to be driven through the clay to find support on underlying gravel. The piles of prescribed length proved to be too short. The reason was a sharp downfold in the clay and underlying gravel that had not been indicated by exploratory borings which formed the basis for specifying pile lengths. This example points to the difficulty in drafting meangingful geologic profiles of Beacon Hill, profiles that correctly identify surficial geologic units. A certain flexibility in foundation design has been found desirable so that changes can be readily made in the field as excavation progresses.

Foundation excavations in and around Boston Peninsula have encountered various seepage problems. Sand beds in or at the base of the clay are frequently responsible for unanticipated seepage. During construction of a Boston Edison substation on Kingston Street, relief wells had to be drilled to eliminate seepage of this type into deep, open caissons. In the excavation for the underground garage in lower Boston Common, a large fold brought water-bearing gravel above grade, flooding the excavation until a well-point system had been installed (Kaye, 1961). The folding and the seepage problems had not been anticipated from borings.

Bedrock

Soft-rock alteration probably is responsible for most of the bad tunneling ground in the Boston Basin. Unfortunately, much of the alteration is restricted to relatively narrow zones or beds that are readily missed by exploratory borings. The effect of this soft rock on foundations for large buildings has not been fully tested because few such buildings are supported by this material. An exception is the 41-story Boston Company Building on Washington and Court Streets, near the foot of Beacon Hill. One of four large-belled piers at the corners of this tower is successfully supported by moderately softened argillite (Johnson, 1972).

Cleavage and joints in deeply buried argillite have been found to be a source of water under considerable artesian pressure. The sockets drilled into argillite at the base of the caissons under the Prudential Tower rapidly filled with water that could not be controlled sufficiently to allow close inspection of the sockets (Ball, 1962). In building the new Charles River Dam between Boston and Charlestown, borings showed that hydrostatic pressures in fissured argillite were such as to threaten a blowout of the overlying till I inside the construction cofferdam. A ring of relief wells was drilled into bedrock, and these reduced uplift pressures to a satisfactory level. It was noticed here that the hydrostatic head varied with the tides in Boston Harbor, an observation that had been made much earlier by Lathrop (1800) in a deep well for the then new State House near the top of Beacon Hill.

SOME THOUGHTS FOR THE ENGINEERING GEOLOGIST

When viewed from the general perspective of much of New England's bedrock geology, with its intensely deformed metamorphic and igneous terrane, the Boston Basin seems like an island of calm set in a sea of turbulence. The rocks are practically unmetamorphosed, folding is open rather than tight, and faulting, though dense, is not severe, at least not to the point of becoming a difficult problem to the engineer. The paucity of outcrops in the central Boston area is a disadvantage to both the geologist and the engineer, for what we don't see, we don't know.

This means that in tunnel studies, faults and localized zones of soft-rock alteration are difficult to identify by the usual method of randomly spaced exploratory borings. Nor can bedrock surface be defined precisely with borings, and it is because of this that geophysical methods are generally called on to eliminate the possibility of unknown deep bedrock depressions along tunnel lines.

The Quaternary geology is a challenge to engineering geologists in many areas, most particularly, in the moraines. The problem of recognizing and separating the several drifts, particularly, where they occur in isolation, may seem academic to some, but, in truth, it is the key to understanding ground water movement and the existence of potential avenues of seepage. A new area that remains to be investigated is the subtle "folded" structure and the stratigraphy of the clay (outwash III). Surely, studies along these lines will prove valuable, both from a scientific and from an engineering point of view. Another subject that merits investigation is the nature of deposits beneath the clay in much of the Back Bay, which all too commonly have been classified as "till" on geological profiles.

Lastly, a word should be said about the special role engineering geologists play in the geology of Boston. In a covered terrane of few outcrops, the geology is subsurface. Learning about it occurs mainly through borings, and it is the engineering geologist who has access to borings, not the academic geologist. The engineering geologist, therefore, should make an effort to get the most from his borings. Rather than see the samples once and, then, only briefly on the way to the lab, or on the way through the lab, he should follow the entire exploratory process and then follow the samples until there is no more to be learned from them. He should be concerned about "lost" samples, or stratigraphic intervals that were not sampled. "No data" does not mean "no data of significance." Later, foundation excavations should be studied, not only to check reality against borings and the interpretations made from them, but also so that the engineering geologist can see, face to face, the true nature of the geology (Figure 8). The engineering geologist will find this to be the ultimate reward for his efforts.

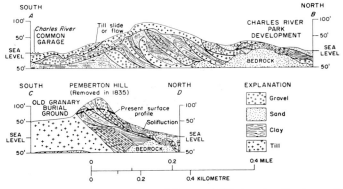

Figure 8. Two cross sections of Beacon Hill showing the type of complexity revealed by deep foundation excavations.

REFERENCES CITED

Aldrich, H. P., 1970, Back Bay, Boston: Boston Society of Civil Engineers Journal, v. 57, p. 1–33.

Ball, D. G., 1962, Prudential Center Foundations: Boston Society of Civil Engineers Journal, v. 49, p. 229–244.

Billings, M. P., 1929, Structural geology of the eastern part of the Boston Basin: American Journal of Science, 5th ser., v. 18, p. 97–137.

—— 1976, Geology of the Boston Basin: Geological Society of America Memoir 146, p. 5–30.

Billings, M. P., and Rahm, D. A., 1966, Geology of the Malden Tunnel, Massachusetts: Boston Society of Civil Engineers Journal, v. 53, no. 2, p. 116–141.

Billings, M. P., and Tierney, F. L., 1964, Geology of the city tunnel extension, Greater Boston, Massachusetts: Boston Society of Civil Engineers Journal, v. 51, no. 2, p. 111–154.

Boston Society of Civil Engineers, 1961, Boring data from Greater Boston: Boston Society of Civil Engineers, 280 p.

—— 1969, Boring data from Greater Boston, Sec. 1—Boston Peninsula: Boston Society of Civil Engineers Journal, v. 56, p. 131–291.

—— 1970, Boring data from Greater Boston, Sec. 2—Roxbury: Boston Society of Civil Engineers Journal, v. 57, p. 185–291.

—— 1971, Boring data from Greater Boston, Sec. 3—South Boston: Boston Society of Civil Engineers Journal, v. 58, p. 51–63.

Casagrande, A., and Fadum, R., 1944, Application of soil mechanics in designing building foundations: American Society of Civil Engineers Transactions, v. 109, p. 382–490.

Chute, N. E., 1959, Glacial geology of the Mystic Lakes-Fresh Pond area, Massachusetts: U.S. Geological Survey Bulletin 1061-F, p. 187–216.

Crosby, I. B., 1937, Ground water conditions of parts of Middlesex, Worcester, and Norfolk Counties in the buried valleys of the preglacial Merrimack, Sudbury, and Charles Rivers: Massachusetts Department of Public Health, Public Document 34, Annual Report year ending November 30, 1937, p. 219–224.

—— 1939, Ground water in the pre-glacial buried valleys of Massachusetts: New England Water Works Association Journal, v. 53, p. 372–383.

Crosby, W. O., 1899, Geological history of the Nashua Valley during the Tertiary and Quaternary periods: Technology Quarterly, v. 12, p. 288–324.

Dreimanis, A., and Goldthwait, R. P., 1973, Wisconsin glaciation in the Huron, Erie, and Ontario Lobes: Geological Society of America Memoir 136, p. 71–106.

Emerson, B. K., 1917, Geology of Massachusetts and Rhode Island: U.S. Geological Survey Bulletin 597, 289 p.

Evenson, E. B., Farrand, W. R., Mickelson, D. M., Eschman, D. F., and Maher, L. J., 1976, Great Lakean Substage—a replacement for Valderan in the Lake Michigan Basin: Quaternary Research, v. 6, p. 411–424.

Grant, D. R., 1980, Quaternary stratigraphy of southwestern Nova Scotia—glacial events of sea-level changes: Geological Association of Canada Annual Meeting, Halifax, Guidebook to Excursion 9, 60 p.

Johnson, E. G., 1972, Unique foundation features—the Boston Company Building, Boston, Massachusetts: Boston Society of Civil Engineers Journal, v. 59, p. 170–193.

Johnson, F., ed., 1942, The Boylston Street Fishweir, Papers: Robert S. Peabody Foundation for Archeology, v. 2, 212 p.

—— 1949, The Boylston Street Fishweir II, Papers: Robert S. Peabody Foundation for Archeology, v. 4, no. 1, 133 p.

Judson, S., 1949, The Pleistocene stratigraphy of Boston, Massachusetts, and its relation to the Boylston Street Fishweir, *in* Johnson, F., ed., The Boylston Street Fishweir II: Robert S. Peabody Foundation for Archeology, v. 4, no. 1, p. 7–48.

Kaye, C. A., 1950, Principles of soil mechanics as viewed by a geologist, *in*

Trask, P.D., ed., Applied sedimentation: New York, John Wiley & Sons, p. 93–112.

—— 1961, Pleistocene stratigraphy of Boston, Massachusetts, *in* Short papers in the geologic and hydrologic sciences: U.S. Geological Survey Professional Paper 424-B, p. B73–B76.

—— 1967a, Kaolinization of bedrock of the Boston, Massachusetts, area, *in* Geological Survey research 1965: U.S. Geological Survey Professional Paper 575-C, p. C165–C172.

—— 1967b, Erosion of a sea cliff, Boston Harbor, Massachusetts, *in* Farquhar, O. C., ed., Economic geology in Massachusetts: Springfield, Massachusetts University Graduate School Publication, p. 521–528.

—— 1976a, The geology and early history of the Boston, Massachusetts area—a bicentennial approach: U.S. Geological Survey Bulletin 1476, 78 p.

—— 1976b, Beacon Hill end moraine, Boston—new explanation of an important urban feature, *in* Coates, D. R., ed., Urban geomorphology: Geological Society of America Special Paper 174, p. 7–20.

—— 1976c, Outline of the Pleistocene geology of the Boston Basin, *in* Geology of southeastern New England, New England Intercollegiate Geological Conference, 68th Annual Meeting: Princeton Science Press, p. 46–63.

—— 1979, Engineering geologic framework of the Boston Basin, *in* Hatheway, A. W., ed., Engineering geology in New England: American Association of Civil Engineers Convention, Boston, Preprint 3602, p. 1–17.

—— 1980a, Late Wisconsinan glaciation of Martha's Vineyard and a peripheral ice cap for coastal New England [abs.]: Geological Society of America Abstracts with Programs, v. 12, no. 2, p. 44.

—— 1980b, Bedrock geology, Boston North, Boston South, and Newton quadrangles, Massachusetts: U.S. Geological Survey Map MF-1241.

—— (in press), Discovery of a late Triassic basin in a major Early Paleozoic suture zone north of Boston, Massachusetts, and its implications as to post-Paleozoic faulting in eastern Massachusetts: American Journal of Science.

Kaye, C. A., and Barghoorn, E., 1964, Late Quaternary sea-level change and crustal rise at Boston, Massachusetts, with notes on the autocompaction of peat: Geological Society of American Bulletin, v. 75, p. 63–80.

Kaye, C. A., and Zartman, R. E., 1980, A Late Proterozoic Z to Cambrian age for the stratified rocks of the Boston Basin, Massachusetts, U.S.A., *in* Wones, D. R., ed., The Caledonides in the U.S.A.: Virginia Polytechnic Institute and State University, Department of Geological Sciences, Memoir 2, p. 257–264.

King, A. F., 1980, The birth of the Caledonides—late Precambrian rocks of the Avalon Peninsula, Newfoundland, and their correlatives in the Appalachian-orogen, *in* Wones, D. R., ed., The Caledonides in the U.S.A.: Virginia Polytechnic Institute and State University, Department of Geological Sciences, Memoir 2, p. 3–8.

LaForge, L., 1932, Geology of the Boston area, Massachusetts: U.S. Geological Survey Bulletin 839, 105 p.

Lathrop, J., 1800, An account of the springs and wells on the peninsula of Boston, with an attempt to explain the manner in which they are supplied: American Academy of Arts and Sciences Memoirs, v. 3, p. 57–67.

Lenk, L., Strother, P. K., Kaye, C. A., and Barghoorn, E. S., 1982, Proterozoic Z age of the Boston Basin, Massachusetts—new evidence from microfossils: Science, v. 216, no. 4546, p. 619–620.

Lincoln, E. H., 1978, Influence of geologic conditions on building foundation engineering in Boston, Massachusetts: Cambridge, Harvard University, Dept. of Geology, (Undergraduate thesis), 65 p.

Marbut, C. F., and Woodworth, J. B., 1896, The clays about Boston, *in* Glacial brick clays of Rhode Island and southeastern Massachusetts: U.S. Geological Survey 17th Annual Report, 1895, pt. 1, p. 989–1004.

Phleger, F. B., Jr., 1949, The Foraminifera, *in* Johnson, F., ed., The

Boylston Street Fishweir II: Robert S. Peabody Foundation for Archeology, v. 4, no. 1, p. 99–108.

Rahm, D. A., 1962, Geology of the main drainage tunnel, Boston, Massachusetts: Boston Society of Civil Engineers Journal, v. 49, p. 319–368.

Skehan, J. W., 1973, Subduction zone between PaleoAmerican and PaleoAfrican plates in New England: Geofisica International, Instituto de Geofisica, Cuidad Universiteria, Mexico City, v. 13, p. 291–308.

Terasmae, J., and Dreimanis, A., 1976, Quaternary stratigraphy of south Ontario, *in* Mahaney, W. C., ed., Quaternary stratigraphy of North America: Stroudsburg, Pennsylvania, Dowden, Hutchinson, and Ross, p. 51–63.

Upson, J. E., and Spencer, C. W., 1964, Bedrock valleys of the New England coast as related to fluctuations of sea level: U.S. Geological Survey Professional Paper 454-M, p. M1-M44.

Whitehill, W. M., 1968, Boston, a topographical history: Cambridge, Harvard University Press, 299 p.

Willman, H. B., and Frye, J. C., 1970, Pleistocene of Illinois: Illinois State Geological Survey Bulletin 94.

Worcester, J. R., 1914, Boston foundations: Boston Society of Civil Engineers Journal, v. 1, p. 1–30; Discussions, p. 179–248 and 395–417.

Manuscript Received by the Society May 11, 1982
Manuscript Accepted June 1, 1982

Geological Society of America
Reviews in Engineering Geology, Volume V
1982

Geology and deep tunnels in Chicago

T. C. Buschbach
Illinois Geological Survey
Champaign, IL 61820

R. T. Cyrier
The Metropolitan Sanitary District of Greater Chicago
Chicago, IL 60611

G. E. Heim
Harding Lawson Associates
Oak Brook, IL 60521

ABSTRACT

Low-gradient streams and generally flat topography have always presented a problem of flooding within the Chicago area. As settlement expanded, the flooding produced greater and more serious results. As early as 1816, the city's leaders began major engineering work to solve these problems. The latest efforts toward a solution currently include a system of over 100 miles (161 km) of large-diameter tunnels in the Chicago area bedrock. These tunnels will intercept overflow from combined sanitary and stormwater systems and convey it to temporary storage reservoirs prior to its being pumped to sewage treatment facilities.

Geologic investigations made during a study for the tunnel sites included test drilling and coring, geophysical logging of boreholes, laboratory testing of samples, seismic surveying, and testing for groundwater. The drilling, coring, and logging furnished data that have been of considerable help in mapping and describing the individual units of Silurian and Ordovician strata of the area. The seismic survey indicated numerous closed depressions on the surface of the bedrock and also suggested that several faults are present with displacements of 10 to 50 feet (3 to 15 m).

INTRODUCTION

The Chicago metropolitan area encompasses about 800 square miles (2072 km^2) of northeastern Illinois. As defined in this report, the area includes the City of Chicago, most of Cook County (Fig. 1), and narrow portions of eastern Du Page and northern Will Counties. The topography of the area is relatively flat, the maximum relief being not much more than 200 feet (61 m). The geomorphology is a relic of the recession of the Lake Michigan lobe of the Wisconsinan Stage of Quaternary glaciation. The terrain is characterized by a series of recessional end moraines separated by ground moraines and intermorainic lacustrine deposits, all of which are underlain by till. These glacial deposits lie upon an irregular weathered surface of Silurian dolomite. As a consequence of the topography and geomorphologic history, most streams and rivers have low gradients and are subject to flooding.

While the latest glacier still occupied the northern Lake Michigan Basin, a lake was formed at the southern end of the basin. Drainage from this lake (glacial Lake Chicago) was to the Mississippi River via the Illinois River. Continued recession of the glacier eventually exposed a lower outlet through the Straits of Mackinac to the St. Lawrence River. This outlet drained Lake Chicago to a point where a resistant dolomite ridge was exposed within

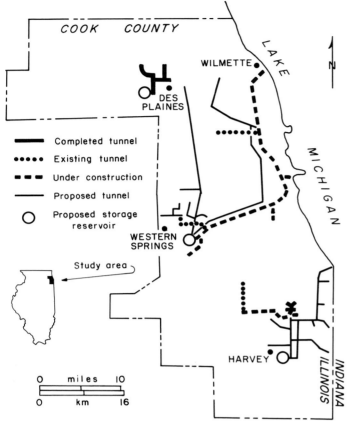

Figure 1. Study area showing status of rock tunnel construction in the greater Chicago area.

the southern outlet. This ridge, located approximately 10 miles (16 km) inland from the present Lake Michigan shore, constitutes a divide separating the Great Lakes Drainage Basin from the Mississippi-Missouri River Drainage Basin.

The lake side of the divide was left with wide areas of swampy ground, a few low dunes and small knolls, and a number of small streams with low gradients. The divide itself was low and flat, approximately 1½ miles (2.4 km) in width. Generally, it consisted of impassable swamps and marshes. At times of high lake levels or heavy rains, some water flowed across the divide.

As the population grew, additional lands were required, and ditches were dug to drain vast areas of swamp and marsh. Sanitation consisted of outdoor privies, and most drinking water was obtained from private shallow wells or from vendors who sold lake water from large water carts. Due to the low relief and poor drainage, flooding from heavy rainfall was common. At such times, many privies overflowed and contaminated the water wells.

In 1816, a tract of land through the marshy divide was purchased from the Indians to construct a canal. The canal (Illinois and Michigan Canal), 6 feet (2 m) deep and 80 feet

(24 m) wide, was completed in 1848. Coincident with the canal construction, water intake pipes were built out into the lake, and a water distribution system was constructed. A system of sewers was built to drain privies to the canal and rivers. In 1854, 6 years after the canal's completion, a rainstorm occurred which exceeded the canal's capacity. The city was flooded, and the water supply was contaminated. A resulting cholera epidemic wiped out more than 5.5 percent of the population.

In reaction to this epidemic, the water intakes were extended farther into the lake, the sewer and water systems were expanded and improved, the canal was deepened, and large pumps were installed in the canal to increase its flow. This work was not completed until 1881, due to reconstruction of the city after the great Chicago Fire of 1871. In August, 1885, more than 6 inches (15 cm) of rain fell. The pumps, canal, and rivers were overwhelmed. A great flush of polluted water was driven out into the lake beyond the water intakes. Within days, cholera, typhoid, and dysentery raged through the city. It is estimated that 175,000 people died that year from those diseases.

In 1890, the Chicago Sanitary District, now known as the Metropolitan Sanitary District of Greater Chicago, was established to formulate plans and direct work that would avoid repetition of those tragedies. The solution decided upon by the District was a total breach of the divide, interconnecting and regrading the rivers to reverse their flow, installing controlling locks at the river's mouth and about 30 miles (48 km) downstream at Lockport, Illinois, and modernizing the sewerage system. Construction began on the Main Channel (Chicago and Sanitary Ship Canal) in September, 1892, and it was completed in January, 1900. This canal, besides reversing the flow of the drainage, provided a navigable waterway 60 to 250 feet (18 to 76 m) wide and 24 feet (7 m) deep which connected the Mississippi River to the Great Lakes. From 1908 to 1922, the North Shore Channel and the Cal-Sag Channel were dug, and additional rivers were intercepted to divert their flows from the lake to the Main Channel.

The city's sewers continued to empty into the rivers and canals, and large quantities of lake water were required to dilute the wastes and flush them down the waterway. Canada and the bordering lake states protested Chicago's diversion of such large quantities of water. The Sanitary District was ordered by the courts to reduce its water usage. To maintain sanitary conditions in the waterways with the reduced diversion, the Sanitary District initiated a massive construction program to build large-diameter sewers and sewage treatment plants. Construction and process refinement are still in progress.

Presently, the greater Chicago area includes more than 5.5 million people and a multitude of industries. The latter adds a pollution load equivalent to approximately 4.5 million additional persons. Removal of storm water runoff and domestic and industrial wastes from an area such as this poses a tremendous challenge. The City of Chicago and the 117 suburban cities, towns, and villages generally install and maintain their own local sewers, but they are in the Sanitary District's service area. Throughout this service area, the Metropolitan Sanitary District of Greater Chicago built and maintains a system of intercepting sewers to collect the sewage and combined sewage-stormwater flow from these municipalities and direct the flow through one of its seven treatment plants.

The central 360 square miles (932 km^2) of the Chicago area have a combined sewer system that was built to receive both stormwater and raw sewage. Urbanization has increased the runoff of stormwater to the extent that the limited capacities of sewers and stream outlets in the existing system are inadequate at times of heavy rainfall. In some areas, the excess water collects in basements, underpasses, and streets. The water is polluted and becomes a hazard to health as well as to property. When the sewer and treatment system is inadequate to handle the stormwater, some relief is obtained at overflow points by the discharge of a mixture of stormwater and raw sewage into Illinois streams. On very rare occasions, when the overflow is too large for the waterway system, the mixture must be discharged into Lake Michigan.

To find a means of alleviating these conditions, the Metropolitan Sanitary District of Greater Chicago, the City of Chicago, and the Illinois State Division of Waterways began, in 1966, to study several possible solutions, including (1) separate storm and sewage systems, (2) temporary storage of polluted stormwaters in widely distributed surface sites until they can be processed through a treatment plant, and (3) a system of large-diameter deep tunnels and reservoirs for the temporary storage of polluted stormwaters.

Complete separation of the combined sewer systems would reduce the pollution due to spillage of excess stormwaters into the waterways. The cost of building separate sewer systems in the Chicago area, however, would be economically impractical. The disruption of traffic on nearly every street in the city and the inconveniences of reworking plumbing in so many houses and buildings are also almost inconceivable. This solution was rejected.

Temporary storage sites at the surface in and near Chicago would be expensive and difficult to obtain because urbanization is so extensive. It was determined, also, that even if the surface storage sites were available, the combined sewer overflows probably could not be delivered to the reservoirs at high enough rates to prevent local flooding. This solution was also rejected.

A system of deep, large-diameter tunnels and reservoirs was determined to be the most feasible and economical solution to the problem. Based on this decision, the Sanitary District proceeded to investigate and study the

scheme. Consultants were hired, and subsurface investigations were begun. By 1970, a distinctive plan was decided upon, and design studies were initiated. Preliminary geologic investigations of rock tunnels in the Chicago area are discussed by Buschbach and Heim (1972). The final concept was named the Tunnel and Reservoir Plan (TARP).

TUNNEL AND RESERVOIR PLAN

The Tunnel and Reservoir Plan is a definitive plan to provide for total capture and treatment of polluted sewer overflows and the detention of excess stream-storm flows. This plan calls for two distinct systems.

The first system includes a series of detention basins to be built along stream courses. These basins hold excess stormwater until the stream has the capacity to accept it. This system is applicable to newer suburban areas where separate storm and sanitary sewer systems have been installed. The purpose of this system is to retard the stormwater runoff, thereby lowering the impact of the stormwater arriving at the canals. This, in effect, increases the storage capacity of the canals so that they can accept the run-off from the central combined sewer area.

The second system is applicable to the City of Chicago and 52 older suburbs which have combined sanitary and storm sewers. In times of heavy rains, these sewers have inadequate capacity and overflow to the rivers and canals. On occasion, when overflows are too large for the waterways to handle, and to protect the central city from flooding, the lake lock must be opened, and the polluted water must be allowed to discharge to the lake. This second system was originally planned as a single unit but was revised to include two separate but integrated parts. These parts are referred to as Phase I and Phase II.

Phase I consists of three essential parts. First, a series of vertical drop shafts will be located to intercept the combined sanitary and stormwater overflow points of the existing sewer system. Second, a network of over 100 miles (161 km) of rock tunnels, 9 feet (3 m) to 33 feet (10 m) in diameter, located in dolomite formations about 150 to 350 feet (46 to 107 m) below the surface, will convey the overflow water from the vertical shafts. Third, large pumping stations will convey the polluted water to waste treatment plants for complete treatment before being discharged into the waterways.

Phase I is designed to provide for the temporary storage of mixed storm-water and sewage overflow. Upon completion, this project is expected to (a) protect the Illinois Waterway System and Lake Michigan from pollution by removing approximately 85 percent of the pollution load now released to the waterways, (b) partially reduce channel flows, thereby increasing the channel's capacity for capturing storm flow, (c) increase the hydraulic gradient on the local sewers, (d) reduce the flooding of basements, streets, and underpasses, (e) improve the degree of sewage treatment by maintaining an even flow through the treatment plants, and (f) increase the recreational potential of the water-ways by the reduced pollution.

Phase II is presently under evaluation for cost-effectiveness by the appropriate federal agencies responsible for its funding. It is the hope of the Metropolitan Sanitary District of Greater Chicago that the study will verify the original concept and that design and construction will be authorized in the near future.

The concept calls for continued interception of overflow water beyond the capacity of Phase I by an additional 22 miles (35 km) of 33 and 35 feet (10 and 11 m) diameter tunnels and conveyance of both this water and that of Phase I to large surface reservoirs (Fig. 2). Pumping stations will direct all the water to treatment plants. It is estimated that such a system would intercept all overflow from a 100-year storm. The system will virtually eliminate flooding and the resultant opening of the lake locks. The reduced pollution load on the canal and rivers will also result in an even greater increase in water quality.

Ultimately, TARP (Phase I and II) will consist of approximately 131 miles (211 km) of tunnels with diameters ranging from 9 to 35 feet (3 to 11 m). It will intercept the major overflows throughout the Chicagoland area. The rock tunnels will increase the hydraulic gradients of the existing sewers and, thereby, reduce flooding. The excavated reservoirs will provide temporary storage for the severe storm that might occur once in 100 years. All the stored water will be treated prior to release, thereby reducing pollution of the waterways by more than 95 percent.

The geologic requirements for the Tunnel and Reservoir Plan include: (1) rock strata thick enough for the tunnels and reservoirs, so that operation of the system can be chiefly by gravity, (2) rock capable of providing long term stability with a minimum of support and lining, (3) rock with fairly uniform characteristics, suitable for excavation by mole-tunneling machines, and (4) a minimum of groundwater flow.

During the course of study for the Tunnel and Reservoir Plan, from the technical feasibility through the individual project designs, a large number of geologic and hydrologic investigations were performed. Quarries and natural outcrops in northeastern Illinois and mines in northwestern Illinois and southwestern Wisconsin were studied to evaluate weathering characteristics, jointing, and mining characteristics of the various stratigraphic units that are present in the Chicago area. Data from wells in the Chicago area were used to prepare maps showing the structure and thickness of selected rock units. The subsurface exploration included seismic surveying, test drilling, geophysical borehole logging, laboratory testing of core samples, and drilling and testing for groundwater. The subsurface data from this project have contributed greatly to the understanding of the detailed geology and groundwater hydrology in the Chicago area.

GEOLOGIC SETTING

The greater Chicago area is located on the Kankakee Arch, a broad, gently sloping arch of Paleozoic sediments that connects the Wisconsin Arch lying to the northwest with the Cincinnati Arch to the southeast. It also separates the Illinois Basin from the Michigan Basin (Buschbach, 1964, Fig. 1). The area studied is northeast of the crest of the Kankakee Arch, and thus, the regional dip of the bedrock units is eastward into the Michigan Basin.

Most of the area is mantled by Quaternary surficial

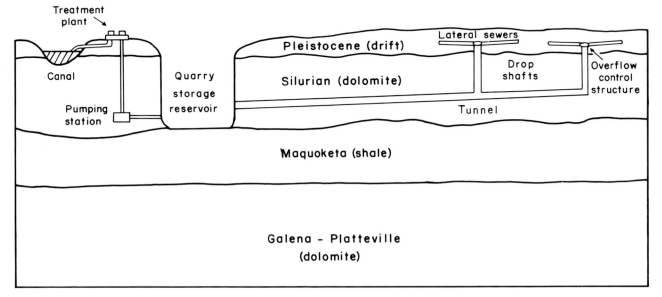

Figure 2. Diagrammatic sketch of proposed cross section of Tunnel and Reservoir Plan.

material, as much as 200 feet (61 m) thick, that was deposited by Pleistocene glaciers that repeatedly covered the area and by the various high-level stages of Lake Michigan. Beneath the mantle of glacial drift and lacustrine deposits, the bedrock consists of Silurian dolomite, which is about 50 to 500 feet (15 to 152 m) thick. The surface of the bedrock is a dissected, undulating plain, in which a well-developed pattern of stream valleys is entrenched. At some places, the valleys are more than 100 feet (30 m) deep and appear to have steeply sloping sides. Glacial deposits filled the valleys, and present drainage patterns have little relation to the earlier valleys.

Underlying the Silurian rocks in northeastern Illinois are from 700 to 1100 feet (213 to 335 m) of Ordovician strata and from 2000 to 3500 feet (610 to 1067 m) of Cambrian strata. Below the Cambrian are Precambrian basement rocks, composed chiefly of granite. The sequence of rock formations in the Chicago area is shown in Fig. 3.

QUATERNARY SYSTEM

Quaternary deposits are assigned to the Pleistocene Series and include all the unconsolidated rock formations that overlie the Silurian bedrock in the Chicago area. The deposits consist chiefly of glacial drift, but they also include deposits made by rivers, by slopewash and slumping, by sedimentation in lakes and ponds, and by work of man.

Repeated fluctuations of glaciers caused deposition of many different units in the area. When the ice melted, it deposited glacial till, a poorly sorted mixture of rock fragments of all sizes. Continued melting of the glaciers provided running water that picked up rock debris and sorted the material by size. Outwash deposits formed valley trains and outwash plains. Near the lake shores, sand and gravel were deposited in beaches, bars, spits, and deltas, while clay, silt, and fine sand were deposited in deeper water. The Modern Soil is developed directly on these glacially-controlled deposits.

Man-made fill has modified the area by creating land in areas that previously had been lake bottom. Along Lake Michigan, mostly sand was used to build islands and peninsulas. The fill used to build up the Lake Calumet area, in southern Chicago, is largely rubbish from the city.

Pleistocene stratigraphy of the Chicago area was described by Bretz (1955) and by Willman (1971).

SILURIAN SYSTEM

The Silurian System is represented in northeastern Illinois by dolomite that ranges from very pure to very silty and is argillaceous and cherty (Fig. 3). The upper part of the Silurian is characterized by randomly distributed reefs of pure dolomite surrounded by well layered, silty, interreef dolomite. The lower part of the Silurian consists of regularly bedded dolomite units that range from pure to argillaceous or cherty. They are distinctive units that can be traced widely in this area (Willman, 1971). The Silurian System generally thickens to the southeast. It is locally less than 50 feet (15 m) thick in the northwestern part of the area, but it reaches a thickness of nearly 500 feet (152 m) in the southeastern part (Suter et al, 1959, Fig. 27). Significant unconformities occur at the top and base of the Silurian. In this area, the Silurian strata are differentiated into two series: the Alexandrian below and the Niagaran above. Much of the proposed tunneling is to be done in Niagaran rocks. Silurian rocks were described by Bretz (1939) and by Willman (1943, 1962, 1971).

Racine Dolomite. The Racine Dolomite, at the top of the Niagaran Series, is a variable unit consisting of pure, gray, massive, vuggy dolomite in large reefs, and of argillaceous, silty, fine-grained, thin-bedded, grayish-brown dolomite in interreef areas. The Racine is about 300 feet (91 m) thick along the eastern edge of the Chicago area. It thins westward by truncation and is absent in the northwestern part of the area.

Sugar Run Dolomite. The Sugar Run Dolomite is a fine-grained, silty, well-bedded, gray dolomite. It is present in the southwestern part of the area, where it is as much as 20 feet (6 m) thick. The Sugar Run appears to be absent in the eastern and northern parts of the area.

Joliet Dolomite. The Joliet Dolomite is 40 to 70 feet (12 to 21 m) thick in the area. It consists of three distinctive members. An upper unit, the Romeo, is a light gray to white, pure, porous dolomite. It is 10 to 25 feet (3 to 8 m) thick. A middle unit, the Markgraf, consists of silty and slightly argillaceous dolomite that is light gray and very fine grained. It is 20 to 30 feet (6 to 9 m) thick. A basal unit, the Brandon Bridge, is argillaceous dolomite with red or green shales. It is present in the northern and western parts of the area, where it varies from a few to 20 feet (6 m) thick.

Kankakee Dolomite. The Kankakee Dolomite, at the top of the Alexandrian Series, consists of light gray to pinkish gray, fine-grained dolomite in beds 1 to 3 inches (2.5 to 7.6 cm) thick, which are separated by thin green shale partings. Chert nodules are present but not abundant. Scattered sand grains and a little glauconite are common at the base. At the top of the formation, there is a massive bed of white dolomite that is about 2 feet (61 cm) thick. The Kankakee ranges from 20 to 50 feet (6 to 15 m) thick in the area, but it is commonly about 40 feet (12 m) thick.

Elwood Formation. The Elwood Formation consists of a few to 30 feet (9 m) of slightly argillaceous, brownish-gray dolomite. It typically contains numerous layers of white chert.

Wilhelmi Formation. The Wilhelmi Formation is a brown to gray, shaly dolomite. The formation has a maximum thickness of about 100 feet (30 m) where it fills broad channels that were cut into the underlying rocks of the

System	Series	Stage	Mega-group	Group	Formation	Graphic Column	Thickness (ft.)	Kinds of Rock
QUAT.	PLEIS.						0-200	Till, sand, gravel, silt, clay, peat, marl, loess
SILURIAN	NIAGARAN		Hunton		Racine		0-300	Dolomite, pure in reefs, mostly silty, argillaceous, cherty between reefs
SILURIAN	NIAGARAN		Hunton		Sugar Run		0-30	Dolomite, even bedded, slightly silty
SILURIAN	NIAGARAN		Hunton		Joliet		40-80	Dolomite, shaly and red at base; white, silty, cherty above; pure at top
SILURIAN	NIAGARAN	AL.	Hunton		Kankakee		20-50	Dolomite; thin beds; green shale partings
ORDOVICIAN	CIN.	RICHMOND.		Maquoketa	Neda \ Elwood		0-15 \ 0-30	Oolite & shale, red \ Dolomite, cherty, slightly argillaceous
ORDOVICIAN	CIN.	RICHMOND.		Maquoketa	Brainard (Ord) \ Wilhelmi (Sil)		0-100 \ 0-100	Shale, dolomitic, greenish-gray \ Dolomite, very shaly; Shale, dolomitic, dk. gray
ORDOVICIAN	CIN.	RICHMOND.		Maquoketa	Ft. Atkinson		5-50	Dolomite; green shale; coarse limestone
ORDOVICIAN	CIN.	MAY.		Maquoketa	Scales		90-120	Shale, dolomitic, gray, brown, black
ORDOVICIAN	CHAMPLAINIAN	ED.	Ottawa	Galena	Wise Lake		170-210	Dolomite, buff, pure
ORDOVICIAN	CHAMPLAINIAN	TR.	Ottawa	Galena	Dunleith		170-210	Dolomite, pure to slightly shaly; locally limestone
ORDOVICIAN	CHAMPLAINIAN	TR.	Ottawa	Galena	Guttenberg		0-15	Dolomite, red specks and shale partings
ORDOVICIAN	CHAMPLAINIAN	TR.	Ottawa	Platteville	Nachusa		0-50	Dolomite and limestone, pure, massive
ORDOVICIAN	CHAMPLAINIAN	TR.	Ottawa	Platteville	Grand Detour		20-40	Dolomite and limestone, medium beds
ORDOVICIAN	CHAMPLAINIAN	TR.	Ottawa	Platteville	Mifflin		20-50	Dolomite and limestone, shaly, thin beds
ORDOVICIAN	CHAMPLAINIAN	TR.	Ottawa	Platteville	Pecatonica		20-50	Dolomite, pure, thick beds
ORDOVICIAN	CHAMPLAINIAN	CH.	Ottawa	Ancell	Glenwood		0-50	Sandstone and dolomite, silty; green shale
ORDOVICIAN	CHAMPLAINIAN	CH.	Ottawa	Ancell	St. Peter		100-400	Sandstone, medium and fine grained; well rounded grains; chert rubble at base
ORDOVICIAN	CANADIAN		Knox	Prairie du Chien	Shakopee		0-20	Dolomite, sandy; oolitic chert; algal mounds
ORDOVICIAN	CANADIAN		Knox	Prairie du Chien	New Richmond		0-10	Sandstone, fine to coarse
ORDOVICIAN	CANADIAN		Knox	Prairie du Chien	Oneota — Blodgett			Dolomite, pure, coarse grained; sand grains
ORDOVICIAN	CANADIAN		Knox	Prairie du Chien	Oneota — Arsenal		120	Dolomite; oolitic chert
ORDOVICIAN	CANADIAN		Knox	Prairie du Chien	Gunter		0-15	Sandstone, dolomitic
CAMBRIAN	CROIXAN	TREMP.	Knox		Eminence		50-100	Dolomite, sandy
CAMBRIAN	CROIXAN	TREMP.	Knox		Potosi		90-150	Dolomite; drusy quartz (Q) in vugs
CAMBRIAN	CROIXAN	FRAN.			Franconia		50-140	Sandstone, glauconitic (G); dolomite; shale
CAMBRIAN	CROIXAN	DRESBACHIAN	Potsdam		Ironton		100-150	Sandstone, partly dolomitic, medium grained
CAMBRIAN	CROIXAN	DRESBACHIAN	Potsdam		Galesville		10-100	Sandstone, fine grained
CAMBRIAN	CROIXAN	DRESBACHIAN	Potsdam		Eau Claire		370-450	Siltstone, dolomite, sandstone and shale, glauconitic (G)
CAMBRIAN	CROIXAN	DRESBACHIAN	Potsdam		Mt. Simon		1700-2400	Sandstone, fine to coarse; quartz granules in some beds
PRECAMBRIAN ROCKS								Granite

Figure 3. Sequence of rock strata in the greater Chicago area (modified from Willman, 1971, Fig. 5). Abbreviations: Al.—Alexandrian; Ch.—Chazyan; Cin.—Cincinnatian; Ed.—Edenian; Fran.—Franconian; May.—Maysvillian; Pleis.—Pleistocene; Quat.—Quaternary; Richmond—Richmondian; Tremp.—Trempealeaun; Tr.—Trentonian.

Maquoketa Group. It thins over divides between channels and is locally absent where a full section of Maquoketa is present.

ORDOVICIAN SYSTEM

The Ordovician System in Illinois is divided, from the top, into the Cincinnatian, Champlainian, and Canadian Series. The Cincinnatian Series is represented in the Chicago area by shaly strata assigned to the Maquoketa Group. A significant unconformity occurs at the top, and as much as 100 feet (30 m) of shale were removed from some localities before the overlying Silurian rocks were deposited. Recent paleontologic studies have shown that the upper beds of the underlying Galena Dolomite Group should be assigned a Cincinnatian age (Fig. 3).

The Champlainian Series in this area is represented by three groups of rocks (Templeton and Williams, 1963). At the top, the Galena Group consists chiefly of medium to thick-bedded dolomite with a little limestone. The underlying Platteville Group consists of dolomite and limestone formations that are somewhat thinner bedded than the Galena strata. At the base of the Champlainian is the Ancell Group, which consists chiefly of sandstone that unconformably overlies older Ordovician and Cambrian formations.

The strata of the Canadian Series are chiefly dolomite and a few thin beds of sandstone. The four formations in the series compose the Prairie du Chien Group. In some places, these strata were entirely removed by solution and erosion before deposition of the overlying St. Peter Sandstone (Buschbach, 1961; 1964).

Maquoketa Group

Neda Formation. The Neda Formation, at the top of the Maquoketa, consists of a few feet of red shale that locally contains hematitic oolites. In this area, the Neda is present only where the underlying Brainard has not been eroded appreciably and the total Maquoketa thickness exceeds 190 feet (58 m).

Brainard Shale. The Brainard Shale is a greenish-gray, silty, dolomitic shale with interbedded layers of silty dolomite. It has a maximum thickness of about 100 feet (30 m), but in places, it has been entirely removed by pre-Silurian erosion.

Fort Atkinson Formation. The Fort Atkinson Formation consists chiefly of fine- to coarse-grained, fossiliferous dolomite or limestone and some interbedded green or brown shale. It ranges from 5 to 50 feet (1.5 to 15 m) thick.

Scales Shale. The Scales Shale, at the base of the Maquoketa Group, is grayish-brown shale that is silty and dolomitic. It contains interbeds of silty dolomite, most of which are an inch or two (2.5 or 5 cm) thick. The Scales is

present and easily recognized throughout the area. It varies from 90 to 120 feet (27 to 37 m) thick.

Galena Group

Wise Lake and Dunleith Formations. The Wise Lake and Dunleith Formations at the top of the Galena Group consist of thick-bedded, pure, fine- to medium-grained, light brown dolomite that grades to fine-grained limestone in some places. Oil-stained vugs are common in the upper few feet of this dolomite sequence, and a concentration of pyrite occurs at the very top. The Wise Lake and Dunleith are quite similar and cannot be separated consistently in this area. They have a combined thickness of 170 to 210 feet (52 to 64 m).

Guttenberg Formation. The Guttenberg Formation consists of brown dolomite or limestone that characteristically contains red specks and thin reddish-brown shale partings. It can be recognized everywhere in the area when good drilling samples or cores are available, and it serves as a good marker bed. The Guttenberg ranges from about 4 inches to 15 feet (10 cm to 5 m) thick.

Platteville Group

Quimbys Mill Formation. The Quimbys Mill Formation is a thin unit at the top of the Platteville that has been recognized in cores for the tunnel project. It consists of a few inches to a few feet of dolomite or limestone that is light brownish gray and very fine grained. Thin layers of dark gray or dark brown shale are present in some places.

Nachusa Formation. The Nachusa Formation consists of fine- to medium-grained, light brown dolomite or fine-grained limestone. It reaches a maximum thickness of 50 feet (15 m) in this area, but it is locally absent.

Grand Detour Formation. The Grand Detour Formation is a light, brownish-gray, fine-grained dolomite or limestone that has dark gray mottling. Thin zones of dark gray or reddish-brown shale partings are common near the top of the formation. The Grand Detour is 30 to 40 feet (9 to 12 m) thick.

Mifflin Formation. The Mifflin Formation is light gray, very fine-grained, thin-bedded dolomite or limestone with green or gray shale partings. It is 20 to 50 feet (6 to 15 m) thick.

Pecatonica Dolomite. The Pecatonica Dolomite is a relatively pure, vuggy, light brown to grayish-brown, fine-grained dolomite with floating sand grains in the lower few feet. It grades to light brown, very fine-grained limestone in some localities, but it is commonly the most dolomitic of all the Platteville formations. The Pecatonica is 20 to 50 feet (6 to 15 m) thick.

Ancell Group

Glenwood Formation. The Glenwood Formation consists of sandstone with some shale and dolomite. The sandstone is slightly coarser grained and not as well sorted as the underlying St. Peter. The Glenwood is not recognized in the southern part of the area. To the north and west, it is as much as 50 feet (15 m) thick.

St. Peter Sandstone. The St. Peter Sandstone is a clean, fine- to medium-grained, well sorted sandstone. It is generally porous and permeable. At its base, the formation includes a unit of shale and chert rubble (Kress Member) that varies from a few inches to over 100 feet (30 m) thick. The thickness of the St. Peter is commonly a little less than 100 feet (30 m) to a little over 200 feet (61 m) in the area, but locally it is more than 400 feet (122 m) thick where it fills older valleys and sinkholes that have been cut into the underlying surface.

Prairie du Chien Group

Shakopee Dolomite. The Shakopee Dolomite consists of fine-grained dolomite with oolitic chert nodules and thin beds of sandstone and shale. The Shakopee immediately underlies the prominent sub-St. Peter unconformity and, consequently, has been entirely removed from most of the area. Where present it is a few to 20 feet (6 m) thick.

New Richmond Sandstone. The New Richmond Sandstone is a medium-grained sandstone interbedded with a little sandy dolomite. It is recognized only in the southwestern part of the area, where it is a few feet thick.

Oneota Dolomite. The Oneota Dolomite consists of relatively coarse-grained dolomite with some interbedded fine-grained units. The upper half of the formation is relatively pure, with only a few scattered chert nodules. Some of the chert is oolitic. The lower half of the formation contains numerous layers of chert nodules and some thin layers of green shale. The Oneota is 150 to 200 feet (46 to 61 m) thick.

Gunter Sandstone. The Gunter Sandstone consists of discontinuous lenses of fine- to medium-grained sandstone interbedded with dolomite and green shale. The Gunter is absent throughout much of the Chicago area, and where it is present it is not known to be over 15 feet (5 m) thick.

CAMBRIAN SYSTEM

The Cambrian strata of this area are assigned to the Croixan Series of late Cambrian age, although it is possible that the thick Mt. Simon Sandstone may include older deposits. Cambrian rocks were described in detail by Buschbach (1964).

Eminence Formation. The Eminence Formation, the uppermost Cambrian formation, is composed of light colored sandy dolomite, with a few thin layers of sandstone at or near its base. The dolomite is fine- to medium-grained and contains oolitic chert nodules. In much of the area, the Eminence has been removed by pre-St. Peter solution and erosion. Its reconstructed thickness increases southward from a little less than 50 feet (15 m) to about 100 feet (30 m).

Potosi Dolomite. The Potosi Dolomite is a light gray to brown, fine-grained dolomite. The formation is relatively pure and was apparently subjected to a considerable amount of solution by groundwater. It is commonly vuggy, and locally it is cavernous. The vugs are lined with drusy quartz crystals. The caverns appear to be vugs that are enlarged and joined by solution. They are most common from 5 to 50 feet (1.5 to 15 m) below the top of the Potosi, but they have been reported throughout the formation. These caverns and fissures cause difficulties in drilling wells through the Potosi; quite commonly, the drill bit drops 3 to 5 feet (1 to 2 m) without encountering solid rock. The Potosi is 90 to 150 feet (27 to 46 m) thick throughout much of the area, but it has been locally thinned or removed by pre-St. Peter solution and erosion.

Franconia Formation. The Franconia Formation, below the Potosi, consists of fine-grained, pink to gray, dolomitic, argillaceous sandstone that is commonly very glauconitic. It contains thin layers of red or green shale. The Franconia is 50 to 140 feet (15 to 43 m) thick.

Ironton Sandstone. The Ironton Sandstone is a clean, medium-grained, moderately sorted, dolomitic sandstone. The dolomite is present as cementing material, and up to 25 percent of the formation consists of layers, a few inches to a few feet thick, of very sandy dolomite or sandstone that is well cemented by dolomite. The Ironton is 100 to 150 feet (30 to 46 m) thick in the area.

Galesville Sandstone. The Galesville Sandstone, below the Ironton, is a fine-grained, well sorted sandstone that varies from a few to 100 feet (30 m) in thickness. The Galesville is friable, porous, and permeable. It is an excellent aquifer.

Eau Claire Formation. The Eau Claire Formation underlies the Galesville and consists of alternating thin layers of fine-grained sandstone, siltstone, shale, and dolomite. In northeastern Illinois, the upper member of the formation is commonly a pink to grayish-orange siltstone with a high feldspar content. It is very dolomitic in the upper few feet and contains thin interbeds of red and green shale. The middle member consists of glauconitic dolomite or limestone. It contains numerous layers of green shale that become increasingly prominent southeastward in the area. The lower member of the Eau Claire is a fine-grained sandstone that is interbedded with thin layers of red or green shale. The Eau Claire is 370 to 450 feet (113 to 137 m) thick.

Mt. Simon Sandstone. The Mt. Simon Sandstone consists of white to pink, fine- to coarse-grained sandstone that unconformably overlies the Precambrian basement. This sandstone is coarser grained, more poorly sorted, and more angular than any of the other Cambrian or Ordovician sandstones. It is generally friable and porous, but it contains lenses of sandstone that are well cemented with quartz. Red and green micaceous shales are presented in very thin layers, especially from 300 to 500 feet (91 to 152 m) below the top of the formation. An arkosic zone with abundant pink feldspar is commonly present at the base of the Mt. Simon. The Mt. Simon is estimated to be 1700 to 2400 feet (518 to 732 m) thick in the area.

PRECAMBRIAN ROCKS

Although no wells have been drilled to the Precambrian in this area, data from wells just outside the area permit inferences concerning the surface of the basement rocks. The top of the Precambrian is estimated to be from 3000 to over 4000 feet (914 to 1219 m) below the surface in the Chicago area. Nearby wells that have penetrated the Precambrian encountered red granite that is about 1.3 billion years old. The topographic surface of the Precambrian at the beginning of Mt. Simon deposition probably had local relief of several hundred feet (91-122 m).

GEOLOGIC INVESTIGATIONS

Initial geologic investigations for the Tunnel and Reservoir Plan included the investigation, collection, analysis, and evaluation of existing data. Quarries and natural outcrops in the area were visited, as were mines in the Ordovician rocks of northwestern Illinois and southwestern Wisconsin. A thorough search of publications and subsurface data was made, and more than 3000 logs of boreholes that had reached bedrock in the area were plotted. These data were used to develop the drilling and testing programs.

The drilling and testing programs involved the exploration of the subsurface to confirm and refine the initial interpretations and, later, to obtain specific engineering parameters required for the design of the systems. The explorations included test drilling with recovery of soil samples and rock core, laboratory testing of the rock and soil samples, geophysical logging of boreholes, groundwater testing, and seismic surveying.

Test Drilling

Approximately 500 holes were drilled by a number of contractors (including Dikor-Groves, ATEC, Continental, and SEECO) to obtain rock cores. The cores provided rock samples for laboratory analyses, positive stratigraphic control, and correlation between the rock layers. The water bearing properties of the rocks were evaluated and monitored in the boreholes. Also, several hundred soil explora-tion holes were drilled to sample the glacial drift and drift-bedrock contact for the various drop-shafts, connecting structures, pumping stations, and reservoirs throughout the project area.

More than 170,000 feet (51,816 m) of rock has been cored for this project. The deepest hole, 1696 feet (517 m) deep, reached the top of the Cambrian Eau Claire Formation. Numerous holes were cored into the St. Peter Sandstone at an average depth of 1000 feet (305 m), although most of the holes were cored only through the Silurian rocks into the Brainard Formation at the top of the Maquoketa Group. These holes had a depth of 400 to 450 feet (122 to 137 m). Core recovery was excellent throughout all formations.

Geophysical Logging of Boreholes

Geophysical logging of boreholes produced a record of the in-situ response of the rock strata to various measuring devices lowered into the borehole. Logging devices were calibrated to provide uniform results from one borehole to another. Variations in borehole conditions, caused by changes in diameter, the presence or absence of fluid, or the presence or absence of casing, will affect the response of the rock strata to some of the measuring devices. The logging program conducted by Birdwell Division included gamma-ray, neutron, formation density, 3-D velocity, temperature, and caliper logs.

A total of approximately 110 test holes and water wells were logged by geophysical methods.

Laboratory Testing of Samples

Selected rock and soil samples were analyzed by various engineering companies in their laboratories to determine the range of properties of the various strata. In general, the rocks were analyzed for their specific gravity, unconfined compressive strength, modulus of elasticity, drillability, natural water content, absorption, abrasion, porosity, permeability, solubility, and reaction to wetting and drying. Petrographic and x-ray determinations were made to ascertain the mineralogy of the rocks.

The samples of soils and glacial drift were analyzed to determine their grain-size distribution, water content, Atterberg limits, unit weight, unconfined compressive strength, triaxial compression, consolidation, and permeability.

Groundwater Testing

A groundwater testing program was carried out to evaluate the technical and economic feasibility of the system proposed for protecting the aquifers and to estimate the amount of groundwater that would seep into the conveyance tunnels and storage reservoirs (Heim, Mossman, and Lawrence, 1971). The groundwater studies included a review of the existing data, analog model studies, an extensive field testing program, and laboratory analyses of the groundwater. Aquifers in the Silurian, Ordovician, and Cambrian strata were evaluated. Seepage into tunnels proved to be difficult to estimate because it was impossible to predict the presence of local porous zones or joints in the rocks (Papadopulos, Larsen, and Neil, 1969). The tunnels located in the Silurian strata, however, will be below the present piezometric surface, and the maximum internal head in these tunnels will be less than the external head. Natural recharge appears to be sufficient to maintain the groundwater levels in the Silurian because of the modest amount of pumpage from the aquifer. Therefore, outward seepage should not occur.

Seismic Survey

A seismic exploration program was conducted by Seismograph Service Corporation in the Chicago area to map both the bedrock topography and the geologic structure of the top of the Galena Group. The seismic survey was laid out on a basic 4 mile (6 km) grid spacing in what was referred to as the Master Plan Area and on a basic 2 mile (3 km) east-west spacing and 4 mile (6 km) north-south spacing in the Lake Calumet area. Minor modifications in the basic layout were made to accommodate variations in the city street system and to obtain more detailed subsurface information in certain areas. Approximately 420 miles (676 km) of seismic traverses were made. No seismic program approaching this magnitude had ever before been conducted in the Chicago area. The 33,600 data points derived from the program provide important subsurface information, especially in areas that lack drilling data. However, contouring of the seismic points and borehole data is necessarily interpretative, and it must be further refined as new data become available.

The Vibroseis (Continental Oil Company) system of seismic exploration was selected by the Metropolitan Sanitary District of Greater Chicago for this investigation because, of several seismic systems considered, it was the most adaptable to an urban environment (Mossman et al., 1971). Seismic operations in a municipal area require that there be a minimum interruption of traffic, relatively little noise produced, no damage to streets or underground structures, and an ability to filter out or distinguish the seismic signal from the high ambient noise level.

The Vibroseis system utilizes a low-power signal that is readily distinguishable from the background noise. The signal is produced by a vibrating source placed directly on the surface of the pavement, and its duration and frequency can be varied to obtain optimum results.

The bedrock surface was mapped by refraction tech-

niques, and the top of the Galena was mapped by reflection techniques. Continuous profiles were obtained along each line of traverses.

Good correlation was obtained between the seismic data and the depth to formation tops reported in most drill hole logs. Fault displacements reported along the seismic traverses are expected to be accurate within plus or minus 15 feet (5 m).

The results of the seismic survey were presented in contour maps and cross sections. The maps (Figs. 4 and 5) are based on all available borehole data from the files of the Illinois State Geological Survey and on the calculated seismic depths. They present new interpretations of the configuration of the bedrock surface and the surface at the top of the Galena Group. To include borehole information obtained since the seismic survey, the maps have been modified slightly for this report and have been expanded along the west side to tie them in with existing regional maps.

A structural anomaly, the Des Plaines Disturbance, occurs in the northern part of the area. The disturbance is an area of about 25 square miles (65 km²) that includes many high-angle faults. The bedrock consists of dolomites, sandstones, and shales of various ages. Because this locality is anomalous to the regional structure and bedrock surface, it is not treated in this report. The Des Plaines Disturbance is discussed by Emrich and Bergstrom (1962) and mapped in detail by Buschbach and Heim (1972).

Bedrock Surface. The bedrock in the Chicago area is chiefly Silurian dolomite. It is overlaid by glacial drift and, locally, by artificial fill. The thickness of the overburden ranges from zero, where the rock crops out, to about 200 feet (61 m). The configuration of the bedrock surface is the result of structural deformation, weathering, and erosion. The duration of weathering and erosion to which the bedrock was subjected was sufficiently long to obliterate any structural trends that may have been present.

Previous interpretations of the bedrock topography were based on outcrop data and borehole records (Horberg, 1950; Suter et al., 1959; Hughes et al., 1966) and depicted a gently rolling, dissected bedrock surface with an integrated drainage system. Divides were generally shown to be 3 to 4 miles (5 to 6 km) wide. The valleys had a general east-west trend and sloped to the east. The more prominent valleys were shown to be 50 to 100 feet (15 to 30 m) deep and about a mile (1.6 km) wide at the top. No closed depressions were mapped by either Horberg (1950) or Hughes et al. (1966).

A new interpretation of the configuration of the bedrock surface, based on the 33,600 plotted points derived from seismic refraction data, information from more than 3,000 boreholes, and outcrop data, was prepared by Seismograph Service Corporation (Fig. 4). The range of accuracy of the data to the top of the bedrock obtained by seismic methods is believed to be plus or minus 10 feet (3

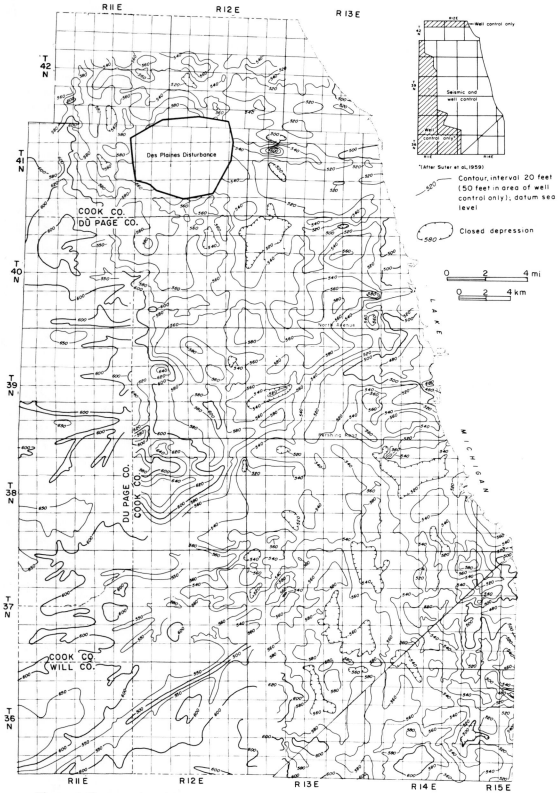

Figure 4. Topography of bedrock surface (modified from maps prepared by Seismograph Service Corporation). The Des Plaines Distrubance boundaries here separate Silurian from non-Silurian bedrock.

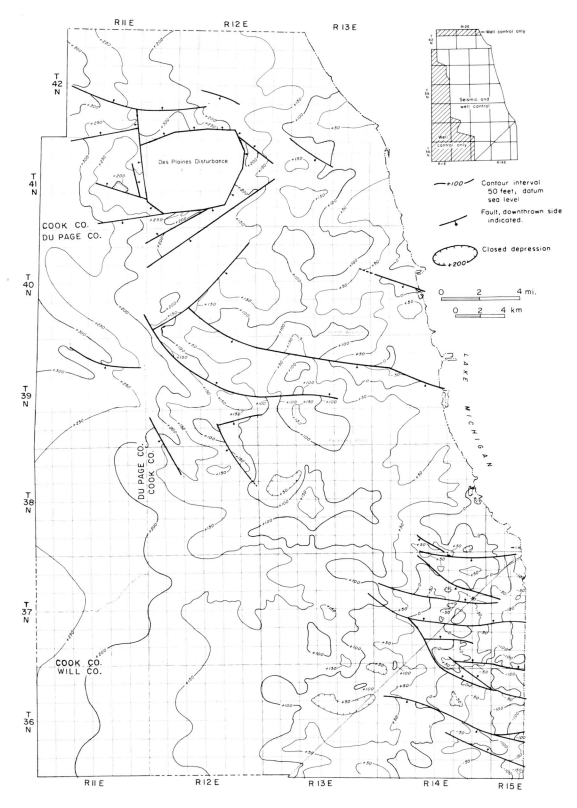

Figure 5. Structure on top of Galena Group (modified from maps prepared by Seismograph Service Corporation). The Des Plaines Disturbance here is bounded by fault lines.

m). Excellent correlation was found to exist in most instances between the seismically derived data and the borehole data. In the few instances where the seismic data and the borehole data failed to correlate, the lack of correlation was probably the result of (1) variations in the seismic velocity of the overburden material, (2) the presence of a zone of weathered rock that could not be identified by seismic methods, or (3) an error in the reported location or elevation of the boring.

The configuration of the bedrock topography (Fig. 4) can be described as a dissected surface with numerous hills, northeast-southwest to east-west trending valleys that slope to the east, and enclosed depressions. The regional slope of the bedrock surface is east and northeast. The elevation of the bedrock surface is generally between 500 to 600 feet (152 to 183 m) above sea level, but it ranges from a high of more than 650 feet (198 m) in the western part of the area to a low of less than 470 feet (143 m) above sea level in the eastern part.

The interpretation of the bedrock topography differs from the previous interpretations in indicating that closed depressions are present throughout the area. The depressions are mostly about 10 feet (3 m) deep, with an interpreted maximum depth of 30 to 40 feet (9 to 12 m). They cover an area of from less than a quarter of a square mile (.65 km^2) to more than 4 square miles (10 km^2). The presence of the depressions suggests that a karst topography had developed. Otto (1963) showed many depressions in the bedrock surface in an area north of Joliet and suggested the possibility of closed depressions on the bedrock surface of the Chicago area.

Faulting in the area is believed to have occurred following the deposition of the Silurian strata. Faults in the Silurian have been reported in natural outcrops and quarries in the Chicago area. However, no offset along any fault was detected on top of the bedrock surface by the seismic study.

Structure on Top of Galena Group. The rocks assigned to the Galena Group and to the underlying Platteville Group are primarily dolomite. The Galena is overlaid by shales of the Maquoketa Group, and the Platteville is underlaid by sandstones of the Ancell Group. The combined thickness of the Galena and Platteville Groups typically ranges from 300 to 330 feet (91 to 101 m).

A structure map of the top of the Galena (Fig. 5) has been modified slightly from one prepared by Seismograph Service Corporation to include borehole data obtained after the seismograph survey. The original configuration was based on the plotted points derived from seismic reflection data and information from more than 300 boreholes that reached the Galena.

Excellent correlation was found in most instances between seismically derived data and the borehole data. Where there is a lack of correlation, local variations that affect the seismic signals or errors in the reported location or elevation of the borings probably are responsible. The range of accuracy of data to the top of the Galena obtained by seismic methods is believed to be plus or minus 25 feet (8 m).

The configuration of the surface of the Galena is the result of structural deformation and minor erosion. The regional structural trends have a north-south strike with a gentle dip to the east, modified by a series of east to west undulations. The elevation of the top of the Galena ranges from a little over 300 feet (91 m) above sea level in the northwestern part of the area to about 150 feet (46 m) below sea level in the southeastern part. Throughout most of the area, the dip is 10 to 15 feet per mile (2 to 3 m/km) in an easterly direction. The east to west undulations are a series of anticlinal noses that plunge eastward. Many of the noses have structural domes along their crests that have 25 to 50 feet (8 to 15 m) of closure. Locally, the adjacent synclines contain structural basins with 25 to 50 feet (8 to 15 m) of closure.

FUTURE UNDERGROUND WORKS

Geologic investigations for the Tunnel and Reservoir Plan furnished a considerable amount of new and detailed information about the rocks in the greater Chicago area. Possibly more is known about the subsurface geology beneath Chicago than is known about any other major city.

The knowledge of subsurface geology in municipal areas is of primary importance in establishing zoning and for engineering projects. For example, potential areas for the sources of construction materials within municipal boundaries can be identified and protected until they are required for construction during the course of development of a municipality. This would include such things as sand and gravel resources and potential quarry sites for rock aggregate and riprap. Knowledge of the subsurface geology is important in assessing foundation conditions for roads, railroads, airports, and large building structures; in laying out tunnel alignments and in anticipating the nature of the type of conditions along such alignments; and in identifying suitable disposal sites. One must also be concerned with protection of the groundwater resource, the potential for development of the groundwater resource, including an assessment of the effect of groundwater lowering through development, and the control of groundwater seepage into excavations. It is not uncommon to read of the tunneling contractor whose tunnel alignment has followed an "unanticipated" sand with large water inflow for a considerable distance when it would have been very easy to recognize that the sand represents a buried beach deposit which has a long linear trend, and possible relocation of the tunnel to one side or another, or above or below, could have avoided the deposit.

Knowledge of the subsurface geology in municipal areas will permit the trained professional to anticipate the types of conditions which may be encountered between boreholes or geophysical survey points.

REFERENCES CITED

Bretz, J H., 1939, Geology of the Chicago region. Part 1—General: Illinois Geological Survey Bulletin 65, 118 p.

Bretz, J H., 1955, Geology of the Chicago region. Part 2—The Pleistocene: Illinois Geological Survey Bulletin 65, 132 p.

Buschbach, T. C., 1961, The morphology of the sub-St. Peter surface of northeastern Illinois: Illinois Academy of Science Transactions, v.54, no. 1-2, p. 83–89.

Buschbach, T. C., 1964, Cambrian and Ordovician strata of northeastern Illinois: Illinois Geological Survey Rept. Inv. 218, 90 p.

Buschbach, T. C., and Heim, G. E., 1972, Preliminary geologic investigations of rock tunnel sites for flood and pollution control in the greater Chicago area: Illinois Geological Survey Environmental Geology Note 52, 35 p.

Emrich, G. H., and Bergstrom, R. E., 1962, Des Plaines Disturbance, northeastern Illinois: Geological Society of America Bulletin, v. 73, no. 8, p. 959–968.

Heim, G. E., Mossman, R. W., and Lawrence, H. W., 1971, Geologic exploration for Chicagoland and other deep rock tunnels to be constructed by mechanical moles, *in* Proceedings from deep tunnels in hard rock: Water Pollution Control Research Services, Environmental Protection Agency, February, p. 141–173.

Horberg, C. L., 1950, Bedrock topography of Illinois: Illinois Geological Survey Bulletin 73, 111 p.

Hughes, G. M., Kraatz, P., and Landon, R. A., 1966, Bedrock aquifers of northeastern Illinois: Illinois Geological Survey Circular 406, 15 p.

Mossman, R. W., Heim, G. E., and Dalton, R. E., 1971, Vibroseis applications to engineering work in an urban area: Preprint Society of Exploration, Geophysicists' Ann. Mtg., November 7–11, 42 p.

Otto, G. H., 1963, Engineering geology of the Chicago area, *in* Foundation engineering in the Chicago area: Lecture Ser. Proc. Am. Soc. Civil Engrs., Illinois Sec. Soil Mechanics and Found. Div., p. 3–1 to 3–24.

Papadopulos, I. S., Larsen, W. R., and Neil, F. C., 1969, Groundwater studies—Chicagoland deep tunnel system: Ground Water, v. 7, no. 5, October, p. 3–15.

Suter, M., Bergstrom, R. E., Smith, H. F., Emrich, G. H., Walton, W. C., and Larson, T. E., 1959, Preliminary report on groundwater resources of the Chicago region, Illinois: Illinois Water Survey and Illinois Geological Survey Coop. Groundwater Rept. 1, 89 p.

Templeton, J. S., and William, H. B., 1963, Champlainian Series (Middle Ordovician) in Illinois: Illinois Geological Survey Bulletin 89, 260 p.

Willman, H. B., 1943, High-purity dolomite in Illinois: Illinois Geological Survey Rept. Inv. 90, 89 p.

Willman, H. B., 1962, The Silurian strata of northeastern Illinois, *in* Silurian rocks of the southern Lake Michigan area: Michigan Basin Geological Society Annual Field Conference, p. 61–68.

Willman, H. B., 1971, Summary of the geology of the Chicago area: Illinois Geological Survey Circular 460, 77 p.

Manuscript Received by the Society May 24, 1982
Manuscript accepted June 1, 1982

Geological Society of America
Reviews in Engineering Geology, Volume V
1982

Effects of geology on
the development of Edmonton, Alberta, Canada

N. W. Rutter
Department of Geology
University of Alberta,
Edmonton, Alberta T6G 2E3, Canada

S. Thomson
Department of Civil Engineering
University of Alberta,
Edmonton, Alberta T6G 2G7, Canada

ABSTRACT

The City of Edmonton is underlaid by a thick sequence of Quatenary glacial deposits overlying gently dipping late Cretaceous clastic sediments. The Quaternary stratigraphy consists of Saskatchewan gravels and sands, two continental till deposits (upper and lower till) separated in places by Tofield sand, all overlaid by Glacial Lake Edmonton sediments. Underground activity has centered on tunneling for sanitary and storm sewer systems and, more recently, for part of Edmonton's Light Rapid Transit system. Nearly all tunneling is in the competent till or bedrock. Other underground activity took place around the turn of the century when coal mining shafts and adits were constructed. Surface subsidence continues today and has to be considered when planning. The greatest hazard in the development of Edmonton is natural landslides that occur along river banks and man-made slopes. Major failures take place mainly in bedrock with small slips in the Lake Edmonton sediments.

INTRODUCTION

Edmonton is 500,000 people living for the most part on the flatlying prairie level of the Western Interior Plains (Figure 1). The city is dissected by the northeastward flowing North Saskatchewan River that has formed a narrow post glacial valley 50 to 60 m deep. The city sits mainly on glacial lacustrine silts and clays bordered on the outlying areas by ground and hummocky moraine, undulating pitted deltas, dunes and outwash gravels (Bayrock and Berg, 1966). It is the intent here to discuss the subsurface activity in the area, the major hazards to development, and only briefly mention other aspects.

GEOLOGY OF THE EDMONTON AREA

The Upper Cretaceous Edmonton Formation crops out throughout the Edmonton area along the valley of the North Saskatchewan River and its tributaries. It consists of grey, clayey sandstones and mudstones, dark carbonaceous shales, bentonite, ironstone beds, and coal seams (Westgate *et al.*, 1976). The units are derived mainly from continental environments and are poorly lithified. Beds dip gently to the southwest at about 5 m/kilometer (Ower, 1960) but locally have been folded and faulted by overriding continental glaciers.

Although the present landscape is a reflection of geological processes operating in preglacial, glacial, and post glacial times, major elements of the preglacial landscape are still clearly discernible. Preglacial topographic highs coincide with present-day upland areas, whereas low-lying areas are located over preglacial valleys. The preglacial drainage

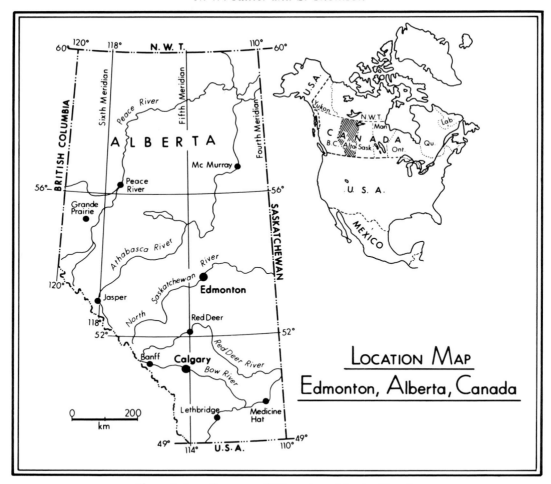

Figure 1. Location map of Edmonton, Alberta, Canada.

pattern is dendritic, showing a regional flow direction to the northeast. The North Saskatchewan River closely follows its preglacial course.

The distribution and description of Quaternary landforms and surficial deposits are given in simplified form in Figure 2. The succession and character of rock-stratigraphic units are shown in Figures 3 and 4. The oldest Quaternary deposits are fluvial gravels and sands, referred to as the Saskatchewan gravels and sands. They lie unconformably upon bedrock and, in most places, are covered by glacial drift. These sediments are found within preglacial valleys as terrace deposits, up to 5 m thick, and as valley-fill deposits, in places 20 m thick. Resistant quartzose sandstone and black chert make up the bulk of the clasts, but arkosic sandstone, jasper, and local bedrock material (mainly coal fragments, petrified wood, and clay ironstone) are also present. The lithology of the Saskatchewan gravels and sands definitely points to an original provenance in the Cordilleran region to the west, but the immediate source for some of these deposits in the Edmonton area is late Tertiary conglomerates that covered former local preglacial uplands.

A greyish brown (10YR 5/1) till overlies the Saskatchewan gravels and sands or sits directly on bedrock. Its maximum observed thickness is in the order of 7 m. This lower till ranges in texture from sandy loam to silty clay loam, has a low carbonate content, and possesses a high percentage of igneous and metamorphic material derived from the Canadian Shield. A characteristic attribute is its highly fractured nature with the resultant tendency to break up into small angular fragments. Some fractures are primary joints, whereas others are shears that developed during a later glaciation (Westgate et al., 1976). The lower till was derived from a Continental ice sheet that flowed from the area of the Canadian Shield. The exact age of the till is not known, but ^{14}C dates from nearby areas suggest that it is older than 50,000 years.

The lower till is overlaid in places by a stratified sand deposit called the Tofield sand. It ranges up to 1 m thick but is generally missing with the lower till in direct contact with the overlying upper till.

The upper till is about 5 m thick, yellowish brown (5Y 7/2), dense, and massive and possesses a pronounced columnar structure that is due to the presence of several well-

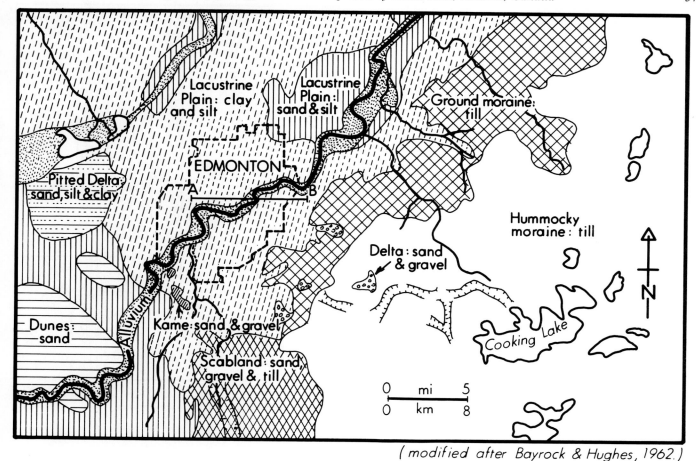

(modified after Bayrock & Hughes, 1962.)

Figure 2. Simplified map of Quaternary landforms and deposits of the Edmonton area.

developed, vertical joint sets. As a result, it usually forms vertical cliffs at outcrops. It is more sandy than the lower till, but its composition is not significantly different. Elongated stones are preferentially oriented in a northeast-southwest direction indicating continental ice movement from the northwest (Westgate *et al.*, 1976). The age is believed to be Late Wisconsin, deposited between 10,000 and 25,000 years ago. The morainal topography in the Edmonton area is underlaid by the upper till.

Glacial lakes formed against the active ice margin during deglaciation. Glacial Lake Edmonton covered much of the lowland in the central and western part of the region. It was bounded by uplands to the west and south and the glacier margin to the north and east. Up to 15 m of sands, silts, and clays, called Lake Edmonton sediments, accumulated. The lake sediments contain pieces of till-like material and thin discontinuous seams of highly plastic clay. Associated deltas are found at various places in the area, as well as scabland in the southern part where the lake drained. Dunes found in the western part of the area are derived, in part, from reworked lake sands.

As ice retreated to the northeast, post-glacial drainage began to develop. This is most noticeable along the North Saskatchewan River Valley where four post-glacial terraces have been recognized. These are underlaid by clay, silt, sand, and gravel.

The geology of the Quaternary deposits within the city is discussed in detail by Bayrock and Berg (1966); Westgate (1969); Westgate *et al.* (1976); Kathol and McPherson (1975); and May and Thomson (1978).

TUNNELING

General

There are over 160 km of tunnel ranging from 1.6 to 5 m in diameter underneath Edmonton; the majority of which is for sanitary or storm sewers (Beaulieu, 1972). Nearly all tunneling is in competent till or bedrock. Surface subsidence is normally less than 1 cm, and inward movement of tunnels is also in the order of 1 cm. This movement can generally be assessed by an elastic analysis (Eisenstein and Thomson, 1977; Thomson and El Nahhas, 1980).

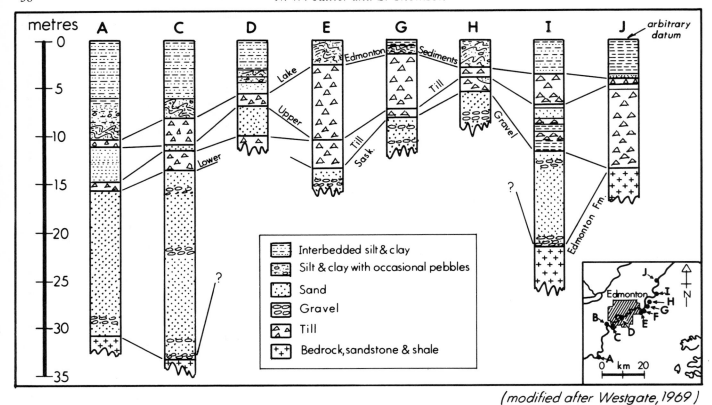

Figure 3. Stratigraphy of Quaternary deposits exposed along the North Saskatchewan River Valley.

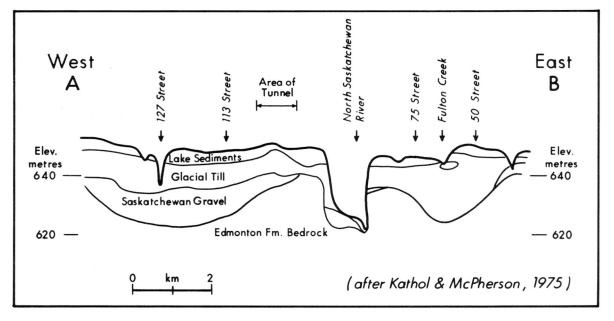

Figure 4. Generalized geologic east-west cross section through Edmonton. See Figure 2.

Tunneling for part of Edmonton's Light Rapid Transit system is probably the most interesting of recent tunneling projects and is discussed briefly below.

Edmonton's Light Rapid Transit System

Introduction

Two parallel tunnels were built in 1976 as part of the first phase of the Light Rapid Transit system. The tunnels, approximately 250 m long, 6 m in diameter, and having centers 12 m apart, were driven in downtown Edmonton with an average of 7.5 m overburden above the crown. The subsurface stratigraphy is shown on Figure 5. Note that the tunnels are located entirely within a dense, jointed till sequence.

The tunnels were advanced using a shielded mole followed by two systems of soil support. The temporary supporting system consisted of steel ribs and timber lagging while the permanent lining was cast-in-place reinforced concrete. Two principal geotechnical problems associated with the tunnel project were: 1. The magnitude and distribution of the surface settlement above the tunnels as a function of the loss of ground in the tunnel. 2. The magnitude and distribution of earth pressures acting on the temporary and permanent linings.

Both concerns were successfully analyzed (Eisenstein and Thomson, 1977). A typical set of observed displacements is shown on Figure 6. In this project, it was concluded that the most important factor that influenced the performance of the tunnels was the character of the till, particularly the jointing. Also, the study indicated that the characteristics of the till must be derived by considering it as a soil mass rather than by extrapolating results from small samples.

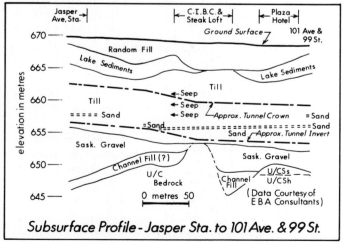

Figure 5. Subsurface profile along the tunnel. See Figure 4 for general locations.

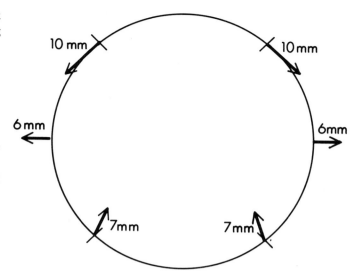

(after Eisenstein & Thomson, 1977)

Figure 6. Observed displacement vectors of points on ribs.

Geology of the Tunnel Area

The tunnels pass through both units of Continental till (Figure 5). The lower till is rectangularly jointed and separated from the upper till by thin beds of Tofield sand. In the area of interest, the lower till is generally less than a meter thick. The upper till displays a columnar jointing but otherwise is, geotechnically, similar to the lower till. Its thickness is 4 to 6 m.

The till contains a high percentage of the local bedrock. Typical grain size distribution shows pebbles and boulders less than 5%, 40 to 45% sand, 25 to 35% silt and 20 to 30% clay. The clay size fraction contains a significant portion of montmorillonite. The bulk unit weight is in the order of 20.6 to 21.2 kN/M^3, and the natural moisture content varies from 10 to 20%, with an average of about 15%. The liquid limit of the matrix material varies from 20 to 40% and the plastic limit from 10 to 20%. The Standard Penetration counts range from 41 to 60, but values of over 100 have been reported (Dejong and Morgenstern, 1973). Unconfined compressive strengths of intact samples of the till above a depth of 12 m vary from 140 to 245 kPa. At greater depths of 21 to 25 m, the unconsolidated-undrained strength varied from 350 to 700 kPa (Morgenstern and Thomson, 1971).

Till Behavior

There was little difficulty in tunneling through the till and maintaining its integrity. Probably the greatest difficulties were with sand pockets within the till and the Tofield sand. The sand pockets vary in lateral extent from one to several meters in diameter and from several to 50 to 60 cm thick. These pockets were commonly saturated and under pressure. When these pockets were intercepted by the mole, water and sand flowed into the tunnel, ceasing in about 1 hour. Although this phenomenon was short-lived, it caused anxious moments until the water source became clear. Unfortunately, there is no economical way of predicting the occurrence of sand pockets.

Dislodging of blocks of till along the natural fractures and joint systems caused problems also. The blocks were in the order of 45 by 60 cm and up to 30 cm thick. A fully shielded mole has only about 2 cm clearance between the shield and the soil so the blocks could only drop down this distance. However, this is enough to cause surface settlement. In the case of an unshielded mole, the blocks were a particular hazard to the moling crew, and the voids left in the crown had to be grouted to prevent serious surface subsidence. An instance of a series of block falls was reported by Matheson (1970).

Buried preglacial valleys have, on occasion, been a hazard in tunneling operations. When the crown of a tunnel comes too close to the underside of a buried channel, the joints in the bedrock open up due to stress release, and the tunnel may be flooded with fine sand and water. In one instance, the tunnel was rerouted vertically and passed under the buried valley. In another instance, the inflow of sand partially buried the mole, resulting in the tunnel crown area having to be sealed by freezing it to free the mole. The costs involved in installing the brine freezing system and the delays in the construction program were considerable.

OLD COAL MINE SHAFTS

Parts of Edmonton are underlaid by abandoned, near surface, coal mining shafts and adits, a result of mining that took took place around the turn of the century (Taylor, 1971). Surface subsidence has resulted and has to be considered when planning. Certain landslides along the river bank have, at least in part, been caused by this subsidence. The ground cracks open up and allow ingress of water which leads to eventual failure (Hardy, 1957).

SLOPE INSTABILITY

Probably the greatest hazards in the development of the City of Edmonton are natural landslides that occur along the banks of the North Saskatchewan River and along the slopes of tributary valleys, and the failure of man-made slopes formed during construction activities. Damage to structures and the necessary remedial work have required an expenditure of millions of dollars (Thomson and Yacyshyn, 1977).

About half of the slope failures occur in the poorly

indurated bentonite-rich clay shales of the Upper Cretaceous Edmonton Formation. Bentonite strongly influences the geotechnical properties of the shales. Clay-rich strata are subject to rebound and swelling when the load is removed and water becomes available. These materials range in natural moisture content from 10 to 70%, liquid limit 50 to 400%, plastic limit 20 to 60%, peak angle of shearing resistance from 14 to 24°, peak cohesion from 40 to 60 kPa, and residual angle of shearing resistance 5 to 17°. Landslides associated with bedrock occur mostly on the steep sided valley walls where bedrock forms more than one half of the 50 m or so height, commonly overlaid by Saskatchewan gravels and sands, till, and lake sediments. The slides are initiated by lateral stream erosion, subsidence from old coal mines, and construction activities such as overloading crests and installation of sewer outfalls (gully erosion). A recent slope stability project in connection with the creation of a park along the North Saskatchewan River required a gravel berm at, and just above, river level to prevent lateral river erosion of the bedrock and to act as a toe load (Thomson and Townsend, 1979).

Landslides in glacial Lake Edmonton sediments account for about 25% of the slides in the Edmonton area. The lake sediments contain 40 to 60% clay sizes, of which nearly one half is montmorillonite and are weakly overconsolidated. The average moisture content below a depth of 3 m is 35%. The liquid limit commonly varies from 65 to 75% and the plasticity index from 25 to 35%. The unconfined compressive strength decreases from an average $240 \, \text{kN/m}^2$ near the surface to $125 \, \text{kN/m}^2$ at a depth of 6 m. Laboratory tests yield a peak angle of shearing resistance of 22° and a cohesion of $14 \, \text{kN/m}^2$ (Fredlund and Dahlman, 1971). Landslides in glacial lake sediments are associated mostly with construction activity in the form of road cuts and landscaping. Field evidence suggests that in instances where failure occurred, the water table was from one third to one half the height of the slope. General experience indicates that long term stable slopes in glacial lake clays are in the order of 3 horizontal to one vertical. Lake sediments have also failed as a result of leaking sewers and from overloaded slope crests.

A few slides are located in fill sections, but practically no failures are seated in till, which is a stable material in the Edmonton area.

Construction activity accounts for nearly three quarters of the landslides in the Edmonton area. Coupled with those that are induced naturally, about 37 substantial slides have been identified to 1975.

The preglacial valleys within the city area have, for the most part, been infilled with Pleistocene deposits, floored with clean water bearing Saskatchewan gravels and sands (Carlson, 1967). The presence of a buried valley enhances slope stability by locally drawing down the water table. In effect, they are deep subsurface drains. An illustration is the valley wall along the north side of the University of Alberta campus. At the east end of this stretch, the valley walls slope at about 10° and comprise slump topography. On the west end, where a preglacial tributary valley is cut by the modern river, the valley walls stand at nearly 30 degrees (Thomson, 1970).

OTHER ASPECTS

Foundations

The City of Edmonton has generally good foundation conditions except for shallow depths in the lake sediments where swelling can occur. This affects homes and other light structures. Large buildings are founded in the competent till on spread footings or belled piles. Settlement of large buildings is determined solely by elastic analysis (Dejong and Morgenstern, 1973). Foundations in bedrock must not rest on bentonite seams because of possible settlement.

Aggregate Supply

Gravel is getting scarce. Gravel and sand are obtained from Saskatchewan gravels and sands and glaciofluvial outwash. There is no deleterious material in Saskatchewan gravels and sands as far as concrete goes, but the well-sorted (or poorly-graded) nature of the deposit is unacceptable for use in concrete, either Portland cement or asphaltic. Outwash sands often contain clay-shale lumps and pieces of coal that have to be removed in order to use the material for concrete. Both gravel sources must be beneficiated, the former to improve gradation and the latter to remove the deleterious material.

CONCLUSIONS

The geology under Edmonton exerts a profound influence on the design and construction of nearly all development projects. With the exception of slope failures, hazards are relatively minor. Good engineering practice, fortified by an understanding of the geology, can usually avoid unnecessary remedial activities and costs. Fortunately, in the Edmonton area, geologists and engineers have worked together in harmony for years.

REFERENCES CITED

Bayrock, L. A., and Berg, T. E., 1966, Geology of the City of Edmonton, Part I: Central Edmonton: Research Council of Alberta. Rept. 66-1, 30 p.

Bayrock, L. A., and Hughes, G. M., 1962, Surficial geology of the Edmonton district, Alberta: Research Council of Alberta, Preliminary Report 62-6, 40 p.

Beaulieu, A. C., 1972, Tunneling experiences, City of Edmonton, Alberta, Canada: Proceedings of the First North American Rapid Excavation and Tunneling Conference, American Institute of Mining Engineers. v. 2, p. 933–964.

Carlson, V. A., 1967, Bedrock topography and surficial aquifers of the Edmonton District, Alberta: Alberta Research Council, Rept. 66-3, 21 p.

Dejong, J., and Morgenstern, N. R., 1973, Heave and settlement of two tall buildings in Edmonton, Alberta: Canadian Geotechnical Journal, v. 10, p. 261–281.

Eisenstein, Z., and Thomson, S., 1977, Geotechnical performance of a tunnel in till: Canadian Geotechnical Journal, v. 15, p. 332–345.

Fredlund, D. G., and Dahlman, A. E., 1971, Statistical geotechnical properties of glacial Lake Edmonton sediments: Proceedings, 1st International Conference on Applications of Statistics and Probability to Soil and Structural Engineering, Hong Kong, p. 204–228.

Hardy, R. M., 1957, Engineering problems involving preconsolidated clay shales. Trans. Eng. Inst. Can., p. 5–14.

Kathol, C. P., and McPherson, R. A., 1975, Urban geology of Edmonton: Alberta Research Council Bulletin 32, 61 p.

Matheson, D. A., 1970, A tunnel roof failure in till: Canadian Geotechnical Journal, v. 7, p. 313–317.

May, R. W., and Thomson, S., 1978, The geology and geotechnical properties of till and related deposits in the Edmonton, Alberta area: Canadian Geotechnical Journal, v. 15, p. 362–370.

Morgenstern, N. R., and Thomson, S., 1971, Comparative observations on the use of the Pitcher Sampler in stiff clay: American Society for Testing and Materials, Special Technical Publication 483, p. 180–191.

Ower, J. R., 1960, The Edmonton Formation: Alberta Society of Petroleum Geologists, v. 8, p. 309–323.

Taylor, R. S., 1971, Atlas: coal mine workings of the Edmonton area: Edmonton, Alberta, 33 p.

Thomson, S., 1970, River bank stability study at the University of Alberta, Edmonton: Canadian Geotechnical Journal, v. 7, p. 152–168.

Thomson, S., and El Nahhas, F. 1980, Field measurements in two tunnels in Edmonton, Alberta: Canadian Geotechnical Journal, v. 17, p. 20–33.

Thomson, S., and Townsend, D. L., 1979, River erosion and bank stabilization. North Saskatchewan River, Edmonton, Alberta: Canadian Geotechnical Journal, v. 16, p. 567–576.

Thomson, S., and Yacyshyn, R., 1977, Slope instability in the City of Edmonton: Canadian Geotechnical Journal, v. 14, p. 1–16.

Westgate, J. A., 1969, The Quaternary geology of the Edmonton area, Alberta: *in* Pawluk, S., ed., Pedology and Quaternary Research, Edmonton, University of Alberta Press, p. 129–151.

Westgate, J. A., Kalas, L., and Evans, M. E., 1976, Geology of Edmonton area: Geological Association of Canada, Field Trip C-8 Guide Book, Annual Meeting - May 19–21, 1976, Edmonton, 49 p.

MANUSCRIPT RECEIVED BY THE SOCIETY MAY 11, 1982
MANUSCRIPT ACCEPTD JUNE 1, 1982

Geological Society of America
Reviews in Engineering Geology, Volume V
1982

Geology and space beneath a city—Kansas City

Eldon J. Parizek
Professor of Geology and Dean,
College of Arts and Sciences
University of Missouri—Kansas City
Kansas City, Missouri

ABSTRACT

Kansas City geology is favorable to secondary development of subsurface space created by mining for commercial activities. Upper Pennsylvanian shales and limestones, including the Bethany Falls limestone, which is the principal source of limestone products for western Missouri, comprise the bedrock. Activities like warehousing, controlled temperature food storage, manufacturing, and office and laboratory space, have been relocated below the surface to the extent that Kansas City has become the world leader in secondary subsurface space utilization.

Problems, most importantly, floor heave from volume changes caused by oxidation of sulfides in black shales, present limitations to growth of underground usage. Many surface facilities throughout the region are similarly affected, and measures used to counter heave problems in both surface and subsurface facilities have proved only moderately successful.

Metropolitan Kansas City, with an area exceeding 3,300 square miles and a population of 1-1/2 million, is located in a region distinguished by comparatively simple geologic structure. Like many growing areas, this region has its share of urban-related environmental problems. However, the adaptation and use of space mined out beneath the surface has countered the impact of environmental concerns to some degree and is the basis for inclusion of Kansas City in this volume on Geology Beneath Cities. Consequently, the discussion which follows is primarily concerned with the relationship between the geology at Kansas City and this innovative and highly important subsurface dimension in space.

Kansas City is located in a belt of nearly horizontal Pennsylvanian rocks that dips northwest from the Ozark Uplift toward the Forest City Basin at 10-20 feet per mile. The Pennsylvanian section is 900 feet thick at Kansas City, one-third of which is exposed. The rocks are mostly cyclical marine shales and limestones that range in bed thickness from a few inches up to units 30-40 feet thick (Parizek, 1975). The Kansas and Missouri Rivers join at Kansas City and continue eastward in a course that parallels the physiographic boundary which separates the Dissected Till Plains

and Osage Plains (Figure 1). The surface is dissected glacial till and loess north of the river, while outcrops of limestones and shales form east-facing escarpments in the Osage

Figure 1. Location map of Missouri and eastern Kansas, showing location of Greater Kansas City and physical features noted in text.

Plains to the south. Several northerly trending scarps occur between the Missouri Ozarks and the Flint Hills region of Kansas. One escarpment, the Bethany Falls, passes through the Kansas City region (Figure 1) and is critical in the development and use of underground space. The escarpment is less than 50 feet high and is usually concealed by glacial deposits in the area of the Dissected Till Plains. The escarpment is capped by the 20-25 foot thick Bethany Falls limestone. It lies at shallow depth over wide areas downdip from the escarpment and is extensively quarried at Kansas City.

SUBSURFACE SPACE INDUSTRY AT KANSAS CITY

A substantial increase in the use of subsurface space has occurred in the Kansas City metropolitan area since 1955. Prior to that date, the space created by more than a century of mining, together with the areas nearby, was considered wasteland of little value. In the mid 1950s, it was recognized that some of this space could be secondarily adapted and used for certain commercial purposes (Figure 2A). Initially, it was used entirely for vehicle storage. In time, however, developers found that other surface activities could be relocated into the underground beneficially with the result that Kansas City is now the world leader in the use of underground space for many traditional surface functions, including record storage (Figure 2B), warehousing (Figure 2C), cold food storage, manufacturing, commercial sales, and engineering and research laboratories (Stauffer, 1975). Unique among tenants is the Kansas City Foreign Trade Zone, larger in area utilized than the combination of all other commercial trading marts in the continental United States (Figure 2D). More than 2,500 persons are employed in 15 underground locations; about twenty million square feet of space are currently occupied by 200 tenants, covering a wide variety of commercial activities. Several times that amount of space is in various stages of development. All operations are located in single-tiered openings located anywhere from 30-175 feet below the surface.

Open pit mining characterized early exploitation of rock at Kansas City. A thick overburden soon led to extension of operations into the subsurface. With little exception, mining has concentrated in a single limestone, the Bethany Falls, which is among the thickest and most suitable beds for commercial use in northwestern Missouri. Several factors have contributed to the concentration of mining in the Bethany Falls. For example, the layers are nearly horizontal, so floors and roofs in mines are level and smooth; erosion of the rolling surface at Kansas City has provided extensive outcrops; the limestone is easily adapted to room-and-pillar mining; and shales enclosing the Bethany Falls have effectively restricted water seepage into

the mines (Fredericksen and Gentile, 1972). In addition, physical and chemical properties of the Bethany Falls meet Missouri State Highway Department specifications for aggregate better than most strata in the region. Therefore, the Bethany Falls is the principal source of limestone products in western Missouri.

Pillars comprise about 20 percent of the mine area. Questionable practices in the past, particularly "rob and run" mining, have given rise to roof subsidence and surface collapse in a few localities. But the space created is now considered a more valuable resource than the exploited rock. Therefore, designed space, alignment of pillars, and retention of proper roof thickness for secondary use are now common practices.

Industry, roadways, and rail lines have been located along valley bottoms throughout the history of Kansas City. Concurrent with this development has been the concentration of mining and quarry operations along bordering valley slopes. Once the value of mined-out space for secondary use was recognized, it was simple to move into the subsurface (Figure 3A). As the market for space improved, abandoned mines were reopened, and new mines were developed. Sale of the rock has usually paid the costs of mining operations. Each year, mining adds 6-7 million square feet of designed space to the underground inventory (Stauffer, 1976).

Mines in the Bethany Falls have ceiling heights of 12-15 feet. The upper 6-9 feet of the Bethany Falls are left for roof support. Roof bolts are unnecessary in many mines, but in some locations, roof bolts have been tied to a strong limestone unit above. Railroad lines, large trucks, and drilling rigs enter some underground sites (Figure 3B). The normal ceiling height is too small where this occurs, and it is necessary to excavate the 4-5 feet of Hushpuckney shale subjacent to the Bethany Falls. Mine floors then rest on the thin Middle Creek limestone below the Hushpuckney shale (Figure 4). Underground openings have ceiling heights of 16-20 feet where the Hushpuckney shale has been excavated.

Although the favorable nature of Kansas City geology has been basic to the success of this innovative industry, other factors have contributed to its growth and development (Fredericksen and Gentile, 1972). The central location is attractive to producers and shippers from the east and west coasts. Low-cost storage rates in underground space sites compared with surface charges, combined with the geographic location, have made Kansas City a convenient in-transit storage depot for frozen and processed foods and other kinds of goods. For developers and on-site users of underground space, there are other factors equally significant. (1) The cost of adaptation and development of space is comparatively inexpensive. Ceilings, foundations, and supporting pillars already exist, eliminating sizable construction costs that are necessary in developing comparable

Figure 2A, 2B, 2C, 2D. Underground space facilities at Great Midwest Corporation, Kansas City, Missouri. Floor shown in Figures 2A and 2C is on the Middle Creek limestone. Concrete aprons around the Hushpuckney shale in Figure 2A enhance the decor and help inhibit swelling of the shale. Figure 2B shows a portion of the record storage area for International Harvester Corporation, a tenant, protected from fire by an inert gas system originally developed in the outer space program to control fires in space capsules. Elaborate entry into Great Midwest Corporation offices and display rooms 150 feet below the surface is shown in Figure 2C. Modern underground facilities blend contemporary architecture and lighting with the rock pillars. Figure 2D shows portal entries into Great Midwest Corporation's Foreign Trade Zone. Access for large trucks and railways is equally convenient. Flags of some nations using the facility are displayed above the entrances.

surface facilities. Custom-mined space now describes the plan of operation in the rock industry. (2) Rental costs in the subsurface are inexpensive in comparison with charges for comparable space in surface facilities. Comparative savings of 40-50 percent are common. (3) Convenience of space accessible to highways and rail lines is attractive to industrial development. Spurs which connect rail lines with the underground facilities are usually at a gentle grade. (4) Humidity and temperature control, with attendant energy savings, are benefits to users of subsurface space. A constant underground temperature of 56-58 degrees Fahrenheit is an advantageous condition. Between 15-90 percent energy savings have been attributed to use of subsurface

space by operators, depending on the type of activity. One study by Stauffer (1978) involving 13 selected facilities at Kansas City supports the contention that use of the subsurface makes a significant contribution to solving the energy problem. From monitored data of six surface and seven subsurface facilities, he concluded that use of subsurface space contributes energy savings of 60 percent for service operations, 70 percent for warehousing, and 47-60 percent for manufacturing activities. (5) Location in the subsurface has provided a noise- and vibration-free environment that is important to certain manufacturers. One example at Kansas City is the relocation beneath ground by makers of precision instruments. (6) Underground facilities are safe

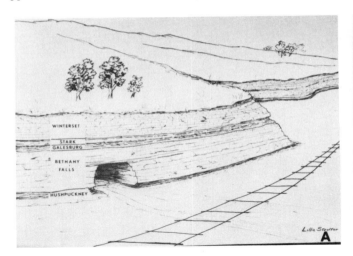

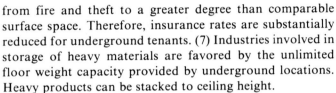

Figure 3A. Representative sketch of an extended face of Upper Pennsylvanian beds with horizontal drift along valley bluffs. Common location of rail lines and mine portals is shown.

Figure 3B. Rail lines set on the Middle Creek limestone at Interstate Warehouse Corporation underground facilities, Kansas City, Missouri. Concrete apron above the tracks and the floor on which people are walking encloses the Hushpuckney shale. Rock bolts in the Bethany Falls are used in this facility to insure stability of the roof.

from fire and theft to a greater degree than comparable surface space. Therefore, insurance rates are substantially reduced for underground tenants. (7) Industries involved in storage of heavy materials are favored by the unlimited floor weight capacity provided by underground locations. Heavy products can be stacked to ceiling height.

Underground facilities at Kansas City have received much attention as potential sites for civil defense. In general, the United States is not geared for protection of its population against nuclear attack and natural catastrophies. Thus, Kansas City's subsurface resource is an asset in time of emergency. Ward (1979) states that roughly 50 million square feet of underground space at Kansas City contain roads, lights, water, and sewer installations. An additional 20 million square feet could become available with the addition of portable generators, medicine, food, and sanitation stations. Facilities are clean and easily accessible to the urban population. The sites are widely dispersed and located along major transportation routes; most citizens reside within 5 miles of one of these possible underground shelters. Ward states that if Kansas City had planned for the location and building of shelters and connecting highway links, it would have been difficult to improve upon that provided by natural conditions.

LITHOLOGIC RELATIONS

The rocks in the region are Upper Pennsylvanian limestones and shales of cyclical origin which extend from western Iowa to Oklahoma. Three hundred feet of the Pennsylvanian section crop out at Kansas City. Most units are less than 10 feet thick, but several are as much as 60 feet

thick. The Swope formation, consisting of three members, the Middle Creek limestone, Hushpuckney shale, and Bethany Falls limestone, in ascending order (Figure 4), is of major economic importance. Above the Swope formation is the Galesburg, a 4-5 foot sequence of shale and nodular limestone, which is commonly overlaid directly by the Stark shale member of the Dennis formation (Howe and Koenig, 1961). These two shales form an effective barrier to water movement and help maintain dry conditions in the open areas created by mining in the Bethany Falls.

MIDDLE CREEK LIMESTONE

Typically the Middle Creek is a hard, fine-grained, single layer of limestone, 6-12 inches thick. In some locations, however, it does thicken to 2-1/2 feet of multi-layered limestone with shale partings (Parizek and Gentile, 1965). The Middle Creek limestone is usually fractured into rectangular slabs. It can be traced for hundreds of miles north and south of Kansas City. The Middle Creek forms the floor in subsurface sites where the Hushpuckney shale has been excavated in order to increase ceiling height.

HUSHPUCKNEY SHALE

Two dissimilar shale types comprise the section above the Middle Creek limestone. The beds are named the Hushpuckney shale and comprise between 4-5 feet of material. The lower portion is dark fissile shale. The beds above are light-colored, thin-layered, and calcareous (Parizek and Gentile, 1965). Finely divided pyrite, in association with other sulfides, occurs throughout both phases. A nodular

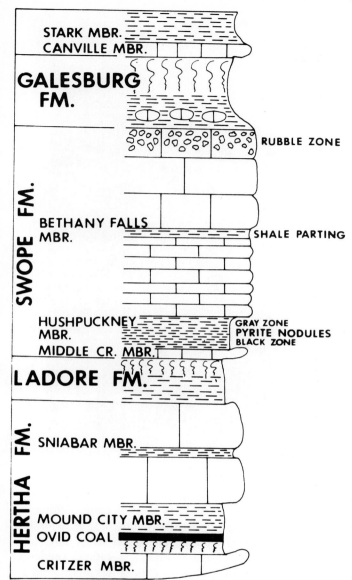

Figure 4. A portion of the Upper Pennsylvanian stratigraphic column at Kansas City, Missouri, showing the relationship of the Bethany Falls limestones to adjacent units. Vertical scale: one inch = 10 feet. (Modified after Howe, 1961.)

pyritic zone exists midway in the section (Figure 4). The Hushpuckney shale is a contributor to a problem of floor heaving in mines, a condition that plagues several underground facilities (Coveney and Parizek, 1977).

BETHANY FALLS LIMESTONE

The Bethany Falls limestone, 14-24 feet thick, forms a prominent escarpment in western Missouri and southeastern Kansas and provides the bulk of crushed rock and aggregate materials used in the region (Figure 5). It underlies more than 200 square miles of the Kansas City area at

shallow depth. The Bethany Falls consists of two distinct limestones that are separated by thin shale midway in the section. The lower 8-10 feet are mostly fine-to-coarse grained gray limestone, while the upper 10-12 feet comprise massive layers that are strongly mottled near the top. The uppermost 2-3 feet appear nodular and lensing, looking like rubble in fresh exposures and unworked concrete when weathered (Parizek, 1975). These beds are left in place during mining (Figure 4). Mine roofs are usually several feet below the upper rubbly zone. The Bethany Falls is cut by two joint sets. Although joints are visible in the mines, they are generally closed and widely spaced. They are most significant in the vicinity of mine portals and surface outcrops.

REGIONAL GEOLOGICAL CONDITIONS

Regional geological conditions are critically important to the success of the underground space industry. Of particular importance are: (1) the karst-free nature of the surface; (2) the minor to moderate structural deformation of the region; (3) the low seismic activity in this portion of the Mid-Continent; and, (4) the rolling configuration of the landscape (Parizek, 1978).

Carbonate rocks in northwestern Missouri are generally free of extensive solution features, in contrast with some other portions of the State. Caves and underground passageways are rare. Small collapse structures exist above a few old mines, as do several small depressions, possibly related to sink holes associated with a deep seated erosional surface on Mississippian limestones. Nonetheless, the sparse occurrence of solution features reduces the concentrated flow of water toward mined-out areas. As a result, remarkably dry conditions exist in the mines.

Stucturally, the Kansas City region is distinguished by beds which dip gently toward the northwest at 10-20 feet per mile. Two joint sets and localized, high angle normal faults cut the nearly horizontal beds.

Joints at underground sites are fairly open where mine portals are mantled with a thin overburden. Within the interior of one underground facility, the length of joints is less than 25 feet. They are at least 50 feet apart. At the portals, however, joints are 100 feet or more in length and 10-15 feet apart. Joints tend to be more open at mine entrances than is the case within the mines, probably due to increased solution work. Downhill creep, release of confining pressure, and solution work have apparently contributed to the increase in length, number, and separation of joints near underground entrances. Similar joint characteristics can be seen at most underground locations.

Faulting has not been observed in the underground sites at Kansas City. Seismic stability has dominated this portion of the North American mid-continent in recent time. By and large, roofs and floors in mines can be characterized as stable, horizontal in attitude, and free of water

Figure 5. Bethany Falls limestone at Kansas City, Missouri. A thin shale parting occurs midway in this section. Horizontal attitude and boundaries of the unit are shown by broken lines.

incursion. Nonetheless, as pointed out by Gentile (1978), Pennsylvanian rocks in west-central Missouri do exhibit localized complex polygonal, rectangular, and triangular-shaped fault systems in the plan view. One structure exists in Jackson County, Missouri, where beds are moderately displaced along northwestern trending, high angle, normal faults. Faulting covers a few square miles and suggests an overall horst and graben structure. Two causes have been proposed for the faults: (1) fracturing and subsidence within the Precambrian basement, or (2) collapse of beds into solution cavities developed within Paleozoic carbonate beds. The faults have not been found in overlying soils. They do cut the Bethany Falls, however, so that similar structures must be considered as possible factors in rock engineering as mining extends into new areas at Kansas City.

The uneven topographic surface combines with the Bethany Falls escarpment to permit easy entrance into the subsurface. The rolling surface is etched by a fine drainage texture, producing zig-zag to dendritic trends along the escarpment face, thus increasing the opportunities for openings into the bluffs. More than 200 square miles of the

Bethany Falls limestone beneath Jackson County, Missouri shown in Figure 6, are potentially minable for secondary space through portals placed along the scarp and valley slopes (Stauffer, 1976). The combined amount of single-tier space currently used at Kansas City is less than 5 square miles of area. The vast area that remains for future conversion, the local and regional geology, and all the other factors favorable to use of the underground, particularly energy savings, very likely guarantee that use of subsurface space will continue to increase in the future.

PROBLEMS RELATED TO USE OF UNDERGROUND SPACE

This bright picture at Kansas City is clouded to some extent with certain limitations. For example, occupancy is limited to a single limestone unit because several feet of competent overlying beds must be left for roof support. Limestones above and below the Bethany Falls are not amenable to excavation for additional ceiling height. Use of the space, therefore, is restricted to functions suited to a ceiling height of less than 20 feet, even where the underlying

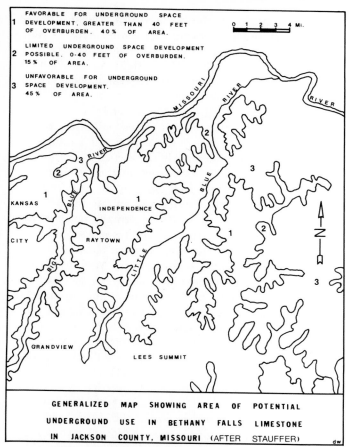

Figure 6. Potential areas of underground development are shown by Numbers 1 and 2, totaling approximately 200 square miles (after Stauffer 1976).

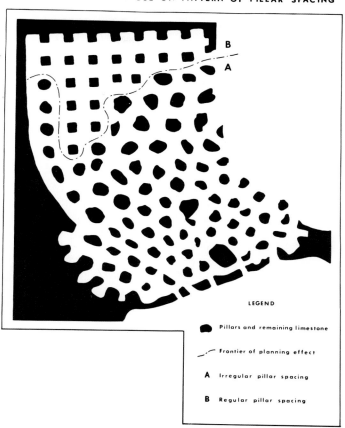

Figure 7. Generalized diagram showing the improved effects of regular spacing of pillars for secondary usage (after Stauffer, 1971).

Hushpuckney shale has been removed. Additional limitations also exist in some old mines because of the random arrangement of pillars. This is not a problem in new mines because the square pillars are aligned and spaced 50-60 feet apart by design (Figure 7). This has increased the amount of usable space and, in some cases, made possible the incorporation of pillars into the subsurface decor.

SHALE HEAVE

The major limitation which affects underground sites, however, is the stratigraphic position of the Bethany Falls limestone between two sulfide-bearing black shales, which are subject to progressive volume increase intrinsic with weathering and mineral alteration (Figure 8). Expansion or heave of floors and walls in the mines may develop when this occurs (Coveney and Parizek, 1977). Similar problems have been reported in black shales from areas as widely separated as Europe (Jangdahl, 1971), Canada (Penner and others, 1970; Penner and others, 1973; Crawford, 1978; Gillot, 1978), and Ohio-Pennsylvania (Dougherty and Barsotti, 1972).

Secondary gypsum crystals develop along bedding planes of sulfide-bearing black shales that are exposed to oxygen (Figure 9). Initial exposure of the shales in urban areas may result from excavations associated with construction. Chemically vulnerable pyrite in framboidal aggregates (less than 2 microns) is the frequent source of sulfur in the fresh shale. As much as 10 volume percent of secondary gypsum may form as veinlets along bedding planes and joints. Enormous pressures are associated with the secondary growth of gypsum, and this can account for rock distortion in the mines. Pressures that can exceed 2,000 atmospheres have been predicted from calculations relating to reactions of this sort (Winkler and Singer, 1972). Gypsum density is about one-half that of pyrite, and its specific volume, therefore, roughly doubles the volume of the original pyrite grains. Two moles of gypsum are formed for each mole of pyrite; hence, the secondary gypsum crystals occupy space about quadruple that of the original pyrite. Gypsum crystals consistently occupy less than one-third the space volume of the secondary porosity created by their formation (Coveney and Parizek, 1977). If all the pyrite in some black shales at Kansas City was com-

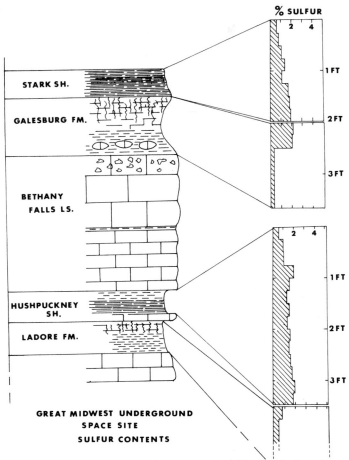

Figure 8. Sulfur content (weight percent) within the Hushpuckney and Stark shales at Great Midwest Corporation's underground facility, Kansas City, Missouri.

pletely altered, calculations indicate that the shale volume could theoretically increase as much as 30-35 percent. Such a tremendous increase is unlikely to occur in full.

Localized heave of mine floors at several Kansas City locations, however, has already reached 6-8 inches, with a pronounced camber between the supporting pillars. Profiles of the floors appear as inverted catenary curves, peaking about 8 inches high at the center and declining sharply near pillars and structural walls. Such profiles correspond to an overall floor heave of 3-5 inches and a volume increase of roughly 8 percent (Coveney and Parizek, 1977). Substantial unaltered pyrite still remains in all observed cases of distorted black shale, indicating that additional heaving is to be expected. Underground developers have tried several measures to counter heave in the black shales, the most common being the immediate application of asphalt or other impervious materials in order to prevent air contact and diminish the effects of moisture variation. This and other measures have proved only moderately successful, particularly when used after the onset of shale distortion.

Volume change in the black shales is also a major problem affecting surface facilities in a wide sector of Kansas City. In addition to the two shales associated stratigraphically with subsurface sites, three additional black shales occur within the exposed Upper Pennsylvanian beds (Howe and Koenig, 1961). Four shales are about 5 feet thick (Hushpuckney, Stark, Muncie Creek, and Eudora), and one (Quivira) is 15 feet thick in places (Figure 10). All contain 1-10 percent fresh pyrite and minor amounts of other sulfides. Volume increase in the vertical direction can theoretically reach 15 inches in each of the 3-5 foot beds and 4-5 feet in the 15 foot bed. Once pyrite alteration begins, the change from sulfide to sulfate is a slow, continuous process. The distortion normally becomes apparent in 4-6 years for surface structures erected upon or within the shale. Concrete slabs in some basements have heaved 10 inches within a single decade. At Kansas City, structures affected by such volume changes include apartments, residential homes, and government and commercial buildings. A classic example occurs in the Country Club Plaza District, site of a tragic flood in September, 1977. The thick Quivira shale crops out in the area. A branch library was built in 1967, with the basement floor located in the upper portion of the shale (Figure 11). Heave began to appear by 1971, and portions of the floor have risen progressively, and a 10 inch rise now exists between the walls. The problem has spread throughout the entire basement, resulting in damage to door frames and interior walls, electrical and plumbing fixtures, and the heating system (Figures 12A, 12B, 12C). Renovation costs exceeded one-half million dollars.

Buckling and cracks in foundations are usually attributed to variations in soil moisture. Volume increase in clay shales at Kansas City from water absorption, however, is only 1-2 percent, as verified by mineralogical and soil tests. This minor volume increase is substantially lower than the amount of heave observed at many localities.

The rolling surface and relief at Kansas City dictate that one or more of the five problem-causing shales should outcrop or lie at shallow depth in much of the region. The west half of Jackson County, Missouri, an area of 250 square miles, is shown in Figure 13. The line pattern depicts sectors where one or more of the sulfide-bearing shales outcrop or are within 10 feet of the surface. Volume increase in these beds by generation of secondary gypsum could potentially occur if the surface is disturbed during construction. Major portions of the lined area are either commercial or residential sections or localities into which urban sprawl will extend in the near future. Thus, if only because of the widespread problem of shale expansion, the geology beneath Greater Kansas City deserves continued, intensive study in the years ahead.

Figure 9. Secondary gypsum development along joint surfaces (A and B, vertical) and bedding planes (B, horizontal) in Hushpuckney shale from Fairmount Industries' underground facility, Kansas City, Missouri. Scale on photos (after Coveney and Parizek, 1977).

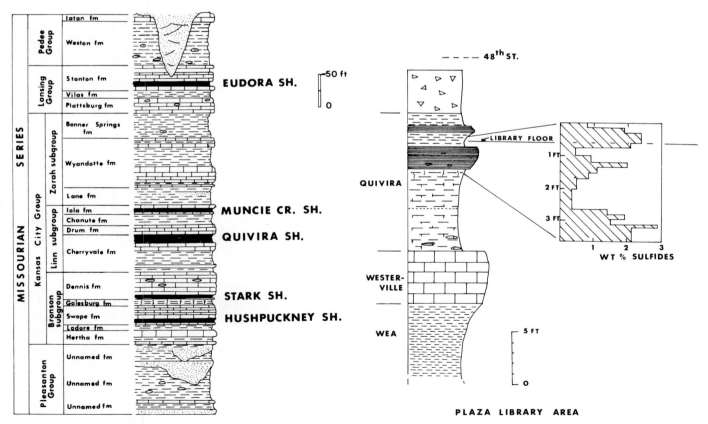

Figure 10. Stratigraphic position of five sulfide-bearing black shales in the Upper Pennsylvanian, Missourian Series, at Kansas City, Missouri. Section shown includes about 250 feet of beds (modified from Howe, 1961).

Figure 11. Stratigraphic relationships at Plaza Branch Library, Kansas City, Missouri. Location of library floor and weight percentages of sulfides in expanding black shales immediately adjacent to it are shown.

Figure 12A, 12B, 12C. Deformation in the basement level of Plaza Branch Library, Kansas City, Missouri, from swelling in the Quivira shale. Figure 12A shows warped door and damaged electrical fixtures. Extension of distortion along basement hallway is shown in Figure 12B. Floor separation near basement pillar in response to 10 inch rise of basement slab at center of room is shown in Figure 12C.

ZONE CONTAINING POTENTIALLY DESTRUCTIVE BLACK SHALES
(WEST-HALF JACKSON COUNTY, MISSOURI)

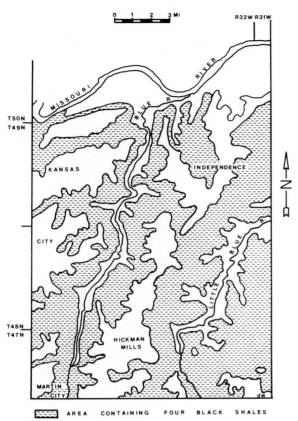

Figure 13. Map of west half of Jackson County, Missouri, outlining areas where four sulfide-bearing black shales either outcrop or are at shallow depth. A considerable portion of the area is urban development or residential.

REFERENCES CITED

Coveney, R. M., and Parizek, E. J., 1977, Deformation of mine floors by sulfide alteration: Bulletin of The Association of Engineering Geologists, Vol. 14, No. 3, p. 131–156.

Crawford, C. B., 1978, Shale expansion: Underground utilization: Proceedings, Eighth International Conference on Soil Mechanics and Foundation Engineering, Vol. 2, p. 427–429.

Dougherty, M. T., and Barsotti, N. J., 1972, Structural damage and potentially expansive sulfide minerals: Bulletin of the Association of Engineering Geologists, Vol. 9, p. 105–125.

Fredericksen, W., and Gentile, R., 1972, Guide to field trips: Association of Engineering Geologists, Kansas City, Missouri, 109 p.

Gentile, R. J., 1978, Faulting of the Bethany Falls limestone and associated strata at Kansas City, Missouri—A preliminary report: Underground utilization: A reference manual of selected works, space construction underground: University of Missouri-Kansas City/National Science Foundation, Vol. 3, p. 433–447.

Gillot, J. E., 1978, Heave in black shales: Underground utilization: A reference manual of selected works, space construction underground: University of Missouri-Kansas City/National Science Foundation, Vol. 3, p. 424–426.

Howe, W. B., and Koenig, J. W., 1961, The stratigraphic succession of Missouri: Missouri Geological Survey and Water Resources, Vol. 40, 2nd ser., 185 p.

Jangdahl, C. E., 1971, Swelling shale in the Owsterund area: National Swedish Building Report, 116 p.

Parizek, E. J., 1975, Geologic setting of Greater Kansas City: Proceedings of the Symposium on the Development and Utilization of Underground Space, University of Missouri-Kansas City/National Science Foundation, Kansas City, Missouri, p. 9–23.

Parizek, E. J., 1978, Geology beneath a city-Kansas City: Geological Society of America Abstracts with Programs, Vol. 10, p. 467.

Parizek, E. J., and Gentile, R. J., 1965, The geology of the Kansas City group at Kansas City: Report of Investigation N. 31, Missouri Geological Survey and Water Resources, 62 p.

Penner, E., Eden, W. J., and Gillot, J. E., 1970, Investigation of heave in Billings shale by mineralogical and biogeochemical methods: Canadian Geotechnical Journal, Vol. 7, p. 333–338.

Penner, E., Eden, W. J., and Gillot, J. E., 1973, Floor heave due to biochemical weathering of shale: Proceedings, Eighth International Conference on Soil Mechanics and Foundation Engineering, Vol. 2, p. 151–158.

Stauffer, T., 1975, Kansas City: A model of underground development: Proceedings of the Symposium on the Development and Utilization of Underground Space, University of Missouri-Kansas City/National Science Foundation, Kansas City, Missouri, p. 29–38.

Stauffer, T., 1976, Underground space: inventory and prospect in Greater Kansas City: Geographic Publication, No. 2, Geosciences Department, University of Missouri-Kansas City, 16 p.

Stauffer, T., 1978, Energy use effectiveness and operating costs compared between surface and subsurface facilities of comparable size, structure, and enterprise classification: Report prepared for City Development Department, Kansas City, Missouri, 42 p.

Ward, D. M., 1979, A preliminary report on the potential use of the Kansas City underground for civil defense: Geographic Publication, University of Missouri-Kansas City, for Director of Emergency Preparedness, Kansas City, Missouri, 23 p.

Winkler, E. M., and Singer, P. C., 1972, Crystallization pressure of salts in stone and concrete: Bulletin of the Geological Society of America, Vol. 83, No. 11, p. 3509–3514.

MANUSCRIPT RECEIVED BY THE SOCIETY MAY 11, 1982
MANUSCRIPT ACCEPTED JUNE 1, 1982

Printed in U.S.A.

Geological Society of America
Reviews in Engineering Geology, Volume V
1982

Engineering geology of New Orleans

C. R. Kolb
Consulting Professor
Institute for Environmental Studies
Louisiana State University
Baton Rouge, La. 70803

R. T. Saucier
Special Assistant for Program Development
Environmental Laboratory
U.S. Army Engineer Waterways Experiment Station
Vicksburg, Miss. 39180

PERSPECTIVE—WATER, WATER EVERYWHERE

Among those who can look beyond the ubiquitous concerns of the "energy crisis," there is a consensus that the decade of the 1980's will witness recognition of widespread regional water shortages as perhaps the next national "crisis." How quickly people tend to forget or ignore the water rationing episodes in several of America's larger cities only several years ago! But the City of New Orleans and its suburbs belong in a small category of major cities in which water in overabundance is the nemesis rather than a scarce natural resource. In fact, it is no overstatement to say that the single greatest regional engineering concern is literally to keep the city from drowning. Coupling this regional concern, with the project-specific one of unusually weak foundation conditions, sets the stage for this overview of the engineering geology of the Crescent City—the location of the French Quarter, the Mardi Gras, and Canal Street (Figure 1).

In an article more than a decade ago by the junior author (Saucier, 1965), the setting of New Orleans was described as being the flattest, lowest, and geologically youngest of any major city in the United States. Quantification of this reveals a maximum relief of about 7 m within an area of 385 km^2, an average elevation of about 0.4 m above mean Gulf level (Schultz and Kolb, 1954, Fig. 2), and no surficial deposits older than 2,500 years (Saucier, 1963). Elaboration on the elevation statistic reveals that over 45 percent of the urbanized area of the city is at or below mean Gulf level, some of it by as much as 2 m. To place this in perspective, one need only mention the following facts: floods on the Mississippi River, where it winds through the city (Figures 1 and 2), have reached a stage of 6.5 m above

mean Gulf level; hurricane surges in Lake Pontchartrain to the north of the city have exceeded a height of 2 m above mean Gulf level, and average annual precipitation (depending on location) varies from 1,500 to 1,600 mm (Lower Mississippi Region Comprehensive Study Coordinating Committee, 1974). Rainfalls of 250 mm in 12 hours have been recorded on several occasions with dramatic consequences. Coping with these conditions, and even the side effects of certain "solutions," has presented interesting challenges in the development and maintenance of an urban complex with a population of nearly 1 million.

PART I: GENERAL GEOLOGY

Location and Physiographic Setting

New Orleans and its immediate suburbs lie wholly within the Holocene deltaic plain of the Mississippi River. Originating as a tiny settlement on the northern bank (locally regarded as the east bank) of the river in 1718, it now sprawls on both sides of the river and as far as the shores of Lake Pontchartrain in both Orleans and Jefferson Parishes. The presence of this lake, plus numerous bayous and extensive wetlands within and adjacent to the city limits, producing a distinctive estuarine setting, suggests immediate proximity to the Gulf of Mexico. However, such is not the case; the Gulf is actually 75 km away, and the mouth of the river is 175 river km distant to the southeast.

Using accepted regional physiographic nomenclature, the fresh-to-brackish-water wetlands (both marshes and

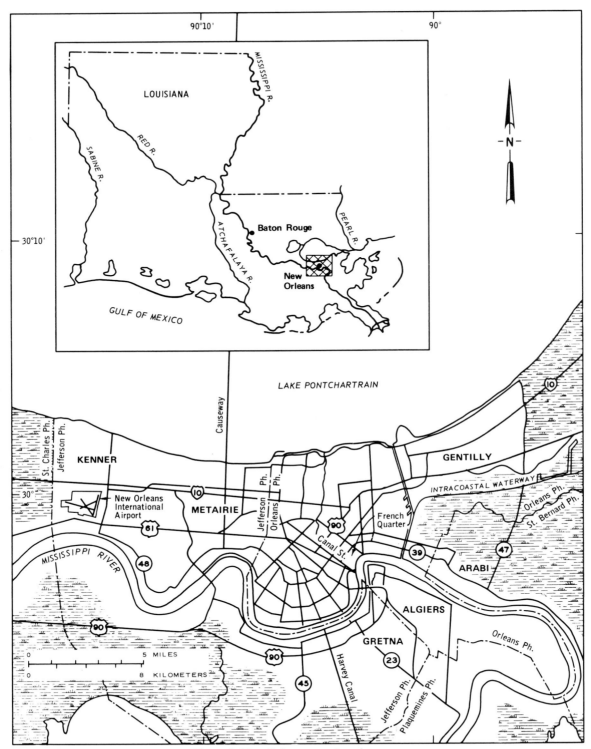

Figure 1. New Orleans area location map.

swamps) of the area occupy interdistributary lowlands or, as they are also sometimes called inter-levee basins. While true wetlands are virtually absent in the urbanized parts of the city as a result of extensive leveeing, canalization, and pumped drainage, they once occupied about half of this area (Fig. 3). The remaining half of the city area is characterized by natural levee ridges. Those flanking the Mississippi River are the best developed in the region, varying in width from 1.5 to 5 km on each side of the stream, and produce the highest elevations in the city. Smaller natural

Figure 2. The Mississippi River in flood as it winds its way through the Crescent City. (Photo courtesy of the U.S. Army Engineer District, New Orleans)

levee ridges, having a total width not exceeding 2 km, trend east-west through the city roughly midway between the Mississippi River and Lake Pontchartrain. Known as the Metairie-Gentilly ridge, this levee system marks the course of the Metairie Bayou and Bayou Sauvage distributaries of an older delta lobe of the Mississippi. Although low (not over an elevation of 1.5 m) and narrow, this ridge system has been important in dictating the routes and patterns of roads and streets and influencing foundation design and surface drainage systems. Other distributary natural levee ridges, of similar but less intense influence, radiate eastward and southward from the New Orleans area as shown in Fig. 3.

Historic and relict beaches of Lake Pontchartrain and other water bodies are not significant physiographic features; however, they are in the shallow subsurface as will be discussed later. A 1 km wide belt of relatively high ground

(1 to 1.5 m above mean Gulf level) flanks the Lake Pontchartrain shoreline in Orleans Parish for over 7 km (Fig. 1), but this is artificial fill dredged from the lake about 50 years ago as part of a reclamation project.

Stratigraphic Relationships and Depositional Environments

New Orleans, as well as all of southern Louisiana, lies directly over the Gulf Coast geosyncline where Neogene deltaic or nearshore marine deposits have accumulated to a thickness of about 12,000 m (Jones, 1969). The alternating transgressive-regressive units consist almost entirely of sands, silts, and clays with abundant organic debris. Quaternary-age deposits comprise the upper 640 m of the sequence (Murray, 1961), with all but the uppermost few

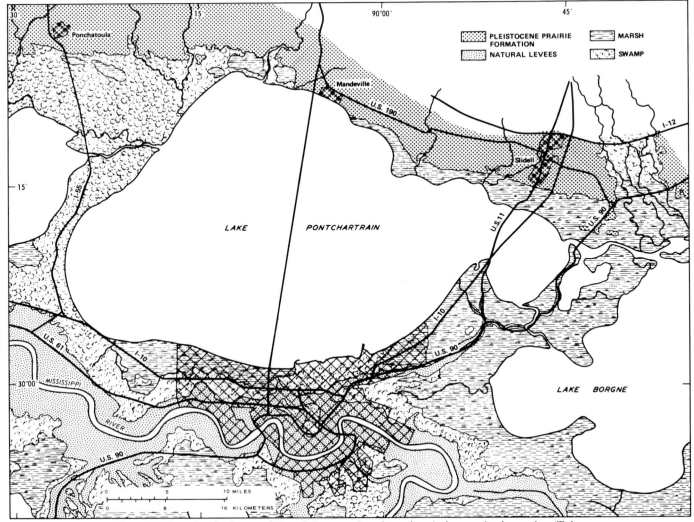

Figure 3. The urbanized area of New Orleans and environs in relation to physiography. (Taken from Saucier, 1963)

tens of meters of this being of Pleistocene age. A regional dip to the south is prevalent.

The uppermost coastwise Pleistocene formation in southern Louisiana is the Prairie formation, which comprises the land surface just north of Lake Pontchartrain (Fig. 3). It represents deposition in nearshore marine, lagoonal, and fluvial environments and has been correlated with the Sangamon interglacial stage (Saucier, 1977).

As a consequence of several processes, including faulting and subsidence, the Prairie formation is exclusively a subsurface feature in the New Orleans area (12 to 30 m deep), and precise correlation of individual strata or units across Lake Pontchartrain to the outcrop area is not possible. Irrespective of correlation, however, the uppermost subsurface Pleistocene unit is distinctive, has been mapped in detail using the logs of thousands of borings (Kolb and others, 1975), and is, for all practical geotechnical reasons,

the local "bedrock." For years, it was presumed that the first (uppermost) unit to be encountered was equivalent to the outcropping Prairie formation to the north. Recent work by the authors (Saucier, 1977; Kolb and others, 1975), however, has revealed the presence of a second unit at a depth of 35 to 50 m. The second unit may be the Prairie equivalent, making the uppermost unit a younger and possibly mid-Wisconsin depositional feature.

Because of its relatively shallow depth, the uppermost Pleistocene formation was exposed to thousands of years of subaerial erosion during the Late Wisconsin glaciation when sea level was lower than present. Streams draining the uplands north and west of Lake Pontchartrain formed narrow entrenchments up to about 12 m deep on the otherwise flat to gently undulating surface (Figs. 4 and 5). Presumably, the second Pleistocene unit was similarly entrenched during an earlier glacial stage, but data are adequate to

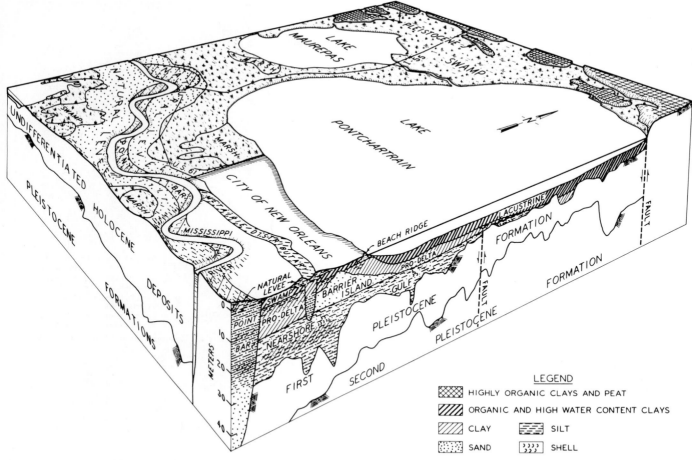

Figure 4. Idealized distribution of depositional environments and soil types in the vicinity of New Orleans. (Adapted from Kolb and Shockley, 1959)

permit only contouring of the general slope of this relict surface.

Inundation of the uppermost Pleistocene erosional surface and initiation of deposition of Holocene sediments in a nearshore Gulf environment began about 12,000 years ago. During the subsequent several thousand years, these deposits completely blanketed the eroded Pleistocene formation to a depth of 3 to over 15 m (Saucier, 1963, Fig. 18). Even though the actual Gulf shoreline moved well north of the city by the latter part of this period, water depths apparently did not exceed 10 to 12 m.

Cessation of these shallow marine conditions in the New Orleans area was highlighted by an event of considerable significance as far as foundation conditions are concerned. This was the formation about 4,600 to 5,000 years ago (Saucier, 1977; Corbeille, 1962) of a 5 to 8 km wide and 55 km long barrier island that now lies directly beneath the northern part of the city between Lake Pontchartrain and the Metairie-Gentilly ridge. Its well-preserved surface, including relict tidal passes and even dunes, has been mapped in considerable detail using thousands of borings (Saucier,

1963). Although far less than 1 percent of the feature, called the Pine Island beach trend, is presently exposed at the surface, there are tens of square kilometers where it is less than 3 m below ground level.

The remarkable state of preservation of the relict barrier island is attributable to the next stage in the geomorphic history of the region, that is, the development of a subdelta (or delta lobe) of the Mississippi River. Abandoning a course well to the west in central Louisiana about 4,600 years ago, the river rapidly introduced fine-grained alluvium eastward into the New Orleans area as part of the St. Bernard delta complex (Frazier, 1967). The oldest distributary channels, their natural levees, and the flanking interdistributary lowland swamps and marshes largely underlie more recent equivalents. They are not significant features from the standpoint of foundation conditions and only came to light as a result of quite detailed stratigraphic correlations (Saucier, 1963; Frazier, 1967). They are, however, of significance because they mark the end of a marine environment and the beginning of a deltaic plain environment.

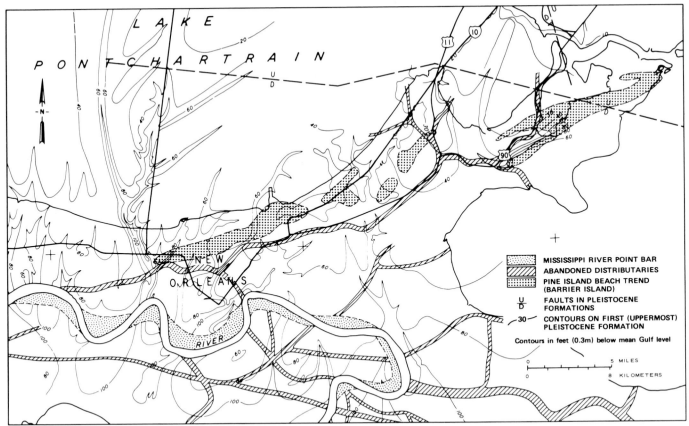

Figure 5. Subsurface geology of the New Orleans area. (Taken from Kolb, Smith, and Silva, 1975)

The Metairie Bayou-Bayou Sauvage distributaries were formed during a later stage of the St. Bernard delta complex about 2,000 to 2,800 years ago (Saucier, 1963). As with the earlier St. Bernard delta complex distributaries, their precise locations and directions of advancement were strongly influenced by the Pine Island beach trend, which was then still a prominent topographic ridge. While the distributary formation marks the beginning of "modern" conditions in the area and establishment of present physiography, the actual present course of the Mississippi River through the city did not form until about 1,200 to 1,500 years ago. Technically speaking, the natural levees continued to develop until the early 18th century, at which time artificial flood control levees put a stop to overbank flooding and incremental alluvial deposition.

From the standpoint of foundation conditions, it is important to note that the various St. Bernard delta complex distributaries individually never carried more than perhaps 30 to 40 percent of the full flow of the Mississippi River. Consequently, the stream channels *per se* were only 15 to 20 m deep and not over 1 km wide. Considering also that they did not meander to any significant degree, channel fill and point bar (channel lag) deposits are not significant subsurface occurrences. Such is not the case along the Mississippi River, however. There, the river has meandered so as to produce a 2 to 3 km wide zone in which all preexisting deposits to a depth of 30 to 45 m have been removed (including the Pleistocene formation) and backfilled with channel sediments in the point bar environment (Kolb, 1962), (Figure 5). This zone is of critical importance in the engineering geology of the New Orleans area, as will be pointed out later.

Structural Processes and Economic Geology

Of the several processes that have been working together to affect a long-term pattern of subsidence in the New Orleans area, faulting is moderately significant. East-west trending, down-to-basin gravity faults are prevalent in southern Louisiana, where displacements of a kilometer or more are not uncommon in Neogene strata (Jones, 1969). These growth faults have been active in Quaternary times, as adjustment of the huge mass of sediments in the Gulf Coast geosyncline continues.

No nearsurface faults are known or suspected in the New Orleans urbanized area; however, minor ones could have escaped detection because of the tendency for the unconsolidated marine and deltaic sediments to warp rather than shear (Kolb and others, 1975). The nearest major fault zone, the Baton Rouge fault zone, roughly parallels the north shore of Lake Pontchartrain, where it has displaced late Pleistocene strata on the order of 15 m or more. A smaller fault, displacing Pleistocene but not Holocene strata, has recently been discovered by acoustic reflection, profiling trending east-west through the center of Lake Pontchartrain to near the mouth of Pearl River (Kolb and others, 1975), (Fig. 5).

Rupturing of the ground surface or shearing of utilities or foundations by faulting *per se* is not an engineering consideration in New Orleans. Similarly, this portion of Louisiana is essentially aseismic with only a minor seismic risk status; this is attributable to events in the New Madrid region of the central Mississippi Valley (McClain and Myers, 1970).

Consolidation of sediments, on both a regional and local scale, is the principal contributor to subsidence. The former involves the entire Neogene and older sequence of the Gulf Coast geosyncline and manifests itself slowly in the form of land sinking, accelerated shoreline erosion, salt-water encroachment in estuaries, and similar effects. Local consolidation, affecting mainly the soft and often highly organic interdistributary lowland and similar deltaic deposits, manifests itself rapidly and frequently with dramatic effects to man-made structures and facilities. Differential settlement, bank failures, and flooding are typical consequences in the New Orleans area.

Taking sea level variations into consideration, the regional long-term subsidence rate probably lies between published estimates of 119 mm/century (Saucier, 1963) and 238 mm/century (Kolb and Van Lopik, 1958). In contrast, local subsidence due to shallow groundwater withdrawal (for drainage) has been as high as 3 m in 50 years in parts of the city, as will be discussed later. Further aggravating the situation is surface subsidence due to deep ground-water withdrawal (for industrial consumption), which has probably been over 500 mm in parts of the city during a recent 26 year period (Kazmann and Heath, 1968).

The structural processes active in the New Orleans area do not include salt domes, although these features abound in southern Louisiana. The nearest ones are 15 to 25 km distant to the south and west. A few small oil and gas fields in stratigraphic or fault traps occur only on the fringes of the urbanized area near Kenner, in Lake Pontchartrain, and in the easternmost undeveloped wetland part of the city. Indeed, the pattern of urban development might have been quite different had the city been located a few dozen kilometers to the west or south, where extensive petroleum production occurs.

Besides oil and gas, the only mineral substance of consequence now produced in the city is sand. Although millions of cubic meters are produced in a typical year, all is consumed within the city as fill, and even this does not meet demand. For many years, a fine to very fine sand has been borrowed from Mississippi River bars and banks within and adjacent to the city for use in filling and maintaining the elevation of residential and commercial sites. Larger construction projects, such as levees, highway embankments, and industrial sites, lately have relied upon the hydraulic dredging of fine to medium sand from Holocene but, more often from Pleistocene marine strata (relict beaches and barrier islands) beneath Lake Pontchartrain. In the early days of the city, clam and oyster shells dredged from Lake Pontchartrain were the primary sources of fill. These resources, although still important, are rapidly diminishing and are less economically competitive. Their specific use is discussed later, as is the overall situation of scarce construction materials.

Physical Characteristics of the Shallow Subsurface

Pleistocene Formations

As determined from thousands of borings to depths of 30 to 60 m and more, the deltaic to marine deposits of both Pleistocene formations consist of interbedded and interfingered clays, silts, and sands with occasional massive sand bodies (Kolb and others, 1975). All sediments are unconsolidated, with no lithified or consistently cemented materials present. Rock, even of gravel size, is completely absent. Although minor sedimentary structures, engineering properties, faunal remains, and other techniques have been used to identify particular depositional environments within the Pleistocene formations, prediction of lithology without borings is not yet possible in these units as it is in the Holocene sedimentary sequence.

Compared to overlying Holocene sediments, the Pleistocene sediments are generally much stronger (or denser in the case of noncohesive sediments), have lower water contents, and are appreciably less organic. The upper several meters of each of the two Pleistocene units, characteristically, are moderately to well oxidized and desiccated as a result of the episodes of subaerial weathering. Highest soil strengths occur in the preconsolidated "crust;" hence, the designation "local bedrock." Beneath the crusts, physical and engineering properties are somewhat more erratic, and even under-consolidated zones may be encountered.

Marine Transgressive Deposits

As best characterized by Kolb and Van Lopik (1958), the Holocene nearshore Gulf (and closely related bay-sound) deposits that veneer the uppermost Pleistocene formation consist predominantly of mixtures of silts and sands of relatively low density. They are easily recognized by their abundant and diagnostic fauna. While shells and shell fragments abound, true reef deposits are seldom encountered.

The nearshore Gulf deposits are of relatively little concern from a foundation viewpoint, and their significance is overshadowed by the overlying Pine Island beach trend. This feature is a massive body of clean and relatively dense but permeable fine sand with a prolific macrofaunal assemblage (Rowett, 1957). It attains a mean maximum thickness of about 10 m. Its engineering significance is, in part, related to its excellent foundation characteristics for light structures, but also to its relationship to the surrounding deltaic deposits as a deterministic factor in patterns of local consolidation and drainage of the latter.

Mississippi River Deltaic Deposits

The most consistently uniform Holocene deltaic deposits are those deposited in the natural levee environment, In the New Orleans area, these are composed of up to 4.5 m of silts, silty clays, and clays with virtually no sand (Kolb, 1962). Oxidation and desiccation have kept water and organic contents relatively low, and soil strengths are second only to those of the Pleistocene formations. In general, strengths decrease and water and organic contents increase with depth. Laterally, as one moves to the levee margins, interfingering with other types of deltaic deposits takes place.

Where natural levees of the Mississippi River or its abandoned distributaries overlie interdistributary lowland or other fine-grained and compressible deltaic deposits (for example, prodelta deposits), they have exhibited marked subsidence. Where they overlie point bar deposits, however, in the zone of river meandering, subsidence has been minimal. This is due to the largely silty and sandy nature of the thick point bar sequence. In the New Orleans area, at least half of the sequence is sand, and the percentage increases with depth. Due to vagrancies in the precise modes and locations of deposition of the sediments in the river channel, point bar silts and sands may range from loose to dense over short horizontal and vertical distances.

In a strict interpretation, those predominantly clayey and silty sediments, laid down in a deltaic area ahead of and along the flanks of an advancing distributary, represent deposition in lacustrine, interdistributary, prodeltaic, and paludal (swamp and/or marsh) environments. For the purposes of this paper, they may be more simply classified in two groups—that is, those where mineral soils prevail, and those where the organic content is high enough to profoundly influence their engineering properties.

In and around New Orleans, these two groups constitute the interdistributary lowland (Fig. 4) and underlie certain natural levees, thereby making them the most widespread areally. Since the inorganic soils represent deposition closest to active distributaries, they are stratigraphically lower than the organic soils that reflect the low sedimentation rates which prevailed during the phase of subdelta inactivity and deterioration.

The largely mineral or inorganic soils of the first group are actually composed of low-strength, high-water-content, compressible, plastic clays and silts in interfingering, lenticular strata. Highest relative strengths and silt (and occasionally even sand) contents can be found in the prodelta deposits and others that were deposited in a brackish water environment. Typically, all soils of this group are a uniform steel gray in color and are highly reduced, making them readily distinguishable from the mottled brown, yellow, and red oxidized natural levee deposits. Except in the area of Mississippi River meandering (Figure 5) and the Pine Island beach trend, these soft clayey deposits extend throughout the area from a depth of about 4 to 13 m (Schultz and Kolb, 1954).

The largely organic soils of the second group are coincident with the extent of the interdistributary lowland and consist of 3 to 4 m of extremely soft, high-water-content, highly organic clays and peat. Wood, ranging from finely divided fragments and leaves to stumps and logs, is present nearly everywhere. Where undrained and still a swamp or marsh environment, the upper 0.5 to 1 m of the deposits typically is an organic muck or ooze wherein the weight of the water in the soil mass is several times the dry weight of the mass. Obviously, upon drainage, these soils will shrink and compress to less than half their original volume. Moreover, oxidation will produce further volume loss, and during prolonged dry spells, the deposits have been known to burn at the surface and below ground to the water table for periods of weeks. It is on soils of this type that much of the expansion of New Orleans over the last several decades has occurred and will do so in the future.

PART II: GEOTECHNICAL PROBLEMS

An Overview

On a clear day, the air approach to New Orleans affords the critical viewer a remarkable vista of a riparian culture that has long since outgrown its natural boundaries. What Bienville had conceived in the early 1700's as a fairly small settlement circumscribed by high land along the river has developed into a major city that daily pushes farther into marshy low-lying tracts that can be made livable only by ingenious and expensive engineering procedures.

When the river is in flood, water levels confined by the artificial levees are as much as 9 m above the lower parts of the city. The integrity of the dikes seems to be taken for granted by most of the citizenry, but protection from flooding, by the river and by wind-driven tides swept in by hurricanes, is a major objective of hundreds of professionals who work for agencies at the federal, state, and local levels.

High-rise buildings reach heights of 210 m above marsh and other deltaic deposits that once could barely support the weight of a man. Concrete ribbons of the Interstate and other arterial highways span and loop their way through soft deltaic mucks.

In the following paragraphs, four groups of engineering problems that are directly affected by the geology of the area are explored: (a) protection from floods and hurricanes; (b) foundations for heavy structures; (c) foundations for light structures; and (d) sources of granular fill and aggregates.

Protection from Floods and Hurricanes

The first levees along the lower Mississippi River were built at New Orleans. Low earthern dikes, only 1 m high, were built by De la Tour, Bienville's engineer, in 1717 to hold back floodwaters from the first settlement. By 1735, the levee lines extended from 50 km above New Orleans to about 20 km below the city. Levees have increased in size to the point where they dwarf these early embankments. They still consist of earth, but they are carefully designed to protect against through-seepage, underseepage, and foundation and slope failures. In parts of the valley, levees reach heights of more than 12 m with base widths of 120 m or more. At the present time, the Lower Mississippi Valley is protected by 2,500 km of levee along both sides of the river.

Levees protecting New Orleans from Mississippi River floods are less impressive than those upvalley, averaging only 5 m above the natural levee ridges on which they were built. Because the differences in elevation between the water contained by these levees and the lowest parts of the city are formidable, the need for a soundly engineered and thoroughly reliable levee system is obvious. Fig. 6 illustrates a fairly typical elevation profile between the river and Lake Pontchartrain.

Artificial levees in the New Orleans area were invariably built along the crest of the natural levees that flanked the stream. In many instances, the natural levees, in turn, overlie sandy point bar deposits (Figs. 5 and 6). Since these deposits are relatively coarse-grained and largely inorganic, they provide some of the best shallow foundation soils in the New Orleans area. Stability of levee foundations, thus, has been a minor problem. Seepage beneath the levees has been of minor consequence, although some under-seepage problems developed within bends during the recent exceptional 1973 and 1975 floods. Where the artificial levees are on natural levees that overlie fine-grained deltaic deposits, the impermeable sequence was thick enough to prevent underseepage. In the river bends at New Orleans, minor seepage paths developed, but there were no known occurrences of the "sand boils" (Kolb, 1976) that formed by the

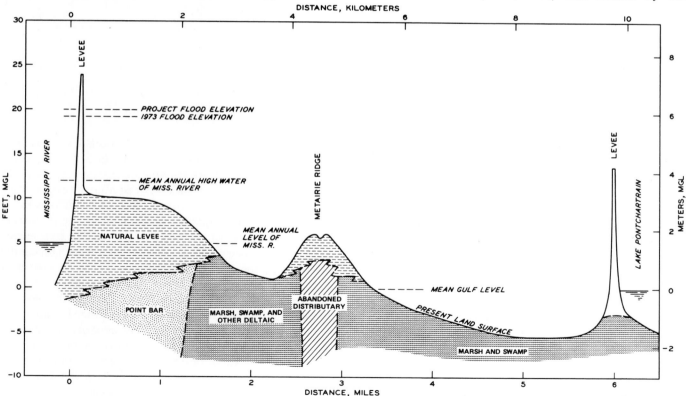

Figure 6. Surface elevations and environments of deposition along a typical transect in the New Orleans area. (Modified from U.S. Department of Agriculture, 1977)

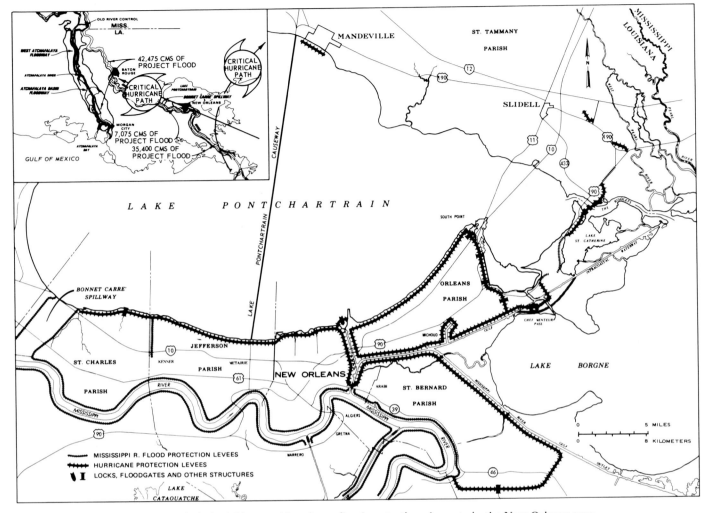

Figure 7. Mississippi River and hurricane flood protection elements in the New Orleans area.

hundreds on the landward side of levees upstream and were of considerable concern. A few levee-bank failures occurred near New Orleans, the most serious one about 90 km downstream from New Orleans (Nairn), which affected the levee as well as the river bank. About 50 km upstream of New Orleans (Montz), a 1,500-m levee setback was hastily constructed when the river bank failed as the flood crest was subsiding. Such failures occur when there is a rapid drop in river level, and the saturated levee and/or bank loses the buoyant support of the water. If the flood continues to subside, the consequences are minimal. The danger lies when a sudden drop in river level is followed by a subsequent rise before the breached or endangered levee can be rebuilt.

Of equal concern to the general welfare of New Orleans is the maintenance of the integrity of the Old River Control Structure, which is used to divert floodwaters coming down the Mississippi River through the Atchafalaya Basin on a direct path to the Gulf (Fig. 7). Half the volume

of water (42,475 cms) carried by a hypothetical "project" flood can be diverted through this structure. Levees downriver from this point are capable of carrying only 42,475 cms to the Bonnet Carre Spillway just above New Orleans. When flood crests in New Orleans reach 5.8 to 6 m, water is usually diverted through this spillway into Lake Pontchartrain to protect the city, since only 35,400 cms can be carried safely between the levees past New Orleans. During the past decade, the Bonnet Carre Spillway has been opened three times to lower flood crests at New Orleans.

There have been justifiable fears that the Mississippi River might choose the shorter route to the sea along the Atchafalaya Floodway and entirely abandon its present course past Baton Rouge and New Orleans. Geologic studies in 1952 (Fisk and others) had concluded that unless a viable engineering structure was built to prevent it, river diversion through the Atchafalaya Basin would reach a critical stage by 1975. To geologists, this impending diversion was merely the latest in a series of similar natural occurrences in the normal sequence of development of the deltaic plain. The control structure has been successful, so far, in preventing the shift of the river while allowing partial, controlled diversion. The situation at the Old River Control Structure during the height of the 1973 flood (the third highest on record) was, however, critical. The roiling floodwaters partially undermined the foundation slab, and a wingwall failed.

The experience in 1973 has opened new inquiries concerning the effectiveness and vulnerability of the structure, the need for such a structure or a new one, and the effect of a carefully planned and controlled diversion of most of the river into its Atchafalaya distributary. One question being entertained is whether the Lower Mississippi would be better served in the long run if the river was not shackled with artificial engineering restraints and was permitted to choose this shorter path to the sea that it would have chosen under natural conditions. The implications to Baton Rouge, to New Orleans, and to the enormous complex of industries that lines the banks of the river in between, are enormous.

Hurricane-induced flooding could be just as catastrophic to the New Orleans area as flooding by the Mississippi River. Hurricanes are a phenomenon natural to coastal Louisiana and occur at a mean frequency of two every 3 years. None have passed directly over the city recently, but Betsy in 1965, which passed to the west of the city, caused total damages of $90 million. Camille, the most intense storm known to have hit the United States, bore down on the Mississippi Gulf Coast just to the east of New Orleans in 1969, causing over $1 billion worth of destruction and a significant loss of lives in that area. The effect of a storm of Camille's intensity passing directly over New Orleans is incalculable. Massive evacuation is a tenuous option. Moving hundreds of thousands of people over the highways that serve the city within a 1 or even 2 day period of time is a virtual impossibility.   Thought is being given to vertical evacuation, i.e., the movement of the citizenry to two-story and higher buildings and other elevations above hurricane flood level. Although loss of life would be lessened, the loss of property still would be enormous.

As a typical hurricane approaches from the Gulf, winds blowing from the south and east result in abnormally high tides that enter Lake Pontchartrain from Lake Borgne. When the eye of the hurricane moves past the city, the winds shift and blow from the north, thus reversing the drive of the water to the south shore of Lake Pontchartrain. This could cause overtopping of lakefront levees and flooding of populated areas.

Hurricane paths that would be most damaging are shown on the inset to Fig. 7. One such path would come inland at about the point where Betsy did and track north along the Mississippi River but then curve northeast across Lake Borgne. Another critical path that a storm might take would be one that approached from the southeast and came

ashore just to the east of New Orleans. It would then follow a path up the Mississippi River toward Baton Rouge. Major hurricanes along either path could cause a disaster of awesome proportions.

To alleviate the effects of these and lesser storms, the series of protective levees shown in Figure 7 are either planned or underway. These, together with the Mississippi River flood-control levees, will completely encircle the city and environs. Major control structures, such as at The Rigolets and Chef Menteur Pass, will prevent hurricane tides from entering Lake Pontchartrain. As of September 1982, the project was about 50 percent complete.

Foundations for Heavy Structures

Early structures built in New Orleans were founded on Mississippi River natural levees and were placed directly on the ground surface using crossed timber supports and masonry footings. The use of piles, however, was soon found expedient for the heavier structures, particularly in the lower, marshy areas. Eustis and Shilstone (1965) report that one of the earliest recorded uses of piles in Louisiana was in 1722 at a French fortification, then known as Balize, at the mouth of the Mississippi River, where a crude pile driver was constructed at the site. Ursuline Convent, located in the French Quarter, was built in 1745. St. Patrick's Church and the Custom House, two massive structures, were completed in 1839 and 1881, respectively. The first "skyscraper" in New Orleans, the 11-story Maritime Building completed in 1895 and still structurally sound, is supported on timber piles set in Mississippi River point bar sands at about 15 to 18 m depths.

Until about 1920, piles were generally driven to the first sand stratum in which driving resistances and pile load tests indicated a safe capacity. Such sand strata and such driving resistances were found at fairly shallow depths within the Mississippi River point bar deposits, along portions of Metairie-Gentilly ridge, and along the Pine Island beach trend. Elsewhere, however, the fine-grained deltaic and nearshore Gulf deposits that form the subsurface afforded little end-bearing resistance and only moderate frictional resistance to shallow piles.

Settlement of pile-supported buildings occurred, cracks developed, and utility lines were broken, but the method was generally accepted until Charity Hospital was built in the late 1930's (Huesmann, 1952). Charity Hospital has a 20-story central portion and 12-story outer wings. It covers a fairly extensive area and is located over deltaic deposits. Blessey (1969) states that 9,701 untreated wood piles, with an effective length of 7 m, were driven to refusal in the first sand layer encountered in the subsurface. Unfortunately, this layer was relatively thin and was underlaid by compressible deltaic and nearshore Gulf deposits. By 1939, when construction was completed, settlement of the building had reached such proportions that the limestone facing on the lower two stories had cracked badly, and the building showed other signs of distress. Measured settlements of 460 mm at the center and 180 mm at the corners had occurred. The building has continued to sink with ultimate settlements estimated at 760 mm in the center and 360 mm at the corners.

The Veterans Administration Hospital was constructed in the early 1950's at a site adjacent to Charity Hospital. Although averaging only about 9 stories in height, the lessons learned at Charity Hospital were effectively applied. By this time, it had become apparent to foundation engineers that the soft soils of the New Orleans area did not extend to unlimited depths and that a competent Pleistocene formation sloped southward beneath Lake Pontchartrain and formed a relatively high-strength horizon beneath the city. The tan colors and increased penetration resistances of the uppermost Pleistocene unit contrast sharply in geotechnical borings with the gray colors of the soft deltaic soils that now cover it. Design of the Veterans Administration Hospital called for piling penetrating to the Pleistocene deposits, which were at a depth of 25 m at the site; 2,030 wooden piles were driven for the foundation. Settlement computations indicate that a maximum settlement of 200 mm and a differential settlement of 130 mm can be expected.

The depth to the Pleistocene deposits in New Orleans is often a controlling factor in the design and economics of a given structure. Where they are found at shallow depths, pile lengths and numbers can be significantly less than where they are deeper. There are deeper strata within the Pleistocene, however, that are compressible when the loads are sufficiently great. For years, the depth to and the strength of the upper Pleistocene layers were important controlling factors in the permissible heights and imposed loads of potential structures. In 1959, the New Orleans Building Code was modified to allow a greater height of buildings in certain areas. These increased loads invariably involve piles driven to greater depths. The Plaza Towers, built in 1968 to a height of 45 stories, has piles 50 m in length. One Shell Square, currently the tallest building in New Orleans, reaches a height of 50 stories. Octagonal concrete piles, 500 mm in diameter, average 64 m in length and have a capacity of 280 tons.

The famous New Orleans Superdome is in a class by itself. The domed stadium is supported by 2,266 concrete piles, each 410 mm square with a design capacity of 175 tons, driven to depths of 50 m. The piles were driven in clusters of from three to nine piles to support the building columns. The maximum differential settlement that will occur between adjacent pile clusters is estimated to be no more than 13 mm.

To summarize, pile lengths in many instances are now reaching to the second Pleistocene horizon beneath New Orleans. Pile characteristics, such as shape, size, composition, and spacing, are, of course, important parameters in the design of the foundations for heavy structures, but in general, the heavier the structure or the imposed load, the deeper the pile. Major modifications to this generalization are due to geological controls, such as the depth to Pleistocene deposits or whether the site is located above Mississippi River point bar deposits, along the Metairie-Gentilly abandoned distributary ridge, or above the Pine Island beach trend.

Foundations for Light Structures

Heavy structures built to current exacting specifications in the New Orleans area seldom show signs of stress caused by settlement. On the other hand, as many as 10 percent of the light residential and commercial structures and fully 30 percent of the older streets and sidewalks show obvious effects of differential settlement. As is the case with the heavy structures, light structures on the competent natural levee and point bar deposits associated with the Mississippi and Metairie-Gentilly ridges have experienced few foundation problems. In between and flanking these ridges, however, the organic swamp and marsh deposits afford a treacherous foundation. Foundation slabs beneath buildings become exposed, patios buckle, and air conditioner slabs settle and crack. Driveways subside to the extent that it is sometimes impossible to drive into carports, or, unsupported, they break into regularly tilted blocks. Underground utility systems rupture, and gas and water leakage commonly result. Sewer lines, storm drains, sidewalks, and streets sink unevenly (Figs. 8 to 10). The amount of damage is almost directly proportional to the thickness of the surficial organic deposits. Fig. 11 shows the thickness of this peaty surface layer. Note that in some areas it reaches a thickness of 5 m.

The major reason for differential settlement beneath light structures is the subsidence caused by dewatering, compaction, oxidation, and destruction of the organic deposits. Urbanization in the area presents New Orleans building authorities with a serious dilemma. They must either accept the subsidence, which in some areas amounts to 2.5 to 3 m, or accept the high water table that prevailed prior to urbanization. The latter solution is, of course, no option where urbanization and subsidence have already occurred. It becomes, at best, a limited option in newly developing areas, areas that in their natural state could hardly support the weight of a man.

Development itself leads to increased subsidence in that the absorptive capacity of the soil is decreased by the artificial, impermeable covering of streets, parking lots, buildings, and other structures. Drainage canals must be deepened, and pumping capacities must be increased to prevent flooding caused by the resultant increased runoff.

Figure 8. Typical view of subsidence around residential foundation slab.

This, in turn, causes additional subsidence, after which drainage canals and pumping capacities must be again increased in a seemingly endless cycle. Eventually, the organic layer is reduced to the point (perhaps one-quarter of its original thickness) where that portion above the water table has reached its minimum thickness due to the imposed load and to desiccation. But biochemical oxidation continues above the water table until, presumably, only the mineral constituents of the organic zone remain. The U.S. Department of Agriculture (1977) lists the choices available vis-a-vis the water table and land use decisions: (1) to use the land without drainage to control subsidence; (2) to use the land with some drainage, but to tolerate wet conditions and minimum subsidence; or (3) to provide better drainage and tolerate subsidence at a greater rate.

Traughber and Gore (1978, unpub. report to the City of Kenner) illustrate the history of subsidence in northern Kenner, between downtown New Orleans and the airport

(Figure 12). Settlement of almost 2 m has occurred here since 1924, when the surface was about 0.3 m above sea level. Initial pumping caused settlement of about 0.3 m. Settlement would have leveled off at about 0.4 m had groundwater levels remained constant. Because the 1947 hurricane caused severe flooding in the area, new Lake Pontchartrain protective levees were built in 1949, and new and more effective pumps caused further lowering of the water table and increased settlement. Settlement might not have increased to much more than 1.4 m except that its newly protected status, coupled with the construction of Interstate 10 and other highway arteries, made the area increasingly attractive for urbanization and development. As of 1978, settlement in the area was approaching 2 m, and continued development and improvements to drainage continue to affect the tenuous balance between the groundwater and overall settlement.

Few structures in organic soil areas are built directly

Figure 9. Carport entrance destroyed by subsidence. In such instances, carports are often enclosed as additional rooms to the house.

on grade. Those that were and are still standing ordinarily show severe distress caused by differential settlement. Most construction during the past 25 years in such areas consisted of pile-supported concrete foundation slabs poured on the ground. Settlement between the ground surface and a pile-supported slab is sometimes so great that, within a few years, one can see completely under the slab. Carport and garage entrances settle below slab level, and the parking spaces are abandoned, used as patios, or closed in as an additional room for the house, with steps often added to compensate for differential settlement at the entrance. Sidewalks tend to buckle and generally slope toward the street. Utility lines to the houses become exposed and strained.

A common practice by homeowners is to periodically have a 20 to 50 mm increment of silty or sandy fill placed on their lots to compensate for the effects of subsidence.

The unsightly gap which develops between the foundation slab and the surrounding ground is sometimes disguised by homeowners, who bank fill against the slab. Thus, the void beneath the house is confined and becomes a potential reservoir for the accumulation of gas in possible explosive concentrations. These gases result from temporary natural gas-line leaks at connections strained by settlement or from the generation of methane by the decomposition of the underlying organic matter. Vents are now recommended in new construction to carry such fumes upward through the roof. For existing structures without such provisions, a number of vents around the periphery of the house is considered prudent.

Although the major source of gas buildup beneath foundation slabs is gas leaking from utility lines strained or broken by shifting foundations, the seepage of methane from subsurface layers is not uncommon in the New Or-

Figure 10. Results of explosion and fire caused by the effects of subsidence on gas utility connections. (Photo courtesy of the Soil Conservation Service, New Orleans)

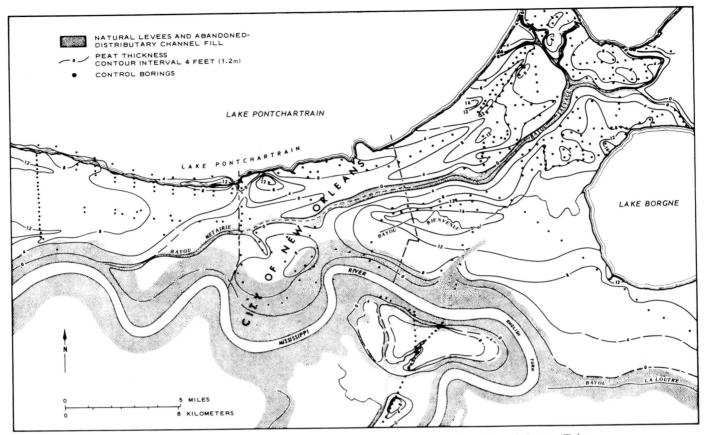

Figure 11. Distribution and thickness of peat deposits in the vicinity of New Orleans. (Taken from Gould and Morgan, 1962)

leans area. It was considered in some detail in the design of the Veterans Administration Hospital more than 25 years ago. A pervious foundation blanket was included in the design to bleed off gaseous accumulations, and vents were provided to permit the gas to escape harmlessly. Gas build-up is usually only a minor consideration in the design of heavy structures. It becomes more important in light installations of large areal extent, such as parking aprons and mall and warehouse foundations. One of the reasons for the construction of the Rummel High School on raised piers founded on pilings was to permit natural venting of marsh gases. Foundation borings made near this site hit a pocket of gas at 22 m that was sufficiently pressurized to send a column of gas, earth, and water to heights of more than 6 m. Several hours elapsed before the pressurized flow ceased.

Founding light structures on piers to provide a free air space beneath the structure has additional advantages. If there is differential settlement of the pilings beneath piers, the structure is easily releveled, thereby eliminating the unsightly raised slabs that result as the surrounding ground surface settles. More importantly, construction on piers has the advantage of increased security from flood damage due to the initially greater floor elevation. Water entering be-

neath the doors on ground level foundations is a continual problem in many of the low areas in New Orleans during flash flooding caused by torrential rains.

Only a few of the difficulties in building on organic soils in New Orleans were discussed in the preceding paragraphs. In a number of recent comprehensive reports that consider these problems in detail (Earle, 1975; Traughber and Gore, 1978, unpub. report to the City of Kenner; and U.S. Department of Agriculture, 1977), innovative methods are proposed to make the most of inherently poor foundation alternatives. One site-development technique proposed is to first build a levee and a pumping station around the tract to be developed so that the water table can be pumped to a level below the surficial organic deposits. Sufficient time would be allowed (1 to 3 years) for initial subsidence. The area then would be backfilled with granular fill to a level consistent with anticipated flooding. The fill would load and compact the underlying organic layers. The water table could then be raised to a level where the organic layers would be permanently inundated. This would preserve the compacted organic materials and provide a stable inorganic or mineral-soil foundation for urbanization, streets, and utility lines.

Arman (1978) reviewed current practices in the treat-

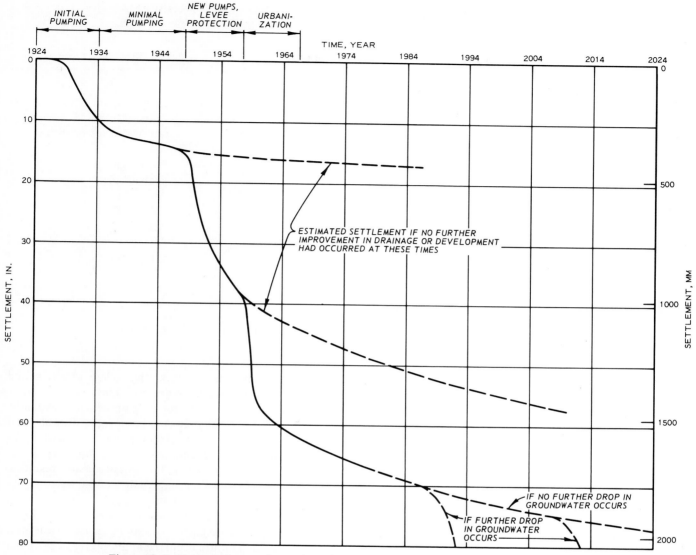

Figure 12. Settlement history of a portion of New Orleans characterized by 2 to 2.5 m surficial organic layer. (Taken from Traughber and Gore, unpublished report to the City of Kenner, 1978)

ment of soft soils on which light to moderately heavy structures are to be placed. Although the costs of many of these methods are economically unjustifiable for residential foundations, the methods are extensively used in designing embankments for major levees and arterial highways, oil tanks, heavy storage facilities, etc. Table 1 is reproduced from this reference. Controlling parameters in the New Orleans area for the methods cited in the table include such factors as whether the soil to be treated is organic, mineral, cohesive or noncohesive; whether the method will cause settlement, be environmentally deleterious, or otherwise adversely affect adjoining areas; and, perhaps of paramount importance, whether suitable mineral soil or rock for surcharging, backfilling, and related procedures is available.

Sources of Granular Fill and Aggregate

Soils for purposes such as backfilling, surcharging, and embankment construction are at a premium in the New Orleans area. Sand and gravel or other suitable aggregates for concrete, base courses, and similar purposes are scarce, and their use depends on long overland transportation by truck and/or even longer hauls by river barge. Rock for riprap and other construction purposes generally must be transported down the Mississippi River or its tributaries from sources in Arkansas or Missouri as far away as 800 to 1300 km.

Sources of Pleistocene and, occasionally, Holocene sands and gravels occur along the Mississippi-Louisiana border north of New Orleans, along tributaries to the Pearl

TABLE 1. METHODS OF TREATING SOFT FOUNDATION PROBLEMS*

Treatment type	Soil type	Structure type
Removal by Excavation	Cohesive and noncohesive	All
Removal by Displacement	Cohesive	Embankment
Controlled Rate of Placement (Increment or Stage Placement)	Cohesive and noncohesive	Embankment tanks, storage facilities
Surcharging and Precompression	Cohesive	All
Lightweight Fills	Cohesive	Embankments
Self-supporting Fills	Cohesive	Embankments
Grouting	Cohesive and noncohesive	All
Electro-osmosis	Cohesive	All
Blasting	Cohesive and noncohesive	All
Reinforced Earth	Cohesive and noncohesive	All
Mix-in-place Pits and Walls	All	Structures
Vibro-densification	Cohesionless	All
Vibro-replacement	Cohesive	All
Dynamic Consolidation	All	All

*Taken from Arman (1978) and reproduced by permission of the American Society of Civil Engineers.

River, and along the Pearl itself. Gravel content (sizes 10 mm or larger) of the deposits is relatively low, but the premium placed on these materials makes mining and hauling them profitable. Barge loads of sand and gravel from pits containing considerably higher gravel content are brought downriver from Pleistocene formations that border the east side of the Mississippi River from areas as far north as Tennessee. Gravel is also dredged directly from the river and hauled downstream to New Orleans from as far north as Tennessee, where the modern river point bar deposits contain high percentages of chert gravels. The point bar deposits along the river below Baton Rouge are almost completely barren of gravel. Thus, material derived from the river in its lower reaches is suitable only as fill, for surcharging, for base course, and for the construction of embankments.

During the construction of I-10, particularly that portion west of its junction with I-55, tens of millions of cubic meters of sand were pumped from the river for fill. Additional quantities were pumped from Lake Pontchartrain for that portion of I-10 in Kenner and New Orleans.

Because of the scarcity and expense of suitable aggregate, two somewhat unusual sources are exploited in the New Orleans area: the first is a light-weight aggregate made from expanded clay; the other is naturally occurring clam (mostly *Rangia*) and oyster (*Crassostrea*) shells.

Lightweight aggregate is made by burning clays at high temperatures. One plant near Baton Rouge exploits extensive local supplies of Holocene backswamp clay. The grain size and clay mineral content, coupled with the proper amount of organic matter, make these clays ideally suited for producing lightweight aggregate. The organic matter becomes gaseous during the burning process and expands, producing a clinker-like material that is light, durable, and satisfactory for use in a variety of concrete structures. In high-rise buildings, tall chimneys, heavy highway interchange structures, and such, the smaller loads resulting from use of the lightweight aggregate permit welcome reductions in pile lengths and numbers.

There have been some instances where use of lightweight aggregate is suspected of having caused structural failures. One such failure occurred at an interchange on the Pontchartrain Expressway (I-10), where large holes developed in the decking, and two concrete spans had to be replaced. Lightweight aggregate had been used in the spans, but evidence that use of the aggregate resulted in the failure is not conclusive. Because pollutants in the air may have reacted unfavorably with the concrete made from lightweight aggregate, the use of such concrete is frequently restricted to building interiors or to exterior walls covered with some type of protective sheathing.

Shells are a product of brackish-water lacustrine environments, such as Lake Pontchartrain and Lake Borgne to the east of New Orleans, and more marine conditions. Relict deposits lie beneath the deltaic plain at variable depths and include ancient shell beaches and shell reefs. A knowledge of the disposition of the various former delta lobes of the Mississippi River and the relationship of these to former bay and sound areas helps in predicting where such shell reefs are most probable.

Huge quantities of shells are dredged from Lake Pontchartrain and in both onshore and offshore areas of southeastern Louisiana. They form a suitable aggregate for many types of concrete construction, but their principal use is in roads and also as a flexible mat for light structures. Shells are considerably superior to chert gravel in this regard in that they are lightweight and tend to interlock, developing strength from internal friction. When placed over fibrous peats, they form a homogeneous, monolithic "slab" with remarkable strength and resilience. Oyster shells, rather than clam shells, are thought to form the best and strongest surface under traffic.

Shells form a mat suitable for highway embankments, parking aprons, heavy industrial fabrication yards, and warehouse foundations when end-dumped in thicknesses of 1 to 2 m on soft soil. They are highly recommended in residential areas where driveways tend to crack and crumble in response to settlement. Railroad ties or other such moveable borders can be used with a 0.5 to 1 m layer of shells in between. Although settlement is not totally eliminated, the light weight and flexibility of the shell bed minimize the effects of differential settlement, and warped surfaces can be easily releveled.

ACKNOWLEDGMENTS

Among those to whom we are indebted for information on geotechnical problems in the New Orleans area are Eustis Engineering Company, Gore Engineering, Inc., and McClelland Engineers, Inc., of New Orleans; the Engineering Division of the U.S. Army Engineer District, New Orleans; the Soil Conservation Service, U.S. Department of Agriculture, New Orleans; and Professor Ara Arman, Chairman, Civil Engineering Department, Louisiana State University, Baton Rouge, LA. Editorial assistance was provided by Ms. D. P. Booth, Environmental Information Analysis Center, Environmental Laboratory; cartographic drafting was accomplished under the direction of Mr. W. C. Park, Engineering Graphics Branch, Publications and Graphic Arts Division; and copy was prepared by the Word Processing Section, Environmental Laboratory, under the supervision of Ms. B. J. Smith—all of the U.S. Army Engineer Waterways Experiment Station, Vicksburg, MS.

REFERENCES CITED

Arman, A., 1978, Soil improvement history, capabilities and outlook: Philadelphia, American Society of Civil Engineers, Special Publication of the Geotechnical Engineering Division.

Blessey, W. E., 1969, The case for high capacity long steel piles: New York, Committee on Building Research and Technology, American Iron and Steel Institute.

Corbeille, R. L., 1962, New Orleans barrier island: Transactions of the Gulf Coast Association of Geological Societies, v. 12, p. 223–229.

Earle, D. W., 1975, Land subsidence problems and maintenance costs to homeowners in east New Orleans, Louisiana: [Ph.D. dissertation]: Baton Rouge, Louisiana State University.

Eustis, J. B., and Shilstone, C. M., 1965, New Orleans soil conditions. . . enigma for builders: Gulf South Home Builder, Winter Edition.

Fisk, H. N., Kolb, C. R., and Wilbert, L. H., Jr., 1952, Geological investigation of the Atchafalaya Basin and the problem of Mississippi River diversion: Vicksburg, Mississippi River Commission.

Frazier, D. E., 1967, Recent deltaic deposits of the Mississippi River: their development and chronology: Transactions of the Gulf Coast Association of Geological Societies, v. 17, p. 287–315.

Gould, H. R., and Morgan, J. P., 1962, Coastal Louisiana swamps and marshes: *in* Rainwater, E., and Zingula, R., eds., Geology of the Gulf Coast and central Texas and guidebook of excursions, Houston, Houston Geological Society.

Huesmann, H. A., 1952, Foundation problems in the New Orleans area: American Society of Civil Engineers, Paper No. 9.

Jones, P. H., 1969, Hydrology of Neogene deposits in the northern Gulf of Mexico basin: Louisiana Water Resources Research Institute Bulletin GT-2, 105 p.

Kazmann, R. G., and Heath, M. M., 1968, Land subsidence related to ground-water offtake in the New Orleans area: Transactions of the Gulf Coast Association of Geological Societies, v. 18, p. 108–113.

Kolb, C. R., 1962, Distribution of soils bordering the Mississippi River from Donaldsonville to Head of Passes: U.S. Army Engineer Waterways Experiment Station Technical Report 3-601, 61 p.

Kolb, C. R., 1976, Geologic control of sand boils along Mississippi River levees, *in* Coates, D. R., ed., Geomorphology and engineering: Stroudsburg, Penn., Dowden, Hutchinson and Ross.

Kolb, C. R., and Shockley, W. G., 1959, Engineering geology of the Mississippi Valley: American Society of Civil Engineers Transactions, v. 124, Paper 2996, p. 633–656.

Kolb, C. R., Smith, F. L., and Silva, R. C., 1975, Pleistocene sediments of the New Orleans-Lake Pontchartrain area: U.S. Army Engineer Waterways Experiment Station Technical Report S-75-6, 7 p.

Kolb, C. R., and Van Lopik, J. R., 1958, Geology of the Mississippi River deltaic plain, southeastern Louisiana: U.S. Army Engineer Waterways Experiment Station Technical Report 3-483, 120 p.

Lower Mississippi Region Comprehensive Study Coordinating Committee, 1974, Lower Mississippi region comprehensive study: Regional climatology, hydrology, and geology, Appendix C, 2 v.

McClain, W. C., and Myers, O. H., 1970, Seismic history and seismicity of the southeastern region of the United States: Oak Ridge National Laboratory Report ORNL-4582, 46 p.

Murray, G. E., 1961, Geology of the Atlantic and Gulf coastal province of North America: New York, Harper & Brothers, 692 p.

Rowett, C. L., 1957, A Quaternary molluscan assemblage from Orleans Parish, Louisiana: Transactions of the Gulf Coast Association of Geological Societies, v. 7, p. 153–164.

Saucier, R. T., 1963, Recent geomorphic history of the Pontchartrain Basin: Louisiana State University Studies, Coastal Studies Series No. 9, 114 p.

Saucier, R. T., 1965, New Orleans—its geologic setting: Geotimes, v. 9, No. 8, p. 9–10.

Saucier, R. T., 1977, The northern Gulf Coast during the Farmdalian substage: a search for evidence: U.S. Army Engineer Waterways Experiment Station Miscellaneous Paper Y-77-1, 39 p.

Schultz, J. R., and Kolb, C. R., 1954, Geological investigation of the New Orleans Harbor area: U.S. Army Engineer Waterways Experiment Station Technical Memorandum 3-391, 23 p.

U.S. Department of Agriculture, 1977, Soil survey of East Bank of Jefferson Parish, La.: New Orleans, U.S. Department of Agriculture in cooperation with the Louuisiana Agricultural Experiment Station.

MANUSCRIPT RECEIVED BY THE SOCIETY MAY 11, 1982
MANUSCRIPT ACCEPTED JUNE 1, 1982

Geological Society of America
Reviews in Engineering Geology, Volume V
1982

The foundation geology of New York City

Charles A. Baskerville
U.S. Geological Survey
National Center, Reston, Virginia 22092

ABSTRACT

Most cities in the United States are within one or two physiographic units, and only a few major rock and soil types must be dealt with in civil works in different parts of a city. New York City's five counties, however, cover three physiographic units (the Coastal Plain, New England Upland, and Triassic Lowland), which contain nine different foundation rock types and dozens of soils. The foundation types range from high-strength gneissoid granite through soluble marble to soft-sensitive, low shear strength, and high moisture content, organic silty clay having very limited bearing capacity. Each rock and soil type has its own engineering characteristics, and, in addition, local problems exist within each major type. Serious problems of foundation support in loosely consolidated materials of the Coastal Plain are solved by use of spread footings, whereas a similar structure in the New England Upland may require the use of caissons where bedrock underlies thick till.

The New York City crystalline rocks are separated into the New York City Group and the Hutchinson River Group by extension of Cameron's Line, a regional north-northeast-trending thrust fault. The formations of these groups are cut by several sets of fault systems, and seismic activity has been noted along the northeast-striking fault system.

Slope stability can be a problem in valleys at the north end of the city or in deep cuts within the moraine areas. The use of reinforced concrete walls and line drilling have helped, where rights-of-way are tight, to control slopes.

Ground water, once used in the city for water supply, is now an engineering problem. As population expanded, salt-water encroachment due to drawdown by pumping and contamination from human activity made the ground water unfit for human consumption. The impotability of the ground water fostered the construction of reservoirs and hundreds of kilometers of rock tunnels and distribution mains, which make up one of the greatest water supply systems in the world. A negative result of the cessation of groundwater use has been the rise in the water table, which has flooded structures, such as subway tunnels, that were built when groundwater pumping had greatly lowered the water level. Sewer tunnels and treatment plants have been built to reduce the pollution problems in the waters surrounding the city.

Erosion is a serious problem on New York City's ocean beaches. Building up the beaches by placement of dredged material and the wiser planning of protective structures are important measures in attempting to preserve these recreational facilities from natural erosion.

The complexity of the geology and the resulting foundation problems in the city have resulted in the writing of a comprehensive building code for New York City. This 1970 code requires a scientific approach to foundation exploration and generally allows the use of modern material and technology not allowed under the pre-World War II codes that were in use through the 1960's.

In addition to the vast number of engineering projects, such as tunnels and bridges for transportation and large buildings in which people live and work, hundreds of hectares of land have been added to the city's perimeter through landfill projects that were started during the time of the English settlers and that continue to date. The latest perimeter landfill is the site of the future Battery Park City in Lower Manhattan in the Hudson River; the landfill consists largely of the spoil from excavation for the Twin Towers of the World Trade Center.

INTRODUCTION

New York City is the largest city in the United States, the most important seaport on the east coast, and one of the leading ports of the world. A factor in the development of this seaport is its location on New York Bay at the mouth of the Hudson River, which has deep, protected, and navigable estuaries (Figure 1). New York City lies within the Humid Continental climatic region. The Gulf Stream, flowing northward along the coast, tends to moderate the temperature range, and the climate is generally mild and semi-marine.

The city covers an area of approximately 950 km² in southeastern New York State, including areas of surface water. Greater New York City presently consists of five boroughs—a term retained from the early English colonial settlers. These boroughs, also known as counties, are: the Bronx (Bronx County), Brooklyn (Kings County), Queens (Queens County), Manhattan (New York County), and Staten Island (Richmond County). These five counties were consolidated into the present City of New York in 1898 through the Act of Consolidation (New York City, 1976).

PHYSIOGRAPHY (AND LAND USE)

New York City straddles parts of three physiographic units: the Atlantic Coastal Plain on the southeast, the New England Upland on the northwest, and the Triassic Lowland on the southwest (Figure 2). The Bronx, Manhattan, and part of Staten Island are in the part of the New England Upland locally known as the Manhattan Prong, whereas, most of Long Island and Staten Island are in two low-lying provinces, the Coastal Plain and Triassic Lowland.

The physiography of the area has had a pervasive influence on the regional pattern of development, transportation, and urbanization. For example, on the southern end of Manhattan Island, where New York (New Amsterdam of the Dutch) was first settled (Figure 3), the streets were laid out in no particular pattern; the land was underlaid by soft glacial materials, and the low hills could easily be leveled for development (Cozzens, 1843). When the settlement started to expand northward, hard bedrock of the New England Upland was encountered. As the ridges and

valleys of Manhattan and the Bronx trend about N. 30°E, the avenues were laid out in the strike valleys, the paths of least resistance, which also parallel the Hudson River (Merrill and others, 1902); most of the main north-south streets still follow the valleys. The rough, hilly areas of Manhattan's Central Park, for example (Figure 2, loc. 15), and the Botanical Garden and Zoo in the Bronx were established as parks.

The Coastal Plain of the New York City area differs from the rest of the Atlantic Coastal Plain to the south in that the New York part was glaciated. Most of Long Island is made up of a gently southward-sloping plain of glacial outwash. The western part of Long Island is transected by a sinuous ridge, a coalesced terminal moraine. Except for the interruption at the Narrows Entrance to New York Harbor (Figures 1, 2), the ridge extends westward across the southern third of Staten Island. The crest of this moraine has been utilized as parks and cemeteries for the most part (Figure 2, locs. 36-38, 53-55, 62) because the colonists and subsequent developers through the 19th century were unable to use this hilly, bouldery land for agriculture or to divide it into regular city lots. The high, undulating terrain is scenic and highly acceptable for park use (Merrill and others, 1902). The southern edges of Staten Island, Brooklyn, and Queens are used as recreational beaches.

GENERAL GEOLOGY

Age of New York City Group[1] and Cameron's Line

The basic foundation of New York City is a sequence of Proterozoic Z to lower Paleozoic crystalline rocks consisting of schist, gneiss, and marble that crop out mainly in Manhattan and the Bronx. These rocks are overlaid unconformably by Triassic and Cretaceous deposits on Staten Island and by Cretaceous deposits in Brooklyn and Queens (Figure 1). All of these deposits are overlain unconformably by Pleistocene glacial deposits and scattered postglacial material.

---

[1]The New York City Group of Prucha (1956).

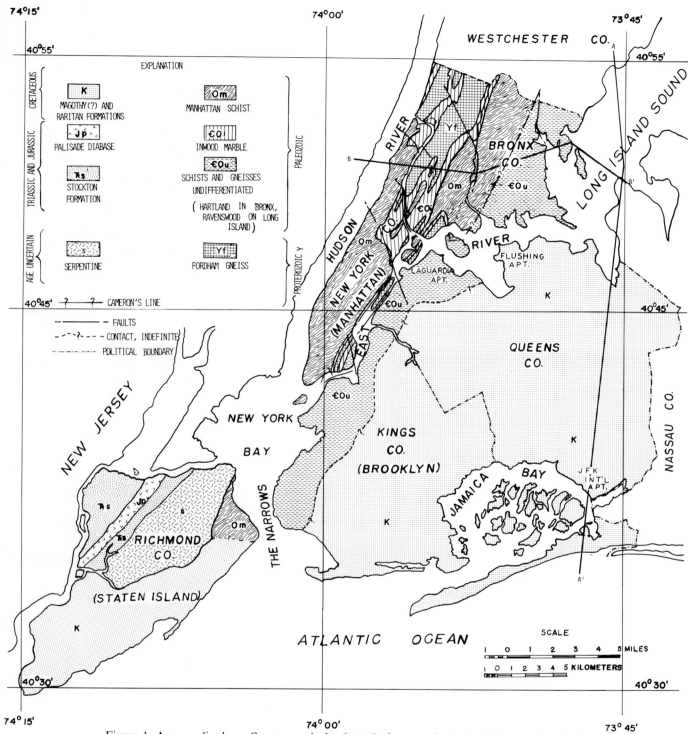

Figure 1. A generalized pre-Quaternary bedrock geologic map of New York City. (Compiled and modified from Perlmutter and Arnow, 1953; Berkey, 1911; Schuberth, 1968; Merrill and others, 1902; New York City, 1976; New York State Museum and Science Service, 1971; and reconnaissance fieldwork by the author.) Sections along lines A-A' and B-B' are shown in Figures 5 and 6.

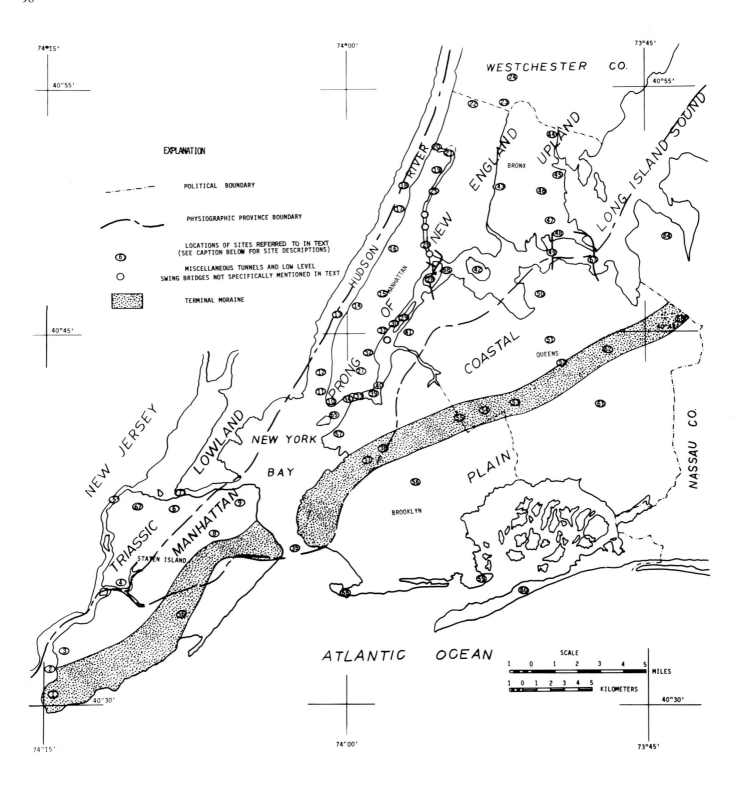

The crystalline rocks of the Bronx and Manhattan have been placed in two major units separated by Cameron's Line, a regional northeast-striking thrust fault whose surface dips eastward (Rodgers, 1970; Gates and Martin, 1976). The rocks west of this line, the New York City Group (Prucha, 1959), are considered to be a metasedimentary miogeosynclinal sequence (Hall, 1976; Gates and Martin, 1976). These rocks have been dated by U-Pb methods on zircons (Grauert and Hall, 1973) and by K-Ar and Rb-Sr methods on micas (Long, Cobb, and Kulp, 1959; Long and Kulp, 1958, 1962; Long, 1962). According to the work of these authors, at least four metamorphic events affected this part of the Manhattan Prong at approximately 1,150 m.y., 840 m.y. 450 m.y. 480 m.y., and 360 m.y. L. E. Long (written commun., 1980) says that these rocks apparently show a complex isotropic age pattern in which he believes zircon ages tend to reflect the times of primary formation of minerals and mica ages correspond to times of regional uplift and cooling. These variations of radiogenic dates have led workers in this terrane to consider the Fordham Gneiss, the oldest formation of the New York City Group stratigraphically, as Precambrian (Hall, 1976) or of uncertain age (Mose and Hayes, 1975), in that the Fordham may range from Precambrian to Cambrian (New York State Museum and Science Service, 1971).

The overlying Inwood Marble and Manhattan Schist are considered to be Cambrian and Ordovician. N. M. Ratcliffe and R. R. Knowles (oral commun., 1968, 1969) discovered crinoid stems in a marble band in the Manhattan Schist. These fossils represent Early Ordovician to Late Devonian age (Moore and others, 1952). The fossil evidence, coupled with the radiogenic metamorphic dates (350 m.y.-405 m.y.) on the Inwood Marble and the Manhattan Schist, conclusively indicates that these formations are of Cambrian to Middle Ordovician age.

Characteristics of New York City Group

The formations of the New York City Group have been subdivided individually into members. The Fordham Gneiss (Merrill and others, 1902) consists of five members, A through E, of which A is the oldest (Hall, 1968a). These members consist of amphibolite, paragneiss, quartzite, and a schist which can be mistaken for similar schist in the Manhattan Schist. The Fordham Gneiss was considered the basement gneiss complex by Hall (1968a).

The Yonkers Granite (Merrill and others, 1902), composed of biotite, hornblende, orthoclase as a main feldspar, and quartz, is found associated with the Fordham Gneiss. A large outcrop of Yonkers Granite can be found in Van Cortlandt Park (Figure 2, loc. 22). This rock usually appears pink when fresh.

The Inwood Marble (Limestone of Merrill and others, 1902) consists of pure calcite marble that weathers quite rapidly, pure dolomite marble units that are a mixture of these marbles, and coarse dolomite containing actinolite-

Figure 2. (Facing page) New York City site location map. Numbers are locations of sites mentioned in text. Refer to following list:

1. Tottenville
2. Outerbridge Crossing
3. Charleston (Kreisherville)
4. Fresh Kills sanitary landfill
5. Goethals Bridge
6. Graniteville abandoned quarries
7. Bayonne Bridge, Shooter's Island due west
8. Staten Island Expressway Interchange at Todt Hill
9. Silver Lake Park and reservoir, St. George to northeast
10. Battery Park
11. Battery Park City site, Twin Towers northeast of site 10
12. Holland Tunnel
13. Lincoln and Pennsylvania Railroad Tunnels
14. Serpentinite pod
15. Central Park
16. 125th Street valley
17. Site of sewage-treatment plant, 145th Street
18. George Washington Bridge
19. Dyckman Street, Inwood area due west
20. Henry Hudson Parkway Bridge, Riverdale on north

side, playing fields to the south
21. Broadway Interborough Rapid Transit (IRT)—vehicular bridge over Spuyten Duyvil
22. Van Cortlandt Park
23. Hillview Reservoir
24. Mile Square quarries
25. Alexander Hamilton, Washington, and High Bridges
26. Conrail lift bridge
27. East Eighth Street
28. Triborough Bridge
29. Roosevelt Island
30. 63rd Street subway-rail tunnel
31. United Nations headquarters, Turtle Bay
32. New York University-Bellevue Medical Center, Kips Bay
33. Manhattan Bridge
34. Brooklyn Bridge
35. Verrazano-Narrows Bridge
36. Ocean View and other cemeteries
37. Greenwood Cemetery
38. Prospect Park
39. Wallabout Bay
40. Williamsburg Bridge
41. Long Island City, Queens end of Queensborough Bridge

42. Rikers Island
43. Bronx River
44. Hutchinson River
45. Co-op City
46. Bronx State Hospital
47. Bruckner Interchange
48. Ferry Point Park
49. Whitestone Bridge
50. Whitestone Expressway near Linden Place
51. Jewel Avenue crossing Flushing Meadow Park-Van Wyck Expressway on east, Grand Central Parkway on west
52. Kew Gardens
53. Forest Park
54. Cypress Hills and other cemeteries
55. Cemetery of the Evergreens
56. Flatbush Avenue IRT subway line-Nostrand Avenue and Clarendon Road
57. Hamilton Avenue-Gowanus Expressway (Hicks Street), Battery Tunnel Plaza
58. Coney Island
59. U.S. Naval Air Station-Floyd Bennett Field
60. Rockaway Peninsula

61. Jamaica
62. Cunningham Park
63. Throgs Neck Bridge
64. Great Neck
65. Brooklyn Battery Tunnel, Governors Island to south
66. Korvette Shopping Center and housing development (sand and gravel pit)
67. Staten Island Expressway-West Shore Expressway Interchange
68. Randalls and Wards Islands

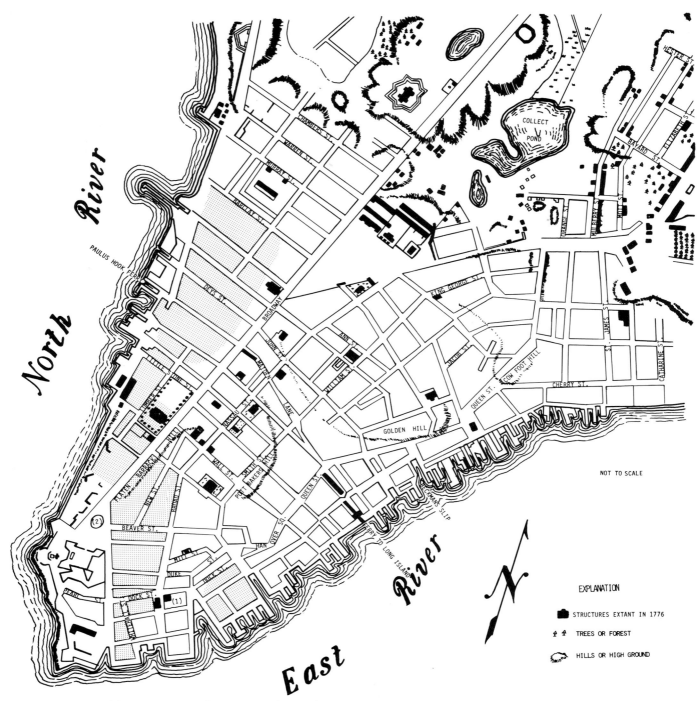

Figure 3. A map of New York City as of approximately 1776. The city occupied the area now called Lower Manhattan, from what is now China Town south to the Battery. Also shown is the Collect Pond, from which the city obtained its main water supply. The shaded areas show the extent of the fire of 1776. Lack of adequate water supply and low pressure impeded fire control. Fraunces Tavern (1) and Bowling Green (2), among others, exist today along with most of the streets shown. Map adapted from New York City (1976)

tremolite and other siliceous minerals. These dolomites, or dolostones, leave a residual fine-to-coarse white dolomitic sand upon weathering. In addition, the Inwood Marble contains foliated calc-schist layers in which the mica is predominantly phlogopite. Outcrops of this overall composition can be found in the Inwood Park section of Manhattan (Figure 2, loc. 19). This variability in the Inwood Marble led Hall (1968a) to divide the formation into five members, A through E, on the basis of his work in the White Plains quadrangle of Westchester County. Subsequent work by Hall (1976) indicated that it is more consistent to divide the Inwood Marble into four members. Unit A overlies the Fordham unconformably.

Hall (1968a) also divided the Manhattan Schist (Merrill and others, 1902) into three members, A through C. He considered the A member as the base of the Manhattan Schist and separated by an unconformity from the underlying Inwood Marble; he correlated this unconformity with a regional unconformity found in New York and New England (Hall, 1968a, b). The Manhattan Schist members B and C probably are Cambrian in age and may have been thrust onto member A (Hall, 1968a, b). The Manhattan Schist contains muscovite, biotite, garnet schist, schistose gneiss, intertonguing schist and marble (Unit A, Hall, 1968a), and amphibolite (Unit B, Hall, 1968a); the marble and amphibolite unit can be found near the base of the formation in Manhattan. For a detailed description of the New York City Group formational subdivisions, see Hall (1968a, 1976).

Crystalline rocks east of Cameron's Line

The rocks east of Cameron's Line from southwestern Connecticut through eastern Westchester County, N.Y., and the east Bronx and possibly the northern edge of Queens and Kings Counties, N.Y., belong to a eugeosynclinal mixture of metamorphosed clastic and volcanic rocks (Pellegrini, 1975, 1977; Ratcliffe and Zartman, 1976, Figure 1). From southwestern Connecticut through Westchester County, N.Y., to the New York City line, this group of rocks belongs to the Harrison Gneiss[2] and the Hartland Formation. Hall (1976) divided the Hartland into four units or members: amphibolite, schist-gneiss-amphibolite, light-gray gneiss, and schist and granulite (Figure 4).

Hall (1968a) considered the miogeosynclinal sequence west of Cameron's Line to be Cambrian-Ordovician in age and considered that the eastern eugeosynclinal sequence had been thrust onto the western sequence. These eugeosynclinal rocks are also considered Cambrian-Ordovician because of correlation with western Connecticut rocks of similar lithologies (Hall, 1976).

[2]The Harrison Gneiss of Merrill (1898) is herein adopted for U.S. Geological Survey usage.

The Harrison Gneiss has not been reported in New York City, but units similar to at least one and possibly two members described by Hall for the Hartland Formation have been noted in work being done in the east Bronx by the author. The formations and other miscellaneous rock units in the Bronx and Westchester County east of Cameron's Line have, because of their stratigraphic relationship,

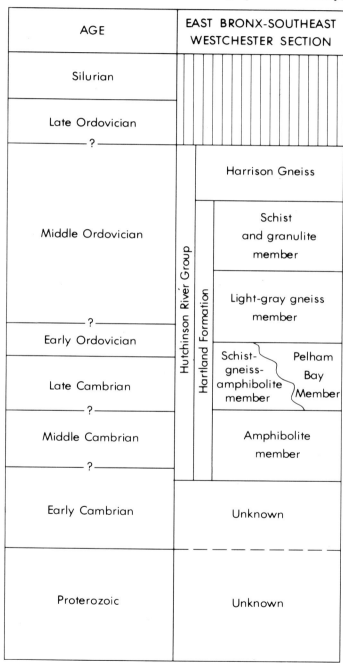

Figure 4. A stratigraphic column of the Hutchinson River Group. Hartland Formation informal members adopted from Hall (1976). Description of the Hutchinson River Group with the Pelham Bay member can be found in Baskerville (1982).

been placed in the Hutchinson River Group[3] (Baskerville, 1967; Seyfert and Leveson, 1968).

These eugeosynclinal rocks truncate the miogeosynclinal rocks along Cameron's Line, as the Hartland Formation truncates the Fordham Gneiss, Inwood Marble, and Manhattan Schist in Connecticut (Hall, 1968a). A similar contact is found in the Bronx in juxtaposed schists but is difficult to locate because both the New York City Group and schists of the Hutchinson River Group can be similar in some cases as Hall (1968a) found in the White Plains area.

Farther south along the East River, the Ravenswood Granodiorite crops out in Long Island City, northern Queens (Figure 2, loc. 41). It is directly juxtaposed to a band of Inwood Marble in the east channel of the river opposite Roosevelt Island. The contact between these two units is believed to be Cameron's Line. In Brooklyn, at depth, is a gneiss that appears to be the westward continuation of the Ravenswood Granodiorite, called "Brooklyn Injection Gneiss" by Blank (1972). This rock was found in test borings for the Brooklyn Battery Tunnel (Figure 2, locs. 10, 57, 65; Sanborn, 1950). The gneiss at the Brooklyn end of the Battery Tunnel was found to be too deep to bore the tunnel through it; therefore, the tunnel was driven by shield and compressed air between the Brooklyn portal and just east of Governors Island. The Battery Tunnel from southeast of Governors Island to Manhattan is in Manhattan Schist. A rock correlative with the Ravenswood Granodiorite was found in boreholes on the lower east side of Manhattan between the Williamsburg and Manhattan Bridges (Figure 2, locs. 33, 40) during exploration for the proposed Lower Manhattan Expressway. Similar rock in the southeastern projection of Manhattan Island was found in exploration work for the Catskill Pressure Tunnel from Brooklyn to Queens (Berkey, 1911).

The southeastern edge of the Ravenswood-"Brooklyn Injection Gneiss" map pattern across northern Brooklyn and Queens in Figure 1 roughly approximates the -15 to -30 m (-100 to -200 ft) below mean sea level contour lines for top of sound rock northeast to southwest in Queens and the -30 to -91 m (-200 to -300 ft) contours from northeast to southwest (to the Narrows) in Brooklyn, as shown on the New York City Board of Water Supply (1963) contour map of parts of Brooklyn and Queens. City Pressure Tunnel No. 2 is in both these rocks at -153 m from the East River opposite Rikers Island in northern Queens to Hicks Street and Hamilton Avenue (Gowanus Expressway) in Brooklyn; the project Record Drawings of geologic profiles for Pressure Tunnel No. 2 indicate the rock to be "Brooklyn Injection Gneiss" for the entire length across Queens and Brooklyn (New York City, Board of Water Supply, 1936).

If the "Brooklyn Injection Gneiss" is a westward extension of the Ravenswood Granodiorite, then the gneiss would be juxtaposed with the Manhattan Schist where the Inwood Marble appears to be missing between Governors Island and Brooklyn (Sanborn, 1950, pl 5). Cameron's Line, therefore, can probably be extended along the eastern shore of the East River, cutting across the southeastern protrusion of Manhattan (Figure 1). The Geologic Map of New York (New York State Museum and Science Service, 1971) indicates a correlation of the Ravenswood Granodiorite with the Harrison Gneiss; the two rocks are similar in fabric and mineral composition. Ziegler (1911) believed the two units to be entirely distinct and separate. The Ravenswood Granodiorite does not have the pronounced gneissic structure throughout that the Harrison Gneiss shows; the former has no muscovite and little biotite, whereas the Harrison Gneiss has far more quartz and biotite than the Ravenswood Granodiorite, as Ziegler (1911) observed. The author has noted the same comparison in the field and in microscopic study of rock thin sections of these units.

Serpentinite rocks

Serpentinite masses are not widespread in New York City. Serpentinite is usually associated with the "backbone" of Staten Island but is also present on Manhattan's west side from the Hudson River to the southwestern side of Central Park (Cozzens, 1843; Gratacap, 1904). The Manhattan pod is now covered by streets and buildings (Figure 2, loc. 14). The largest serpentinite mass, and best known, in New York City, is the one forming Todt Hill, the highest geographic point in the city—124 m. It is an oval body striking southwest from St. George, Staten Island, to Richmond Creek (Figure 1).

Cretaceous rocks lap up on the serpentinite unconformably on the east, and the Triassic Stockton red beds have a similar contact relation on the west (Baskerville, 1965; Ohan and others, 1975). The ultramafic serpentinite shows a sheared concordant contact with the New York City Group (Berkey, 1933, pl. 10; Ohan and others, 1975), and a trend paralleling the general structural axis of these rocks. If the Manhattan Schist unit A is one of the units in contact with the serpentinite, a Late or post-Ordovician time of emplacement is implied. The unconformable relations between the serpentinite and the overlying Triassic and Cretaceous sedimentary units indicate that the serpentinite is definitely pre-Mesozoic. The Staten Island serpentinite mass was originally an ultramafic peridotite composed mainly of olivine and orthopyroxene (Ohan and others, 1975). Serpentinization has altered the rock to antigorite, bastite, serpophite, chrysotile, talc, anthophyllite, and magnetite (Ohan and others, 1975).

At least three major shear zones in the Staten Island serpentinite have engineering implications that will be dis-

---

[3]The Hutchinson River Group is in the process of being proposed for formal adoption (See Figure 4 caption).

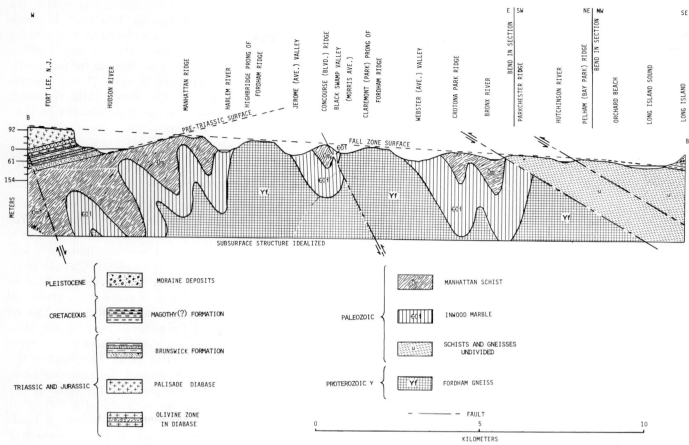

Figure 5. Generalized geologic cross section (B-B' on Figure 1) of New York City. This section parallels Interstate 95 from Fort Lee, N.J., just south of the George Washington Bridge, eastward and parallel to Cross Bronx Expressway (I-95) to West Farms east of the Bronx River. Modified from unpublished field trip guide, Department of Earth and Planetary Science, The City College of the City University of New York, and U.S. Geological Survey topographic maps of the Central Park and Flushing, N.Y., 7.5-min quadrangles.

cussed under *Engineering geology.* Chidester (1968) stated that no high-temperature, contact-metamorphic zones or other diagnostic criteria are associated with the margins of most Appalachian serpentinites; therefore, he believed that the ultramafic rocks were emplaced in solid state at temperatures not too different from that of the host rock and that serpentinization proceeded simultaneously with transport by a "kneading" of the mass through the host rock under tectonic stress. Chidester (1968) considered this transport phenomenon to be spasmodic.

Mesozoic rocks

Staten Island and western Long Island's crystalline foundation surfaces dip westward and southeastward, respectively. West of Manhattan, the eroded surface of the New York City Group dips at about 15° beneath the Hudson River to form the pre-Mesozoic surface upon which the

Triassic and Jurassic Brunswick Formation of the Newark Group lies (Figure 5). Triassic sedimentary rocks unconformably overlie the eroded New York City Group surface in the northwest part of Staten Island (Figure 1). The Newark strata, predominantly arkosic sandstone, siltstone, and shale of fluviatile and continental origin, are "red beds," which probably were originally intermontane deposits. The arkosic sedimentary rocks indicate crystalline rock sources, such as those in the Manhattan Prong to the east and the New Jersey Highlands to the west. Triassic rocks in northeastern New Jersey contain dinosaur footprints, freshwater fish fossils, and some plant remains. The Triassic strata on Staten Island, the Stockton Formation, can be found only in borings, as the Triassic and Jurassic basin here underlies Pleistocene glacial sediments and Holocene marine marsh deposits.

Rodgers (1970) stated that the fanglomerates in the northwestern side of the Newark basin contain pebbles and cobbles of the Proterozoic Z and lower Paleozoic rocks adjoining them to the northwest. In addition to the predominant red beds, there are nonred lacustrine sediments that occupy the basin. This combination, according to Rodgers (1970), indicates that during deposition in the basin, the climate was characterized by warmth and seasonal rains and was similar to the climate of present-day savannas.

According to Gratacap (1904), a small outcrop of Triassic red beds is exposed on Shooter's Island just off the north shore of Staten Island (Figure 2, loc. 7). A diabase dike intruded upon the red beds and extends southward across western Staten Island. This intrusion in New York's Rockland County ranges from 213 to 244 m in thickness (Lowe, 1959). The intrusive relationship of this dike is shown by test borings taken for the Staten Island Expressway-West Shore Expressway Interchange (Figure 2, loc. 67).

On Staten Island, the unconformity between Triassic strata and Upper Cretaceous Cenomanian sedimentary rocks was evident in the Staten Island highway boring program, as the Triassic was penetrated at varying levels in drill holes sufficiently close together to indicate an irregular paleotopographic surface (Baskerville, 1965). In the rest of New York City, Triassic rocks are absent and Cretaceous sedimentary rocks unconformably overlie the eroded crystalline rock surface (Fall Zone, Figure 5), which dips gently southeastward beneath the Long Island Sound, under Long Island, and out onto the Continental Shelf.

The Coastal Plain surface beneath Brooklyn and Queens is covered by unconsolidated Cretaceous sediments—sand, gravel, and clay of predominantly terrestrial origin. In early Cenomanian time, the northern part of the depositional basin was probably depressed to the extent that streams began to dump their sediments into newly formed lakes and swamps on eroded Triassic beds. The Staten Island Cretaceous sediments are fluviatile, as indicated by the crossbedding observed in the white sand layers in the Kreischerville quarry (Charleston) near Outerbridge Crossing (Figure 2, locs. 2, 3).

Lewis and Kummel (1915) and Clark (1916) believed that during the Early Cretaceous the Appalachian axis was raised, rejuvenating eastward-flowing streams. At the same time, the coastal areas were depressed. Therefore, the New Jersey Highlands to the west probably were the source of quartz, feldspar, and mica in the Staten Island Cretaceous unit.

Some of the predominantly arenaceous Upper Cretaceous sediments may have been derived in part from reworking of older Cretaceous sediments and possibly Triassic deposits, as evidenced by the yellow limonitic and reddish clays and hematite-stained quartz.

The Cretaceous Raritan and Magothy Formations, from north to south in section on Long Island, form a cuesta striking northeast and unconformably overlie the Hutchinson River Group (Figure 6). This bluff, in which Cretaceous sedimentary units are exposed in places along the Nassau County shoreline, forms the southern shoreline of Long Island Sound and is the foundation for the overlying Pleistocene glacial deposits. If these glacial deposits were removed and only the Cretaceous ridge remained, Long Island would be approximately one-quarter its present length and width, and the surface topography would average only 8-9 m above sea level.

Pleistocene and Holocene deposits

The Pleistocene in New York City consists of a series of glacial and interglacial deposits ranging from the Wisconsin to at least Illinoian. The oldest glacial deposit is thought to be the Jameco Gravel, probably Illinoian in age. The Jameco Grovel is overlaid by Gardiners Clay, an interglacial moraine deposit of pre-Wisconsin or early Wisconsin Age. The Gardiners Clay is overlaid by a glacial till sheet composed of clayey to sandy boulder till. This till belongs to the Manhasset Formation. Overlying the Manhasset is the youngest Wisconsin drift, related to the terminal moraine of the Harbor Hill Drift. The Harbor Hill Drift has a clayey to sandy ground moraine containing boulders north of the terminal moraine. The terminal moraine has a rough stratification of sand and gravel; till in this moraine is irregularly distributed and variable in thickness. South of the terminal moraine is glacial outwash of well-stratified sand and gravel (Fuller, 1914; Swarzenski, 1959).

Outwash is the most extensive of the Wisconsin deposits on Long Island. The outwash adjacent to the Harbor Hill terminal moraine is fanshaped, like deposits typically made by water issuing from the former ice front at a single point. Where streams were adjacent to each other, confluent plains and compound fans are apparent.

Except for a few bedrock outcrops, most of southern Manhattan is covered by drift to depths of 30 m or more. Manhattan contains many buried stream channels, ancient as well as recent. The deep channels in the ancient category range from 2 to 30 m below sea level. The courses of the streams that once occupied two of them were controlled by the complex fault zones at Dyckman and 125th Streets. A third such channel was found in Lower Manhattan. Several deep borings for the proposed Lower Manhattan Expressway indicated that the average depth of this channel is also about 30 m below sea level (New York City, Division of Design, Department of Borough Works, 1940). This channel appears to be controlled by erosional processes rather than faulting (Berkey, 1911).

Extensive Holocene fresh-water and salt-water swamp and marsh areas still remain in New York City. Many of them have been and are being used for solid waste disposal.

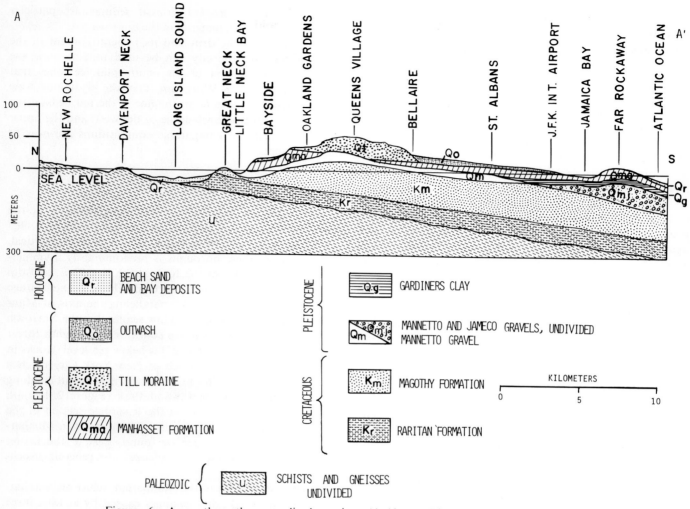

Figure 6. A north-south generalized section (A-A' on Figure 1) through eastern Queens County, Long Island, from about New Rochelle in Westchester County to the Atlantic Ocean. (Compiled and modified from sections by Veatch and others, 1906; Fuller, 1914; and Legget, 1973.)

All marsh areas that were once along the Manhattan shoreline were long ago filled and have been built over. Margins of Brooklyn and Queens Counties, now built up, were once tidal flats below sea level. Three rather large salt marsh areas have been saved from destruction by local government action designating them as wildlife refuges or parks: Pelham Bay Park in the northeast Bronx, Jamaica Bay Wildlife Refuge, and Davis Wildlife Refuge on Staten Island. Flushing Meadow on Queens County's north shore was partly filled in to build La Guardia Airport (Figure 1); the remainder was used for a sanitary landfill, on which the 1939-1940 World's Fair was built. Many parks in the Bronx, Brooklyn, and Staten Island are marshlands that have been filled in.

Many salt marshes were still extant in the early 1800's along the East and Hudson Rivers, as were many glacial till hills in Lower Manhattan, as previously mentioned. Many of the marshes were filled in by leveling adjacent hills, as was done for the construction of Tenth Avenue (Cozzens, 1843; Figure 3, area northwest of Chambers Street). In this century, the salt marsh on the south shore of Spuyten Duyvil on the north end of Manhattan was filled in for baseball diamonds and a soccer field (Figure 2, loc. 20).

Some of the recent freshwater creeks and brooks in the Bronx, Manhattan, Brooklyn, and Queens have been put into culverts and buried. These former waterways are now used as sewers, sewer outfalls, and conduits for effluent discharge from a half dozen or so sewage treatment plants (Barlow, 1971). Many freshwater bogs or marshes formed in kettle holes associated with the terminal moraine. These kettle ponds can be found in such places as Cunningham Park and Forest Park in Queens (Figure 2, locs. 62, 53), as well as in parks in Brooklyn and on Staten Island.

Character of the Pleistocene and Holocene deposits

The Jameco Gravel is composed of fine-to-very coarse sand and gravel. The gravel and pebbles are crystalline and sedimentary rock particles. The deposit also contains biotite, muscovite, hornblende, chlorite, and some feldspar as accessory minerals. The Jameco unit can be found in Kings and Queens Counties (Franke and McClymonds, 1972).

The Gardiners Clay consists of clay, silt, and a few beds of sand and gravel. The deposit is usually grayish green and contains fossil marine shells, Foraminifera, and lignite. The Gardiners Clay in Kings and Queens Counties is found more than 15-100 m below sea level (Franke and McClymonds, 1972).

The Manhasset Formation is composed of a sandy to clayey compact boulder till overlying an outwash gravel. This unit averages 4.5 m in thickness and is interpreted as part of the Ronkonkoma moraine. The Manhasset is immediately followed by the younger deposits of the Harbor Hill Drift. The Harbor Hill contains quartzose fine to coarse sand and gravel outwash beyond the terminal moraine. The moraine is a clay, sand, gravel, and boulder till (Frank and McClymonds, 1972; Swarzenski, 1959). Behind the moraine is a jumbled ground moraine ranging from silt- and clay-sized material to boulders. All the Manhasset and Harbor Hill materials in Queens are mainly gray, brown, and yellow.

The Holocene deposits citywide are made up of artificial fill, salt marsh deposits, alluvium, and shoreline or beach deposits. These sediments consist of sand, gravel, clay, silt, organic silt, peat, loam, and shells. The colors are brown, black, yellow, and gray. The artificial fill contains various mixtures of rubbish.

The Jameco and Gardiners units have not been identified in the Bronx, New York, and Richmond; however, the bulk of the Pleistocene in these counties probably correlates with the Wisconsin Harbor Hill units of Kings and Queens Counties.

The drift in the Bronx is the thinnest in the city and consists of particles derived from crystalline rocks. The drift on Manhattan Island is deep at the south end of the island. The drift on Lower Manhattan tends to be reasonably stratified reddish sand containing clay and boulders. In northern Manhattan, as in the Bronx, the drift is thin except in deep valleys such as the Manhattanville cross valley (Berkey, 1911), locally called the 125th Street fault valley (Figure 2, loc. 16); the drift here tends to be gray, brown, and yellow and to contain erratic diabase boulders. The drift units on Staten Island are similar in makeup and grain size to those in Kings and Queens Counties except that they

are reddish and consist of Triassic sedimentary particles and some Cretaceous material in the outwash.

The color of the drift and its mineral content in the different parts of the city can be used to determine the direction of movement of the continental ice lobes that occupied the area in Wisconsin time; the crystalline New England Upland rocks lie to the north, the red beds of the Triassic and Jurassic lowland lie to the west, and the upper Pleistocene drifts of comparable compositions are near to these provinces.

STRUCTURE

The general strike of the dominant foliation of the metamorphic rocks of Manhattan and the Bronx is N. 30° to 35° E.; dips range from about 45° SE to nearly vertical. The folding in these boroughs is predominantly asymmetric. The axial planes of the folds strike N. 35° E. and dip eastward from 70° to nearly vertical. The fold axes plunge southwestward at 10° to 15°, paralleling the axis of Manhattan Island to about 46 m below sea level at the Narrows. Therefore, all the rock surface south of East Eighth Street in Manhattan (Figure 2, loc. 27) is below sea level. Rocks in the northeast-striking fold belt of New York City reach a maximum altitude of 63 m in northern Manhattan along the Manhattan Ridge in Inwood Park (Figure 2, loc. 19; Figure 4) and almost 92 m in the Riverdale section of the Bronx (Figure 2, loc. 20). South of 34th Street in Manhattan, few rock outcrops can be found. East of the Bronx River valley, the schists and gneisses are generally isoclinally folded.

Detailed analysis of the Manhattan Schist on Manhattan Island revealed fabric changes caused by at least three phases of folding (Langer and Bowes, 1969). For example, the dominant S_1 foliation in the Manhattan Schist is in the axial plane of the tight, isoclinal F_1 folds formed at the time of the main metamorphic event, a high-grade regional metamorphism. Langer and Bowes (1969) suggest that the rubidium/strontium dates of 460 to 480 m.y. on muscovite in the Manhattan Prong may represent F_1. The more open-to-tight F_2 folds are most prominent (asymmetrical), with gentle eastward dipping limbs and steeper west dipping limbs. Plunge is to the south-southwest and S_2 tends to be parallel to the axial plane. The F_3 folds are open and symmetrical with a general northeastern plunge. The 350 m.y. potassium/argon mica date may be partly the result of the F_2 and F_3 phases (Langer and Bowes, 1969). According to Langer and Bowes, these three phases of structural deformation have a direct relationship to the great range in radiogenic dates obtained by workers in this terrane. In general, the K-Ar data are gas-retention ages related more directly to the thermal history of the area than to the history of structural deformation (L. E. Long, written communication, 1980).

Most major fault zones in Manhattan and the Bronx

trend northwest (Figure 1). Examples are: along Mosholu Parkway in the Bronx; Spuyten Duyvil and the Dyckman Street-Burnside Avenue zone (a very complex zone present in the west side sewer tunnel), both between the Bronx and Manhattan; the Polo Grounds-155th Street Bridge zone; 125th Street from the Hudson River to St. Nicholas Avenue, to and crossing the northeast corner of Central Park, thence to the vicinity of 23rd Street and Pearson Street in Long Island City (Manhattan to Queens); and Wallabout Channel in the lower East River to East 17th Street and Avenue A on the lower southeastern side of Manhattan.

Three other major fault zones have an opposite trend, approximately northeast. Two of these parallel Roosevelt Island, one strand in the east channel between the island and Queens and the other in the west channel on the Manhattan side. The third zone is in the East River from the vicinity of Wallabout Bay southward between Governors Island and the Battery (Figure 2, locs. 10, 39, 65). The lower Harlem River follows part of a fault zone that enters the channel from the northwest above 155th Street, and south of High Bridge, and turns south.

The direction of movement on New York City faults also varies. For example, the fault mentioned above, south of High Bridge, trends east across a synclinal fold, as seen in an outcrop along Harlem River Drive, is normal, according to pegmatite sill displacements; the same sense of movement shows up in City Tunnel No. 3, which runs parallel to the synclinal axis at a depth below sea level here of about 153 m (New York City, 1975).

The Mosholu Parkway fault zone is narrow and shows little chemical alteration (T. W. Fluhr, written commun., 1981). It is oblique to the axis of folding, and has two components of movement: normal fault movement on at least three steeply dipping surfaces, as seen underground (New York City, 1975), and strike slip, as indicated by the offset of formations crossed by the fault (Figure 1).

Some faults in New York City are open and act as channels for water flow; others contain gouge or secondary mineralization and are healed. Both open and healed faults can be seen in Fort Tryon Park south of Dyckman Street; they were also observed in the sewer tunnel that runs north-south along the west side of Manhattan where it passes beneath Dyckman Street. The faults in the city probably represent many ages of movement from Late Middle Ordovician time, associated with the Taconic orogeny (Hall, 1968a; Zen, 1968), through Triassic (Rodgers, 1970). No solid evidence indicates that faulting has taken place since the Mesozoic in the city area, although mild earthquakes take place just outside of the city limits from time to time. Engineers are quite concerned in determining whether a fault is active or capable. Active faults are those along which movement has taken place during recorded history and along which movement can be expected at any time

(Krynine and Judd, 1957, p. 78,, 358). Capable faults, a legal term developed for nuclear power plant siting, have had movement in the past 35,000 years, recurrent movement in the past 500,000 years, or instrumentally determined seismicity that can be directly related to the fault (U.S. Office of the Federal Register, 1980, p. 547). The ability to identify whether faults are active would be of inestimable help in New York City; however, very little information exists on the exact age of fault movements in the city area (N. M. Ratcliffe, oral commun., 1980).

In the relatively short distance between the George Washington Bridge and Dyckman Street along the Hudson River on the Manhattan Ridge, most of the fault types can be seen: normal, oblique, strike slip, and reverse, some filled with decaying gouge, others without gouge. A major transverse fault is along the 125th Street valley, where the valley floor is more than 60 m below sea level. In some places along this rock floor, decayed rock extends an additional 60 m below it (Berkey, 1911) because of ground water working along shear surfaces. The offset directions of formations shown on plots of the borings by Berkey (1911) indicate a probable strike-slip component along this zone as well as a vertical component (Berkey, 1911, 1933, pl 36).

A part of City Tunnel No. 2 in Brooklyn and Queens crosses several-major fault zones. One group in Long Island City strikes N. 15°W. to N. 27° W. and has vertical dips; this zone is probably the extension of the Manhattan 125th Street zone. Another zone striking N. 1°W. and dipping 90° is in the Wallabout Basin section of Brooklyn. Most of the fault zones in the Brooklyn-Queens basement strike northwest and have dips ranging from 25° to the south to vertical. Most northeast striking faults appear in the Queens part of the tunnel,though at least three were observed in Brooklyn (New York City, Board of Water Supply, 1936).

Seismicity

Generally, the New York City area has been characterized by few earthquakes, and those were of moderate to low intensity (I to V on the modified Mercalli scale). Several minor shocks (Nuttli magnitudes 1.8 to 3.5) have been caused in the last 20 years by activity along faults either west of the city from south-central New Jersey to the Rockland County, N. Y., area along the Ramapo border fault (N.M. Ratcliffe, oral commun., 1980), or along faults in central Westchester County along a north-south axis between the Bronx and Hutchinson Rivers.

More work is needed to correlate seismicity with specific faults within New York City. Seismic shocks that are felt in the city generally take place consistently along northeast-trending axes that parallel preexisting mapped faults (Aggarwal and Sykes, 1978; N. M. Ratcliff, oral commun., 1980). On November 22, 1976, a shock near

Scarsdale, N.Y., in Westchester County, had a magnitude of 1.9 and a focal depth of about 5 km. Between January and April 1976, three shocks of approximate magnitude 2 at a hypocenter of 4 km took place near Riverdale, N.Y., in Bronx County (Figure 2, loc. 20). In 1978, a 1.8 magnitude shock occurred near Yonkers, N.Y., in Westchester County, which also had a focal depth of 4 km. On January 13, 1979, a 3.5 magnitude quake which occurred in east-central New Jersey near Cheesequake had a hypocenter of about 5 km (Lamont-Doherty, 1976-79). The magnitudes listed are on the Nuttli magnitude scale. Seismic wave attenuation in eastern North America is different from that west of the Rockies; therefore, the Nuttli equations are more accurate for the east than the Richter equations, which were devised for southern California (Nuttli, 1973). A shock of intensity V on the modified Mercalli scale took place on November 22, 1967, in Westchester County, N.Y., 9 years earlier to the day of an event in 1976 in the same county (U.S. Environmental Science Services Administration, C.G.S, 1969).

The first three epicentral areas mentioned above—areas near Scarsdale, Riverdale, and Yonkers—are not far from some northwest-trending fault zones—including one on the Bronx River at White Plains and Cameron's Line. The Cheesequake shock may have taken place along an extension of Cameron's Line (N.M. Ratcliffe, oral commun., 1980). Criteria mentioned above for extension of the line down the East River indicate a trend direction that could reach east-central New Jersey. The fairly constant hypocentral locations could indicate a continuous fault zone. The system of northeast-trending faults (mentioned above) east of the Hudson River valley parallels the Ramapo border fault along which a large number of earthquakes have taken place in the period 1962-78 (Aggarwal and Sykes, 1978). Aggarwal and Sykes (1978) stated that the present maximum stress trends west-northwest, indicating a reactivation of southeast or northwest dipping faults (Figure 5).

WATER SUPPLY—WASTE DISPOSAL

The original water supply prior to the early 1800's was obtained mainly from systems of groundwater wells. One such system was Ridgewood, which supplied Brooklyn from wells and small streams in Kings, Queens, and Nassau Counties. Another, the Jamaica Water Supply Company system, supplied southern Queens from wells. Water on Manhattan Island came from wells and from the old Collect Pond (Figure 3), springs, and other ponds. The quality of Manhattan's water sources began to decline as a result of pollution in the 1700's. A private company, the Manhattan Company, whose main interest was in banking, was given a contract to supply the city with good water. The company

excavated a deep reservoir into bedrock to hold more than 2,000,000 l of water and also dug a well near Collect Pond. They connected these sources by wooden mains to supply the city. Actually, this subsurface source was not what the city fathers had in mind, and, in addition, the water quality was bad. They had thought that the Manhattan Company would provide a large dependable surface water supply from the Bronx River, but banking was more profitable than water (Weidner, 1974).

For many years, these ground water sources supplied the city's water, but the population grew faster than anticipated, and pollution and salt water incursion caused health hazards. Because of additional hookups, the lack of pressure became a problem if fires broke out.

The present main water supply is from reservoirs in the Old Croton system, New York's first aqueduct-reservoir network and sole supply for Manhattan and part of the Bronx until the 1890's when the New Croton Aqueduct was built. Additional water is supplied by the Catskill system and the newer Delaware system of reservoirs and aqueducts in the Catskill Mountains watershed (Berkey, 1933; Weidner, 1974).

The old ground water systems in Brooklyn and Queens were abandoned owing to the large drawdown as the rapidly increasing population in these newer counties placed increased demand on inadequate water supplies in the late 1920's to the early 1930's. This drawdown also caused salt water encroachment on these wells (Geraghty, 1959; Perlmutter and Crandell, 1959; Foxworthy, 1978). An unforeseen result of the cessation of pumping of the western Long Island wells is that the Flatbush IRT Subway Line in Brooklyn (Figure 2, loc. 56) became subject to flooding in the 1950's because of the rising water table. This subway line had been built when the water-supply wells had drawn the water table far below the tunnel invert. Not realizing this, the designers did not provide for sump pumps in the tunnels.

The New York State laws of 1905 created the New York City Board of Water Supply and the New York State Water Supply Commission. Through these agencies and their predecessors, the various water supply systems were built. Tunnels and pipes 45 km long carry water in the Croton system from the Hillview Reservoir in Yonkers just over the city line to the Silver Lake Reservoir on Staten Island (Figure 2, loc. 9). The tunnel (Brooklyn City Tunnel No. 1) from Hillview to Fort Green Park runs approximately 26 km in rock from sea level to about 220 m below sea level in the East River. City Tunnel No. 1 was started in 1907 and finished in 1917; it delivered 945 million l/d. By 1927, when the second stage was complete, 950 million l/d were delivered to the city.

A second tunnel (City Tunnel No. 2) runs beneath the east Bronx, Rikers Island, Queens, and Brooklyn for 32.3 km and is as much as 238 m below the surface. Conduits deliver water from City Tunnels Nos. 1 and 2 to distant parts of Queens, Brooklyn, and Richmond. All the above mentioned deep tunnels are cut through crystalline rocks of the New York City and Hutchinson River Groups.

The Catskill system including City Tunnels Nos. 1 and 2 required 122 km (75 mi) of test borings. The first two stages of the newer Delaware system required 56 km of borings, and together with subsequent borings for the New York City water system, brought the total length of exploratory drill holes for the New York City water supply system to 187.2 km (Berkey, 1911, 1933; New York City Board of Water Supply, 1950). Another city water tunnel is under construction (1980) that will connect the Hillview Reservoir in Yonkers with Manhattan and Queens in a deep-rock excavation averaging 160 m below sea level. Completion of this tunnel will not only bring additional water to the city but will allow the older systems to be shut down for much needed maintenance.

Sewage disposal was originally done by direct discharge into the surrounding estuaries and ocean waters. This practice polluted the sea waters, making them unfit for shell fishing and recreational bathing in some areas (New York State Department of Health, 1961). For the last few decades, with the help of N.Y. State legislation for clean water, ground water and surface water studies by the U.S. Geological Survey and others (Berkey, 1933; Perlmutter and Crandell, 1959; Geraghty, 1959; New York State Department of Health, 1961; Franke and McClymonds, 1972; Foxworthy, 1978), and pressure from environmentalists, sewage treatment plants have been built to combat this type of pollution. For example, a tunnel was bored running north along the west side of Manhattan to intercept the lateral sewage lines emptying directly into the Hudson River. This tunnel will take the raw sewage and carry it into a tertiary treatment plant being constructed in 1980 on the Hudson River. This treatment plant is being built on a concrete platform over the river on hundreds of cast-in-place concrete pipe piles driven into the riverbed (Figure 2, loc. 17).

ENGINEERING GEOLOGY

Building code history

The New York City Building Code has changed since 1936, as more has been learned about the complex geology under the city. The code of 1936 (New York City, 1936) and chapter 5 of the 1942 code (New York City, 1942) are concerned with the bearing capacities of soils or the presumptive bearing capacities of soils and rocks. The 1942 code establishes five classes of foundation materials (Table 1) and gives their maximum allowable presumptive bearing capacities in tons per square foot.

The 1942 code (section C 26-377.0, paragraph a) states, "Satisfactory bearing material shall be ledge rock in its natural bed, natural deposits of sand, gravel or clay, or any combination of these materials. Such bearing material shall neither contain nor overlie an appreciable amount of organic matter or other objectionable material."

In the same 1942 code, provision is made for test pits or borings. Structures less than (15.5 m) 50 ft high and designed for live loads of less than (1463 kg/m²) 300 lbs/ft² could have borings waived. If a structure were to be more than (23 m) 75 ft high or if the total load were to be more than (4890 kg/m²) 1,000 lbs/ft², new test pits or borings to determine soil or rock conditions could be waived if the foundation characteristics of the area had already been determined by previous borings and test pits. In areas where the character of the soil had not been established and the rock was known to be more than (24.5 m) 80 ft below curb level, borings or test pits could be required to establish the general characteristics of the soil.

No specifications are given as to how the borings should be taken (procedure) or how various loadings could be determined except by settlement-tests. "The applied loads shall remain until there has been no settlement for 24 hours." A test was considered unsatisfactory or the results unacceptable if "the proposed safe load showed more than (1.9 cm) 0.75 in. settlement or the increment of settlement obtained under the 50 percent overload exceeded 60 percent of the settlement obtained under the proposed load" (C26-379.0, New York City, 1942).

The 1936 code was considered a major step forward in code writing. The 1942 code proved to be very restrictive 20 years later and caused construction costs to skyrocket owing to inflexibility in allowing the use of new materials and improved modern technology.

The latest code (New York City, 1970), a specifications-type code, allows this flexibility. Detailed specifications are given as to the type of construction permitted, materials that can be used, and, at times, sizes allowed.

TABLE 1. MAXIMUM PRESUMPTIVE BEARING CAPACITIES*

Class	Material	Maximum allowable presumptive bearing capacities[†], ton/ft²	t/m² x 10
1	Hard sound rock	40	40.80
	Medium hard rock	25	25.60
2	Hard pan overlying rock	10	10.21
	Soft rock	8	8.20
	Gravel	6	6.12
3	Coarse sand	4	4.08
	Fine and dry sand	3	3.07
4	Hard dry clay	3	3.07
	Sand and clay, mixed or in layers	2	2.05
	Firm clay	2	2.05
	Fine and wet sand (confined)	2	2.05
5	Soft clay	1	1.02

*From New York City Building Code, 1942.
[†]Considers strength and deformation characteristics.

Anything not covered cannot be used without special permission.

Article 11 of the 1970 code is 90 pages long and covers all types of foundations in all types of soil and geologic conditions; only 6 pages in the 1936 code and 14 pages in the 1942 code were devoted to this topic.

The new code gives minimum driving energy and minimum hammer energy for various pile types driven into various soil and rock classes, all of which are related to pile capacity in tons. Allowable compressive stresses are also given for pile materials. A section in the 1970 code on Soil Load Bearing Tests gives details on procedure, loading, and determination of results. Another section gives details on soil investigations, such as number of borings required for various sized buildings and sampling equipment to be used. A detailed Unified Soil Classification includes identification, description, and laboratory classification criteria.

Allowable bearing pressures are given for various soils and rocks. The 1970 code states, "The tabulated values to basic allowable bearing pressures apply for massive rocks or for sedimentary or foliated rocks where the strata are level or nearly so, and then only if the area has ample lateral support. Tilted strata and their relation to nearby slopes or excavations shall receive special consideration." (C26-1103.4, Notes section, table 11-2, New York City, 1970) The above quotations from and summaries of the 1936, 1942, and 1970 codes show the evolution of a realistic building code for a geologically complex city. The new code takes both geologic complexities and new construction technology into consideration.

Engineering projects

New York City has been a virtual "classroom" on engineering and engineering geology, as so many projects related to transportation, commerce, housing, and waste treatment have been and are being built. In addition to the bridges and tunnels that connect the five counties, many miles of subway, water, sewer, and other utility tunnels have been or are being constructed.

The two major airports in New York City are both in Queens County; John F. Kennedy International is on the south, and La Guardia is on the north side (Figure 1). A smaller general aviation field, Flushing, is a short distance east of La Guardia. These airports have one thing in common: they were built on reclaimed marshland.

All large structures in the city either have foundations excavated to bedrock (the Twin Towers of the World Trade Center extend eight stories into rock) or are supported on bedrock by large caissons (Woolworth Building) or piles. In areas of deep soils having good bearing capacities, smaller structures are founded on spread footings.

This discussion will consider representative engineering projects in the rocks of the New York City Group and

how these rocks have been utilized. Around the turn of the century, the Broadway IRT (Interborough Rapid Transit) Subway System was built, requiring some tunnel excavation in rock. That the rock from the IRT tunnels, Manhattan Schist, was used to construct the Gothic buildings of the City College of New York demonstrates the practical ingenuity of engineers and architects of that era. The Broadway Line exits from below ground onto a viaduct; where it crosses the fault zone of 125th Street (Figure 7), the viaduct has large hinges on the abutments. The idea was that if vertical movement were to take place along the fault, the bridge would move on its hinges but remain intact, and the transportation system would be undisturbed. However, past movement along the fault is now known to have had a strike-slip component (see discussion on faults).

Where the Inwood Marble was found in the excavation for Interstate 95 (Cross Bronx Expressway) across the Jerome Valley (Figure 5), much of it consisted of a coarse dolomitic sand residue from decomposition of the marble. Several thousand cubic meters of this material were stockpiled and used as a base-course filter under the 22.9 cm thick reinforced concrete pavement. This base-course filter blanket prevents the buildup of moisture beneath the pavement that could cause frost heave in winter or "pumping" in spring and summer, which can destroy pavement.

When borings were taken in the marble along the Cross Bronx Expressway for the Bronx abutment of the Alexander Hamilton steel arch Bridge over the Harlem River, a 1136 l/min loss in drilling fluid suddenly took place in one NX (2 1/8 in diameter core) vertical drill hole. As faults are known to be present along the Harlem River Valley, a trigonometric problem was postulated to determine whether a fault had been encountered. On the basis of these computations, an angle hole was subsequently drilled to test that premise. Because the driller was good and extreme accuracy was used in setting up and drilling, the angle hole passed through the questioned vertical hole, a one-in-a-million chance. This hole proved that no fault was present; instead, the bedrock here had been differentially weathered. All the pure lime had been dissolved, leaving open seams (probably soil filled) separating blocks of dolomitic marble. The ground water here is salty, as this abutment is on the flood plain of the Harlem River estuary. The salt water probably hastens solution of fairly pure calcium carbonate. Fortunately, this condition was known prior to construction, which helped in a claim brought by the contractor, who claimed that the foundation was boulders and not bedrock on which he had based his contract bid.

Where the Cross Bronx Expressway crosses the Fordham Ridge between the Jerome Valley and the Harlem River, a deep cut was made through the Fordham Gneiss (Figure 5). When exploration for this section determined the volume of rock cut, exploration was simultaneously

Figure 7. A view looking north along Broadway from West 122nd Street. The IRT subway tracks here are on a viaduct crossing the 125th Street fault valley, which strikes southeast (left to right).

carried out for the Bronx State Hospital along the Hutchinson River Parkway (Figure 2, loc. 46). The hospital site is a postglacial tidal marsh, which contained an average of 30 m of organic silt having a bearing strength of zero. After boring profiles of the marsh indicated its depth and bottom configuration, engineers decided to transport all the rock from the Fordham Ridge excavation to the hospital site. The rock helped stabilize the organic silt. The filling was successful, since no dangerous mud waves were created by the operation. Further discussion of problems related to construction involving marshland will be taken up in the next section of this paper.

The Fordham Gneiss causes the least construction problems of the formations in the New York City Group. The lit-par-lit granite injections help make it a rather tough rock. Roosevelt Island in the East River has been home to a mental hospital, smallpox and tuberculosis sanitariums, and a prison. Some of the older structures, now largely demolished, were built of Fordham Gneiss from quarries on the island by prison inmates (Barlow, 1971). The shell of

the old smallpox hospital still stands today in stark contrast to the ultramodern, middle-income housing complex built to the north (Figure 8).

The Consolidated Edison Gas Tunnel was driven normal to the strike of the almost vertically dipping Fordham Gneiss, where it passes under the East River between the Ravenswood Plant in Long Island City, Queens, and Manhattan. The gneiss is quite stable and self-supporting; therefore, the tunnel has no lining in this rock. There are problems with other rock units encountered in this tunnel.

Another rock unit related to the Fordham, the Yonkers Granite, however, has caused some engineering problems. A portion of City Water Tunnel No. 3 under construction in 1980, with a tremendous valve chamber designed to have angular haunches, was excavated in Yonkers Granite beneath Van Cortlandt Park. The contractor had a problem maintaining the plan shape of this chamber when he blasted, because of the granitic type of sheet jointing inherent in this rock. This rock was quarried for many years in the old Mile Square Quarries just north

Figure 8. A view looking north along the East River from East 43rd Street. Roosevelt Island beneath Queensborough Bridge is shown. Small structures in foreground are the old smallpox hospital constructed of Fordham Gneiss from quarry on the island. To the left beyond the bridge along the shore is a modern middle-income, high-rise housing complex. The large light-colored structure seen under center span of bridge is a hospital. The skeleton like tower structure beneath left span of bridge against the sky is a headframe for shaft 15B, City Water Tunnel No. 3 under construction.

of New York City in Yonkers; the New York State Thruway now cuts through most of them. Most of the walls and bridges of the New York City Parkway system are faced with Yorkers Granite.

Construction materials in the city limits

In the northwestern corner of Staten Island is an abandoned quarry in a Jurassic diabase dike, a southerly extension of the New Jersey Palisades. This tough rock was used to make "Belgian Blocks" for road paving, road metal, quarry run rock for walls, and ornamental touches on some buildings. To the south, the variegated Cretaceous sediments crop out. Clay from these deposits was used earlier in this century and before to manufacture bricks. The "spine or backbone" of Staten Island, the large Todt Hill serpentinite mass, lies between the diabase and the Cretaceous-

Pleistocene Coastal Plain. The serpentinite was mined during colonial times for iron and asbestos (Barlow, 1971).

Long Island has an abundant supply of aggregate, as it consists mainly of a glacial moraine and a vast stratified outwash plain. One of the last sand and gravel pits in the New York City limits was operated south of the Long Island Expressway close to the Queens-Nassau County Line. This area was on the terminal moraine, and the area was far from built up in the 1930's. After World War II, when the urban and suburban expansion and the construction of the Long Island Expressway began, the pit was closed because the site had become a valuable piece of development real estate (Figure 2, loc. 66). Needless to say, fine aggregate is now obtained far to the east in Suffolk County, increasing the cost of transportation of these materials in the New York City area. Inaccessibility of underlying aggregate is one of the common problems of modern urbanization.

Working with reclaimed marsh

Highways built on Flushing Meadows in Queens County illustrate the difficulty of construction and maintenance of projects built on organic silt without adequate stabilization. This meadow extends from the East River south to Kew Gardens (Figure 2, loc. 52). Flushing Creek extends down its midsection. The meadows are underlain to an average depth of 30 m by organic silt. Loading with solid waste during the years between World War I and the 1930's did not completely stabilize the area. Grand Central Parkway, which runs north-south along the western side of Flushing Meadows, was originally built during the 1930's. When the 1964-65 World's Fair at Flushing Meadows was being constructed, Grand Central Parkway had to be rehabilitated, widened, and releveled. At the same time, the Van Wyck Expressway extension was constructed north-south on the eastern side of the meadows. Both these roads had to be releveled in the mid-1970's.

During the 1963-64 construction, a bridge and an associated ramp were built for access to the Van Wyck Expressway from Jewel Avenue (Figure 2, loc. 51). The depth of organic material at this site required piles of 33.5 m average length. The access ramp is supported on hammerhead piers on pile footings. The 33.5 m length of these pile bents was such that no lateral support was given by the organic material to these piles; this lack of support caused the piles to lean under load, resulting in the ramp deck shifting almost off the pads of the pier caps. The deck had to be lifted off the piers in order to underpin them, but the heavy timber mat used to support the 45.5 t cranes used to raise the deck sank into the mud under the load. Eventually, the deck was raised so that the piers could be underpinned by batter piles to take the lateral load.

To the north, the Van Wyck Expressway becomes the eight-lane Whitestone Expressway after crossing Flushing Creek. The Whitestone Expressway in the vicinity of Linden Place, traverses the east edge of Flushing Meadow (Figure 2, loc. 50). Organic matter here had never been surcharged with solid waste or any other substantial fill. Therefore, in order to stabilize the area as much as possible prior to construction, sand drains were installed to speed up the consolidation. Large steel shells were driven into the silt and filled with a fairly homogeneous coarse sand. The steel shell was extracted as the sand was poured into it from a hopper at the top of the leads on the driving rig. The pore water flowed to the surface under pressure of a surcharge embankment placed over the sand drain network. As the pore water drained, the soil compressed to a smaller volume, more of the embankment load was carried by the soil particles, and the stability and shear strength of the soil increased (Baskerville, 1968). Settlement as a result of this method averaged 2 m while the drains were in operation.

In order to prevent a depression from forming during postconstruction consolidation at the approach slab of the expressway overpass bridges, also on the Whitestone project, a structure was built at grade. Precast concrete deck slabs were placed on treated piles supporting grade beams so that a "bridge" was built where normally a compacted approach embankment would have been placed. The settlement of the organic matter would have required an enormous amount of maintenance, such as "mud jacking" the pavement. Mud jacking is the pumping of a soil and cement slurry through holes drilled along the edge of settled concrete pavement to raise it to its proper level.

Geological problems in Kings County are fairly similar to those in Queens, although Kings County does not contain a large marsh area in the north. Rock is reasonably close to the surface along Brooklyn's shore opposite Manhattan, and more than two-thirds of Kings County are underlaid by terminal and ground moraine. Most of the major highways and bridges presented no serious problems. Construction on the southern edge of the outwash plain in Brooklyn between Jamaica Bay and the Atlantic Ocean involved dealing with salt marsh and sanitary landfills on salt marsh. The construction problems here were similar to those described for the Flushing Meadow area of Queens County.

The Manhattan shoreline has been drastically changed since the late 1800's (New York City, Division of Design, Department of Borough Works, 1940). Streams formerly flowed into many bays along the East and Harlem Rivers. For example, Turtle Bay, between East 46th and 48th Streets, has been filled to the bulkhead line, and part of the United Nations Complex now occupies what used to be water between East 42nd and 49th Streets. A similar bay to the south, Kips Bay, has been filled in, and New York University Medical Center, Bellevue Hospital, and high-rise apartment houses have been built in this former bay area. Many of these buildings are on pile foundations, which also support the Con Edison relieving platform and ramps for the F.D.R. Drive through this area. Undisturbed Shelby tube samples, taken for these latter structures, had barely enough cohesion to stay in the tubes.

Artificial ground can create tense moments in subsequent construction. In the late 1930's, pneumatic caissons were placed west of the Manhattan bulkhead line in the Hudson River for the Lincoln Tunnel river connection. The land between the bulkhead line and original ground was artificial fill, consisting, in large part, of huge blocks of rock taken from subway excavations. This land, reclaimed from the river, extended 60-90 m from the original shoreline in places, and fill was found to extend 20 m below the then- existing land surface. Exploration also discovered that the blocks of rock and other rubbish had pushed out the river silt, which took the bulkhead and piles with it. The concrete bulkhead had been fractured and displaced. Because this mass might move again if disturbed, a system of ties had to be designed. Fortunately, the 120 m of tunnel driven through this area caused no displacement (Fluhr, 1941).

Another shoreline change was made when material excavated for the eight-story foundation for the Twin Towers of the World Trade Center was dumped offshore into the Hudson River near the towers. (Legget (1973) contains a short discussion of problems on this project and excellent photographs of the foundation excavation.) In addition to this excavated material, 4.9 million metric tons of sand dredged from New York Harbor has been added to this site (Schlee, 1975; Sanko, 1975). Thus, a large plot of "new land" has been added to Manhattan, on which developers are building (1982) Battery Park City.

The reclaiming of marsh, as well as parts of the river channels, for engineering projects around Manhattan Island during more than two centuries, has been pointed out in this and previous sections to show how the total usable land surface of the city has been increased. To complete the discussion, two very large projects involving land reclamation, which affect thousands of persons, are briefly mentioned.

One of these projects is a large housing development, Co-op City (Figure 2, loc. 45), in Bronx County between the New England Thruway and the Hutchinson River on a former tidal marsh, a site similar to that of the Bronx State Hospital. This project is a middle-income, high-rise total community of about 60,000 persons; it has its own schools, fire and police stations, and shopping centers. The structures are on piles, but the surrounding terrain with its modest "hills and valleys" are actually hydraulic fill from Long Island Sound pumped into the marsh to surcharge height. This surcharged fill was then graded to final topography, and the buildings were constructed.

John F. Kennedy International Airport in south Queens was built in a section originally known as Idlewild on Jamaica Bay (Figure 1). The original site had scattered marsh islands (hassocks) and tidal channels passing among them. This large airfield was founded on hydraulic fill pumped from the Atlantic Ocean onto this marshy area. The fill was spread by bottom scrapers and compacted by heavy sheeps-foot rollers. Terminals and other structures were placed on piles.

In the Co-op City project, the surcharge materials have been settling quite noticeably over the last decade. Sewer structures on piles, for example, have caused large ridges and humps in the streets. Rehabilitation of underground utilities is of prime concern. On the other hand, John F. Kennedy International has not settled noticeably.

Slope-stability problems

Many slopes in the New York City area have failed; some failures have been serious, such as a massive rock avalanche in Westchester County in the early 1960's that blocked half the New York State Thruway; others, such as rockfalls, soil slumps, and earth flows, are more of a nuisance or maintenance problem to highways. Slope stability has generally been taken into consideration in the initial design of highways constructed within the city limits since World War II. The older parkways and drives in Manhattan and the Bronx where high ridges (for example, Manhattan Ridge over Henry Hudson Parkway along the Hudson) exist above the roadway may have occasional single rockfalls. Some rock blocks weigh more than 1 t, but, fortunately, most do not usually roll beyond the road shoulders.

Deep vertical cuts along the Cross Bronx Expressway, where rock was heavily jointed and falls were probable, have been buttressed by brick-faced, reinforced, concrete walls. Areas of sound rock in Fordham Gneiss having few joints were presplit or line drilled; these cuts have been very stable. Heavy stone masonry walls having mortar joints were constructed to cover areas where schist was exposed along the Cross Bronx, and substantial seams of biotite schist tended to weather rapidly to a limonitic soil. In one area (adjacent to the portal of the tunnel that carries the Cross Bronx beneath the Independent Subway Line and the Concourse, Figure 5) where rapidly weathering schist is exposed, and a masonry wall could not be placed, gunite was used in an attempt to stem decomposition. The slope was scaled to sound rock, and then gunite was applied by spray. This coating lasted about 2-3 years; then, the gunite disintegrated as the rock continued to decompose.

An interchange between the Staten Island Expressway and the proposed Richmond Parkway was cut approximately 20 m deep in the serpentinite at the northern end of Todt Hill. Slope stability in this rock proved to be a problem because of the highly complex joint systems and the way the rock weathered. The remedy for this problem was to flatten some of the slopes. The rock still weathers, but it does not fall into the road. Expressway cuts through the Cretaceous sediments on Staten Island were not too deep, and the slopes were laid back to at least 1:1, making them quite stable.

In Brooklyn and Queens, cuts made through glacial deposits were designed to a stable angle of repose, topsoiled, and seeded where the right-of-way was adequate. Otherwise, brick-faced, reinforced, concrete walls were built. On the Grand Central Parkway-Clearview Expressway Interchange, a slope failed in an embankment above a wall. The soil above the wall was exposed to the effects of a heavy rain. During the night, the rain saturated almost a meter into the embankment, the top of which subsequently slid over the wall, dumping about 10 m^3 of earth on the ramp below. Two different soil types were involved. The upper layer that failed contained a high percentage of silt and clay, which held the infiltrating rain. The angle of repose of the original slope above the wall was above equilibrium; therefore, the added weight of the water brought it down. A sandier soil, similar to the soil below the failed mass, was used to rebuild the embankment. This sandier material allowed for a greater infiltration. Additionally, the angle of repose was flattened a bit. Complete flattening was not possible because of space limitations. The solution worked, as subsequent heavy rains infiltrated fast enough to prevent added weight to the soil of a magnitude to cause failure.

Beaches

New York City has approximately 40 km of salt-water, sandy beaches. Attempting to maintain these recreational facilities is a never-ending engineering project. The smallest beach is the manmade Orchard Beach on Long Island Sound in Pelham Bay Park, northeast Bronx (Figures 1, 5); Brooklyn and Queens have 25.5 km of barrier beaches facing the Atlantic Ocean (Figure 2, locs. 58, 60); Coney Island, connected to Brooklyn by artificial fill, contains 5.5 km; Rockaway Peninsula, a barrier bar, contains 18 km; and Staten Island has 15 km extending southwest from the Verrazano-Narrows Bridge.

The Brooklyn-Queens beaches are the least protected from erosion, as they face the direct onslaught of the Atlantic Ocean, its winter erosion, westward longshore drift, and occasional violent hurricanes; whereas, Staten Island is moderately protected by Lower and Raritan Bays. The Brooklyn and Queens beaches are nourished by headland erosion of Montauk Point at the east end of Long Island and subsequent westward sediment transport (Yasso and Hartman, 1976). Staten Island's beaches are nourished by wave erosion of the glacial outwash (Yasso and Hartman, 1976).

Because of filling of East Rockaway Inlet (eastern end of Queens County) by longshore drift and groin construction from the inlet to approximately 6 km to the west, wave and longshore drift erosion devastated great stretches of Rockaway Beach to the west. High tides would range up to and beneath the boardwalk. Until recently, only a very narrow strip, at most, was available at low tide for recreation (Yasso and Hartman, 1976). The strip was built up by placing dredged material from New York harbor navigation channels, and this dredging maintained the channels to the required depth (Schlee, 1975; Sanko, 1975).

According to the U.S. Army Corps of Engineers, New York's Staten Island, Brooklyn, and Queens beaches are included in the area of the United States coastline that is in the greatest danger from erosion (Yasso and Hartman, 1976).

CONCLUSIONS

The geology of New York City is complex; its various

rocks date from parts of all the geologic eras from Proterozoic to Holocene. The soils and rocks vary widely in strengths and competence. The New York City building code has been updated to reflect increases in knowledge of the engineering properties of geologic material underlying the city and improvements in technology. A large percentage of the original ground surface and the surface drainage has been covered by construction projects, and the original shorelines have been drastically altered. Former water areas have been extensively filled and are now occupied by artificial land covered by new streets and buildings. A thorough knowledge of the site foundation geology and history is needed prior to the design and construction of major new civil or architectural works in this city, regardless of the engineering history of adjacent structures. As the city matures and evolves, and the needs of its people change, engineering geology must keep pace by incorporating modern technological methods and new materials without losing sight of past lessons learned, past modifications of the land, or of the ultimate geological foundations.

ACKNOWLEDGMENTS

The author is indebted to K. E. Lowe, Professor Emeritus of City College of New York, for New York City water-supply data and for providing the original incentive to give this paper before the Geological Society of America, Engineering Division Symposium in Toronto. Gratitude is also due L. E. Long, University of Texas, for his constructive help with the radiogenic dating parts of this paper, and N. M. Ratcliffe of the U.S. Geological Survey for his informal review of the structural and metamorphic controversies and the resulting constructive suggestions unstintingly given. The discussions and correspondence that I have had with T. W. Fluhr for this paper and over the years concerning New York geology was like having a human textbook at my side, for which I am greatly indebted. The author has received valuable suggestions and guidance from the formal reviews of A. J. Froelich and R. H. Morris of the U.S. Geological Survey, to whom the author wishes to express his cordial thanks.

REFERENCES CITED

Aggarwal, Y. P., and Sykes, L. R., 1978, Earthquakes, faults, and nuclear powerplants in southern New York and northern New Jersey: Science, v. 200, p. 425–429.

Barlow, Elizabeth, 1971, The forests and wetlands of New York City: Boston, Little Brown and Company, 160 p.

Baskerville, C. A., 1965, A micropaleontological study of Cretaceous sediments of Staten Island, New York: New York, N.Y., New York University, unpublished Ph.D. thesis, 65 p.

—— 1967, Preliminary field study of the gneiss terrane of southeastern Westchester and Bronx Counties, New York [Abs.]: Geological Society of America Northeastern Section, Annual Meeting, 1967, Boston, Mass., Program, p. 13–14.

—— 1968, Geology and foundation treatment of sensitive sediments—World's Fair Highway Complex, New York: Geological Society of America, Case Histories, no. 6, p. 55–63.

—— 1982, Adoption of the name Hutchinson River Group and its subdivisions in Bronx and Westchester Counties: U.S. Geological Survey Bulletin 1529-H, p. H1-H10.

Berkey, C. P., 1911, Geology of the New York City (Catskill) aqueduct: New York State Museum Bulletin 146, 283 p.

—— 1933, New York City and vicinity: International Geological Congress, 16th, Washington, D. C., Guidebook 9, p. 1–23, 36–39, 77–92, 111–123.

Blank, H. R., 1972, Hornblende schists in the Manhattan Formation, in the Bronx, New York: Geological Society of America Bulletin, v. 83, no. 5, p. 1397–1412.

Chidester, A. H., 1968, Evolution of the ultramafic complexes of northwestern New England, in Zen, E-An, White, W. S., Hadley, J. B., and Thompson, J. B., Jr., eds., Studies of Appalachian geology, northern and maritime: New York Interscience, p. 343–354.

Clark, W. B., 1916, Upper Cretaceous deposits of Maryland: Maryland Geological Survey, Report of the State Geologist, v. 6, 986 p.

Cozzens, I., Jr., 1843, A geological history of Manhattan or New York island: New York, W. E. Dean, p. 11–39.

Fluhr, T. W., 1941, The geology of the Lincoln Tunnel: Rocks and Minerals, v. 16, nos. 4–7, p. 115–119, 155–160, 195–198, and 235–239.

Foxworthy, B. L., 1978, Nassau County, Long Island, New York Water problems in humid country, in Robinson, G. D., and Spieker, A. M., eds., "Nature to be Commanded": U.S. Geological Survey Professional Paper 950, p. 55–68.

Franke, O. L., and McClymonds, N. E., 1972, Summary of the hydrologic situation on Long Island, New York, as a guide to water-management alternatives, in Hydrology and some effects of urbanization on Long Island, New York: U.S. Geological Survey Professional Paper 627-F, 59 p.

Fuller, M. L., 1914, The geology of Long Island, New York: U.S. Geological Survey Professional Paper 82, 231 p.

Gates, R. M., and Martin, C. W., 1976, Pre-Devonian stratigraphy of the central section of the western Connecticut highlands, in Page, L. R., ed., Contributions to the stratigraphy at New England: Geological Society of America Memoir 148, p. 301–336.

Geraghty, J. J., 1959, Ground-water problems in the New York City area: New York Academy of Science Annals, v. 80, Art. 4, p. 1049–1059.

Gratacap, L. P., 1904, Geology of the city of New York, 2d ed.: New York, N.Y., Henry Holt and Company, 119 p.

Grauert, B., and Hall, L. M., 1973, Age and origin of zircons from metamorphic rocks in the Manhattan Prong, White Plains area, southeastern New York: Carnegie Institute of Washington, Annual Report of the Director, Department of Terrestrial Magnetism, 1972–73, p. 293–297.

Hall, L. M., 1968a, Time of origin and deformation of bedrock in the Manhattan Prong, in Zen, E-An, White, W. S., Hadley, J. B., and Thompson, J. B., Jr., eds., Studies of Appalachian geology, northern and maritime: New York, Interscience, p. 117–127.

—— 1968b, Bedrock geology in the vicinity of White Plains, New York: New York State Geological Association Guidebook, 40th Annual Meeting, p. 7–31.

—— 1976, Preliminary correlation of rocks in southwestern Connecticut, in Page, L. R., ed., Contributions to the stratigraphy at New England: Geological Society of America Memoir 148, p. 337–349.

Krynine, D. P., and Judd, W. R., 1957, Principles of engineering geology and geotechnics: New York, McGraw-Hill, 730 p. (see especially p. 78–79, 358–359).

Lamont-Doherty, 1976–79, Regional seismicity bulletin of the Lamont-Doherty network: Palisades, N.Y., Columbia University, Lamont-Doherty Geological Observatory.

Langer, A. M., and Bowes, D. R., 1969, Polyphase deformation in the Manhattan formation of Manhattan Island, New York City, in Igneous and metamorphic geology—A volume in honor of Arie Poldervaart: Geological Society of America Memoir 115, p. 361–377.

Lettet, R. F., 1973, Cities and geology: New York, McGraw-Hill, 624 p. (see especially p. 240–242, 337.)

Lewis, J. V., and Kummel, H. B., 1915, The geology of New Jersey: Geological Survey of New Jersey Bulletin 14, 146 p.

Long, L. E., 1962, Isotopic age study, Dutchess County, New York: Geological Society of America Bulletin, v. 73, no. 8, p. 997–1006.

Long, L. E., Cobb, J. C., and Kulp, J. L., 1959, Isotope ages on some igneous and metamorphic rocks in the vicinity of New York City: New York Academy of Science Annals, v. 80, p. 1140–1147.

Long, L. E., and Kulp, J. L., 1958, Age of the metamorphism of the rocks of the Manhattan Prong, Geological Society of America Bulletin, v. 69, p. 603–606.

—— 1962, Isotopic age study of the metamorphic history of the Manhattan and Reading Prongs: Geological Society of America Bulletin, v. 73, p. 969–996.

Lowe, K. E., 1959, Structure of the palisades intrusion of Haverstraw and West Nyack, New York: New York Academy of Science Annals, v. 80, p. 1127–1139.

Merrill, F.J.H., 1898, The geology of the crystalline rocks of southeastern New York: New York State Museum, Annual Report 50, v. 1, p.21–31.

Merrill, F.J.H., Darton, N. H., Hollick, A., Salisbury, R. D., Dodge, R. E., Willis, B., and Pressey, H. A., 1902, Description of the New York City District: U.S. Geological Survey Geologic Atlas, Folio 83, 19 p., 2 sheets.

Moore, R. C., Lalicker, C. G., and Fischer, A. G., 1952, Invertebrate fossils: New York, McGraw-Hill, 766 p. (see especially p. 587–594, 614-648.)

Mose, D. G., and Hayes, J., 1975, Avalonian igneous activity in the Manhattan Prong, southeastern New York: Geological Society of America Bulletin, v. 86, p. 929–932.

New York City, 1936, City of New York Building Code.

——, 1942, Laws, rules, regulations, etc., applicable to the erection, construction, maintenance, and alteration of structures and buildings in the City of New York: New York City Administrative Code, Title C, v. I, Chapter 26.

——, 1970, Building code of the City of New York, Chapter 26 of the Administrative Code, as amended: New York, Van Nostrand-Reinhold Company, p. 266–356.

——, 1976, Official directory (Bicentennial Edition): The City Record, p. 2–9, special section.

New York City Board of Water Supply, 1936, City Tunnel No. 2 record of construction 1928–35: sheets 14–25 in set of 35.

——, 1950, Origin and achievements of the Board of Water Supply: 115 p.

——, 1963, Catskill aqueduct City Tunnel No. 1: Drilling contracts 488 and 495, location maps, and cross sections.

——, 1975, City Tunnel no. 3, stage 1, location maps and geology charts.

New York City Division of Design, Department of Borough Works, 1940, Rock data map of Manhattan: Borough of Manhattan.

New York State Department of Health, 1961, Water pollution control board: New York City Water Survey Series Reports 1–6, 9.

New York State Museum and Science Service, 1971, Geologic map of New York, 1970: New York State Museum and Science Service, Map and Chart Series, no. 15, 6 sheets.

Nuttli, O. W., 1973, Seismic wave attenuation and magnitude relations in eastern North America: Journal of Geophysical Research, v. 78, no. 5, p. 876–885.

Ohan, A. A., Knieshy, A., and Kaarsberg, E., 1975, Geological aspects of Staten Island, New York: New York State Geological Association Guidebook, 47th Annual Meeting, p. 195–212.

Pellegrini, T. L., 1975, Lower Paleozoic metamorphic stratigraphy of the Mamaroneck area, New York: New York State Geological Association Guidebook, 47th Annual Meeting, p. 179–193.

——1977, Geologic map of the Mamaroneck quadrangle, New York-Connecticut: New York State Museum and Science Service, Geological Survey Map and Chart Series 29.

Perlmutter, N. M., and Arnow, T., 1953, Ground-water in Bronx, New York, and Richmond Counties, with summary data on Kings and Queens Counties, New York City, New York: New York State Department of Conservation, Water Power and Control Commission Bulletin GW-32, 86 p.

Perlmutter, N. M., and Crandell, H. C., 1959, Geology and ground water supplies of the south shore beaches of Long Island, New York: New York Academy of Science Annals, v. 80, Art. 4, p. 1060–1076.

Prucha, J. J., 1956, Stratigraphic relationships of the metamorphic rocks in southeastern New York: American Journal of Science, v. 254, no. 11, p. 672–684.

——1959, Field relations bearing on the age of the New York City Group of the Manhattan Prong: New York Academy of Science Annals, v. 80, art. 4, p. 1159–1169.

Ratcliffe, N. M., and Knowles, R. R., 1969, Fossil evidence from the "Manhattan Schist-Inwood Marble" sequence at Verplanck, New York [abs]: Geological Society of America Special Paper 121, p. 368.

Ratcliffe, N. M., and Zartman, R. E., 1976, Stratigraphy, isotopic ages, and deformational history of basement and cover rocks of the Berkshire massif, southwestern Massachusetts: *in* Page, L. R., Contributions to the stratigraphy at New England. Geological Society of America Memoir 148, p. 373–412.

Rodgers, J., 1970, The tectonics of the Appalachians: New York, Interscience, 271 p. (see especially p. 12–28, 66–82, 91–114, and 203–219.)

Sanborn, J. F., 1950, Engineering geology in the design and construction of tunnels, *in* Paige, Sidney, chmn., Application of geology to engineering practice: Geological Society of America, Berkey volume, p. 45–81.

Sanko, P., 1975, Sand mining in New York Harbor, MESA New York Bight Atlas Monograph 21: Albany, N.Y., New York Sea Grant Institute, p. 23–26.

Schlee, J., 1975, Sand and gravel distribution in the Bight, MESA New York Bight Atlas Monograph 21: Albany, N.Y., New York Sea Grant Institute, p. 7–21.

Schuberth, C. J., 1968, The geology of New York City and environs: Garden City, N.Y., The Natural History Press, 304 p.

Seyfert, C. K., and Leveson, D. J., 1968, Structure and petrology of Pelham Bay Park: New York State Geological Association Guidebook, 40th Annual Meeting, p. 175–195.

Swarzenski, W. V., 1959, Ground-water supplies in Pleistocene and Cretaceous deposits of northwestern Nassau County, New York: Annals of the New York Academy of Science Annals, v. 80, Art. 4, p. 1077–1091.

U.S. Environmental Science Services Administration, Coast and Geodetic Survey, 1969, United States earthquakes, 1967: Washington, D.C., Government Printing Office, p. 9–11.

U.S. Office of the Federal Register, 1980, Seismic and geologic siting criteria for nuclear power plants, Appendix A *of* Part 100—Reactor site criteria, *in* code of Federal Regulations, [Title] 10, Energy, Parts 0 to 199. Revised as of January 1, 1980 ***: Washington, D.C., U.S. Government Printing Office.

Veatch, A. C., Slichter, C. S., Bowman, I., Crosby, W. O., and Horton, R. E., 1906, Underground water resources of Long Island, New York: U.S. Geological Survey Professional Paper 44, 394 p.

Weidner, C. H., 1974, Water for a city: New Brunswick, N.J., Rutgers University Press, 323 p.

Yasso, W. E., and Hartman, E. M., 1976, Beach forms and coastal processes, MESA New York Bight Atlas Monograph 11: Albany, N.Y., New York Sea Grant Institute, 50 p.

Zen, E-An, 1968, Nature of the Ordovician orogeny in the Taconic area, *in* Zen, E-An, White, W. S., Hadley, J. B., and Thompson, J. B., Jr., eds., Studies of Appalachian geology, northern and maritime: New York, Interscience, p. 129–139.

Ziegler, Victor, 1911, The Ravenswood Granodiorite: New York Academy of Sciences Annals, v. 20, p. 1–10.

Manuscript Received by the Society May 11, 1982
Manuscript Accepted June 1, 1982

Printed in U.S.A.

Geological Society of America
Reviews in Engineering Geology, Volume V
1982

Toronto's subsurface geology

Owen L. White
Ontario Geological Survey
Ministry of Natural Resources

ABSTRACT

The subsurface geology in the Toronto area, in which much underground construction has taken place in the past 30 years, is, in general, fairly simple, consisting of almost flat-lying Ordovician sediments overlaid by a variable thickness of Quaternary drift deposits.

The Ordovician rocks provide an interbedded sequence of shales, siltstones and limestones; and the Quaternary deposits, which range in age from Illinoian to Late Wisconsinan, consist of several tills interbedded with water-bearing sands and lacustrine clays and silts.

Construction difficulties arising from the local geological conditions are not great, but unexpected encounters with excess ground water do occur. The presence in the bedrock of high horizontal stresses at shallow depths can cause difficulties, especially to the completed structure, unless the stress condition is recognized, designs are modified, and construction procedures are adapted to the unusual stress environment.

INTRODUCTION

When the Geological Society of America first met in an Annual Conference in Toronto in 1953, the first phase of the construction of the subway system of the Toronto Transit Commission was about to be completed. When the G.S.A. again met in Toronto in 1978, what may be the final phase of the system was in its concluding stages. The intervening 25 years saw the construction of 44 km of subway within a system covering 52 km. Although many other underground projects have been constructed in Toronto and the surrounding region in these 25 years, the subway remains the major project of underground construction in the area.

THE GEOLOGY OF THE TORONTO AREA

In general, the geology of the Toronto area is fairly simple and straightforward, consisting of Ordovician sedimentary rocks both flat-lying and tectonically undisturbed, and overlaid by a succession of glacial deposits that may be as thin as a few meters or as thick as 100 m or more (Table 1). However, complexities abound, particularly within the glacial deposits, and it is to these complexities that some attention will be given in this paper.

The surface configuration of Toronto directly reflects the late glacial and postglacial history of the area. A drumlinized till plain left by the last advance of the ice forms the surface of the greater part of Metropolitan Toronto and the surrounding area. Part of this till plain was inundated by the waters of glacial Lake Iroquois while the lake stood some 55 m above the present level of Lake Ontario. These waters considerably modified the original surface, formed a well-defined shoreline bluff, and deposited significant thicknesses of deep water and near shore sediments over the eroded glacial materials. Channels, formed by waters draining the land surface to the north of Lake Iroquois, were deepened in later years as the waters of the lake receded and as Lake Ontario became established. The deeply incised, north-south valleys of the Humber and Don Rivers considerably affected the pattern of development of Toronto in its early years, directing its development northwards rather than to the east and west along the lakeshore (Taylor, 1936). A map of the Quaternary geology of the Toronto

TABLE 1. SIGNIFICANT GEOLOGIC UNITS IN THE TORONTO AREA

Period	Stage/Substage	Formation or Unit	Remarks
Quaternary	Recent		
	Late Wisconsinan	Lake Iroquois Deposits	Sands up to 4 m thick deposited on eroded till surface below the Iroquois bluff.
		Lake Peel Deposits	Thin lacustrine veneer over parts of the Halton Till plain
		Halton Till	Clayey silt to sandy silt till up to 15 m thick. Widespread occurrence at the surface to the north of the L. Iroquois shoreline. Usually underlaid by extensive deposits of sand and silt.
		Wentworth/ Leaside Till?	Dense sandy till. Occurs in northern part of Toronto. Geographic distribution not well know.
	Middle Wisconsinan	Thorncliffe Fm	Interbedded sands, and silts interfingered with two till sheets in the Scarborough area. Not present in downtown area.
	Early Wisconsinan	Sunnybrook Drift Sunnybrook Till	Dark grey, hard clayey silt till up to 20 m thick. Often associated with underlying varved clays.
		Pottery Road Fm.	Channel sands deposited in valleys cut into the Scarborough Formation.
		Scarborough Fm.	Sands and clays 6-7 m thick in downtown area.
	Sangamonian	Don Formation	Dense, water bearing sands up to 5 m thick in downtown Toronto.
	Illinoian	York Drift York Till	Very hard, bouldery, clayey silt till - up to 5 m thick.
Ordovician	Upper	Queenston Fm	Red shale, siltstone - occurs to the west of Metro Toronto.
		Georgian Bay Fm.	Grey shale, siltstones, limestone - forms the bedrock of Metro Toronto
		Whitby Fm.	Black and grey shales - occurs to the east of Metro Toronto.

area was compiled recently for publication by the Ontario Geological Survey (Sharpe, 1980).

BEDROCK GEOLOGY

Metropolitan Toronto is almost exclusively underlaid by strata of the Ordovician Georgian Bay Formation, which are encountered in fairly shallow excavations in downtown Toronto and to the west of Metro in the City of Mississauga (Regional Municipality of Peel). Farther west, the red shales of the Queenston Formation, which overlie the Georgian Bay Formation, outcrop in several localities

and likewise, are often encountered in shallow excavations. To the east of Metro, grey and black shales of the Whitby Formation which underlies the Georgian Bay Formation form the bedrock and have been encountered in recent deep tunneling projects (Liberty, 1969; Hewitt, 1972).

The Georgian Bay Formation consists of a variety of interbedded shales, siltstones and limestones, frequently thinly bedded and rarely with beds thicker than 30 cm. The formation dips regionally to the southwest at about 4 to 6 m per kilometer but in the Toronto area, the beds dip at the same gradient, but to the south. The beds rarely show any signs of true tectonic disturbance, but the recording by White and others (1974) of folded and faulted zones in the upper few meters at 17 bedrock exposures in the Toronto-Hamilton area suggested the existence of high horizontal residual stresses. In recent years, measurements in many rock cuts and tunnels in and around Metropolitan Toronto have shown that high horizontal stresses (for example, Franklin and Hungr, 1978) do exist and are of significance in the design and construction of facilities in bedrock at shallow depths.

QUATERNARY GEOLOGY

Within the Toronto area, five distinct tills are recognized, interbedded with a variety of interglacial and interstadial fluvial and lacustrine deposits. In the downtown area, only two tills have been encountered.

The general stratigraphic sequence occurring in the Toronto area is as follows. The oldest till is the York Till, a very hard, bluish grey, bouldery, clayey silt of probable Illinoian age. It occurs in downtown Toronto directly overlying the Georgian Bay Formation and has been recognized in deep valley sections both to the east and west of downtown. The maximum thickness reported is in the order of 5 m, and this, together with its limited distribution, has meant that the York Till has had little effect on underground construction except to provide more difficult excavation conditions when a so-called 'hardpan' zone is encountered.

Throughout most of the downtown area, the York Till is overlaid by about 3 to 5 m of hard disturbed lacustrine clay, varved in places (water content, 5%; liquid limit, 34; plastic limit, 19) (Lajtai, 1969; Walker, 1978). The York Till and the lacustrine clay are referred to together as the York Drift (Lajtai, 1969).

Overlying the York Drift are the Don Beds of the Don Formation of Sangamonian age. Again present over much of the downtown area, they are dense (Standard Penetration Test—typical blow count N = 80), water-bearing sands up to 5 m in thickness which have become well known to contractors working in the area. Although still carrying considerable water (Walker, 1978), they give much less trouble than in the days of the first subway construction. The cool climate sands and clays of the Scarborough Beds, which marked the onset of the Wisconsinan and were extensively reported elsewhere at up to 50 m thick (Karrow, 1969), are neither as widespread nor as thick in the downtown area. They were encountered in thicknesses up to 6 to 7 m in the first subway excavations but only to a minor extent in the University Avenue subway.

The Sunnybrook Till is the oldest of the Wisconsinan tills in the area but essentially the youngest till in the downtown area. Although generally seen downtown as a hard, clayey silt (Lajtai, 1969; Walker, 1978), lithological variations are known. Up to 20 m thick, the till has been widely encountered in all three subway excavations and in numerous building excavations. The till is associated with overlying glaciofluvial sediments and underlying varved clays and is characterized by its dark grey color and a very low calcite content.

The Thorncliffe Formation overlies the Sunnybrook Till and although it is seen as a series of interbedded sands and silts interfingered with two till sheets in the Scarborough area, the Thorncliffe Formation is not generally recognized in the downtown area. Most of the post-Sunnybrook materials have either been removed by erosion or, perhaps, in some areas, were never deposited. Over what is presumed to be an eroded surface, up to 4 m of sands and clays have been deposited by the waters of Lake Iroquois.

The youngest till in the area, the Halton Till, essentially only occurs above the shoreline of Lake Iroquois and, except for veneers of minor lacustrine deposits, is virtually the surface material over much of Metropolitan Toronto and the surrounding municipalities. The Halton Till is basically a silt till with variations from a clayey silt to a sandy silt. It commonly occurs in thicknesses up to 10 to 15 m and is usually underlaid by extensive sand deposits. These sands are commonly encountered by deep excavations and tunnels and provide the settings of many special construction activities.

UNDERGROUND IN TORONTO

It is in the subsurface environment that has just been described that the 52 km subway of the Toronto Transit Commission has been constructed since 1949. This has resulted in 33.9 km of cut and cover construction, 11.5 km of open cut, 5.5 km of tunneling, and 1.2 km of above ground and bridge construction (Figure 1).

Numerous high rise buildings have risen in the downtown core. Associated with these are not only the below ground floors and multi-level parking garages but also the pedestrian and shopping malls that will soon allow the pedestrian to travel some 1150 m north from the Union Station to the Eaton Centre without encountering the street level environment (Figure 2).

Hidden from everyday sight, but, never-the-less, very important to the life of the city, are the very extensive water supply and sewer systems and their associated intake and outfall tunnels constructed in the shale out under Lake Ontario (Figure 1).

The disposal of the spoil from all these activities conceivably could have presented a major problem of disposal, but the imaginative efforts of the Toronto Harbour Commission led to the use of the excavated material in the construction of a 5.8 km long spit or breakwater out into Lake Ontario to form an Outer Harbour but which now may be used as a marina and for other recreational activities.

Major tunnel construction has not been confined to either downtown Toronto or even Metro Toronto but has also proceeded and is proceeding at a considerable rate in surrounding areas. Service tunnels to the west of Toronto are for a large part constructed in bedrock but those to the north and the east are mostly in drift. Within the Regional Municipalities of York and Durham, a 10 year program of the Ministry of the Environment will see the construction of over 140 km of sewers through tunneling and deep construction.

The passing years have also seen major changes in tunneling techniques in the area. Up to the early 1970's, drill and blast techniques were used in most tunneling operations in bedrock, but since then, the use of continuous boring machines has become quite standard. Rock bolts and steel sets are the usual rock support systems, but since the mid 1970's, shotcrete has become more widely used. Most of the tunnels constructed in recent years have been lined with concrete for service reasons. Tunneling through drift usually involves shields and operations under compressed air.

Although not in Metro Toronto or in the environs considered above, Ontario Hydro has several major underground electric power production projects underway or planned, particularly to the east of the Metropolitan area.

Looking into the future, there are proposals for the construction of underground storage space behind the Niagara Escarpment and for the mining of aggregate below Lake Ontario and the subsequent use of the excavated space for municipal waste storage (Guillet, 1978).

Underground construction in the Toronto area has, in recent years, been of considerable magnitude, and although there may now be a period of slow growth, major projects on the horizon promise to keep knowledge of the subsurface and underground construction experience on the increase.

GEOLOGICAL FACTORS AFFECTING CONSTRUCTION IN BEDROCK

The flat-lying, thinly bedded sediments of the Toronto area have generally given little difficulty with regular, grav-

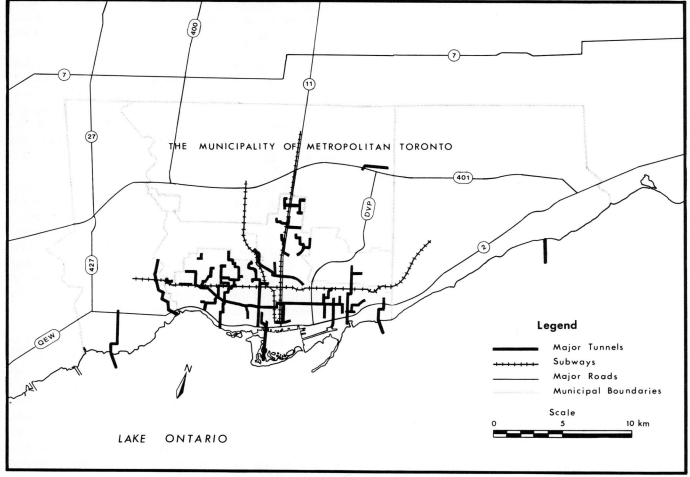

Figure 1. Major Subsurface Construction Projects in Metropolitan Toronto.

ity foundations. Bearing pressures as high as 7.2 MPa have been used for caissons to bedrock (Robinsky and Morton, 1973). (Compare this figure with the foundation bearing stress of 0.6 MPa for the CN Tower, Robinsky and Morton, 1973). The upper 2 or 3 m of the bedrock are often weathered and are usually removed if construction is to be placed onto bedrock. Clay filled joints may extend deeper and may have to be watched for. A greater problem is the rapid deterioration which occurs when the rock is exposed to the atmosphere. If a final dimension is required for the rock excavation, the newly exposed rock surface must usually be coated with a bituminous or cement coating within a few hours of its opening.

Of more concern is the presence of high horizontal residual stresses which are great enough to have caused damage to man-made structures and to have produced numerous postglacial folds and faults (White and others, 1974). Palmer and Lo (1976) measured compressive stresses up to 14.5 MPa at a depth of 18 m in a roof strut of a tunnel under the Welland Canal at Thorold, 65 km south of Toronto, and Franklin and Hungr (1978) estimated ground

stresses at 13 MPa with inward movements of up to 50 mm at a sewer trench site at Hamilton, 65 km southwest of Toronto. To the east of Toronto, horizontal stresses of 6 MPa have been reported at 8.8 to 15.3 m below the rock surface in both the Georgian Bay and Whitby Formations (Lo and Morton, 1976).

Repairs to damaged structures and remedial measures have been costly (Jones, 1973), but when high stresses are suspected, changes in design and in construction schedules can overcome potential problems.

GEOLOGICAL FACTORS AFFECTING CONSTRUCTION IN DRIFT

The tills of the area are generally dense to very dense, reflecting a high degree of overconsolidation (White, 1961) and, usually, good foundation conditions. The dense tills are sometimes difficult to excavate, particularly the tills which directly overlie the bedrock. Boulders are also sources of difficulties, especially during tunneling. An investigation technique to truly characterize the boulder content of

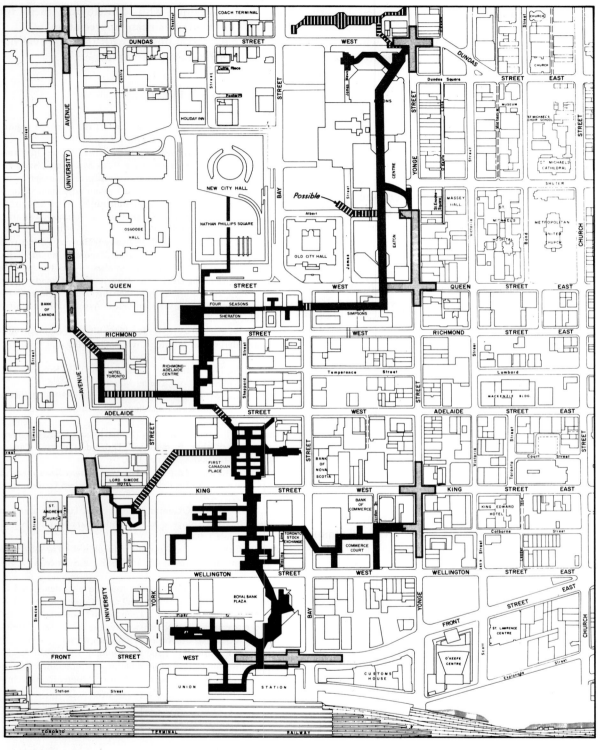

**DOWNTOWN TORONTO
UNDERGROUND PEDESTRIAN
MALL SYSTEM**

FIGURE 2

FROM PLANS BY
CITY OF TORONTO PLANNING AND
DEVELOPMENT DEPARTMENT

1980

tills would, it is certain, be greatly appreciated by sub-surface contractors.

In the discussion of geological factors which affect construction activities in the drift of the Toronto area, the dominant word is WATER!

The water content of many units within the drift may be quite low; for example, many tills have natural moisture contents well below their plastic limits, but it is the unexpected occurrence of water that causes so many construction difficulties.

Artesian conditions, perched water tables, irregular contacts with interstadial sands, lenticular sand bodies within till sheets, and the not infrequent encounters with buried stream channels all contribute their own particular problems. Circumstances such as these have led to the necessity of tunneling with compressed air on many occasions.

Buried stream channels may have one of several origins. Buried bedrock valleys are generally oriented north-south, but the ephemeral buried valleys within the drift sheet are less well organized and are often unexpectedly encountered. Buried valleys that produce real problems are those which have been obliterated through urbanization, but which are generous with their water when intersected. The Ontario Geological Survey has recently started to assemble the records of these buried channels, which have been collected over the years by several interested persons and organizations.

In recent months, one construction project intercepted sands which were a major supply aquifer for a nearby rural community.

THE FUTURE

Despite the early beginings of urban geological mapping in Toronto by the late Professor Coleman (1932) and despite the existence of a geological advisory committee to the Toronto Transit Commission and the detailed recording of subsurface materials (Legget and Shriever, 1960) during the initial subway construction, the interest in mapping and recording the subsurface geological and geotechnical data has been intermittent by both government and university. Despite this situation, some individuals have kept extensive records, which are now proving to be very useful.

Although there have been innumerable lost opportunities, new attitudes and interests in government and academic circles promise an increase in activity in this area.

ACKNOWLEDGMENTS

This paper should be considered a "joint venture" for I owe much to many discussions with friends and colleagues in construction, consulting, academia, and government. To each and everyone who contributed their time and thoughts, I extend my sincere appreciation.

The paper is published with the approval of the Director, Ontario Geological Survey.

REFERENCES CITED

Coleman, A. P., 1932, The Pleistocene of the Toronto region: Ontario Department of Mines, v. 41, pt. 7, 69 p.

Franklin, J. A., and Hungr, O., 1978, Rock stresses in Canada. Their relevance to engineering projects: Rock Mechanics, Supp. 6, p. 25–46.

Guillet, G. R., 1978, Urban minerals—resources in jeopardy or—how to turn a difficult economic climate to your advantage: Canadian Institute of Mining and Metallurgy Bulletin, v. 71, no. 794, p. 101–106.

Hewitt, D. F., 1972, Paleozoic geology of Southern Ontario: Ontario Division of Mines, GR 105, 18 p.

Jones, T. B., 1973, How one driller solved Thorold Tunnel rock squeeze problem: Engineering and Contract Record, v. 86, no. 9, p. 24–26.

Karrow, P. F., 1969, Stratigraphic studies in the Toronto Pleistocene: Proceedings of the Geological Association of Canada, v. 20, p. 4–16.

Lajtai, E. Z., 1969, Stratigraphy of the University Subway, Toronto, Canada: Proceedings of the Geological Association of Canada, v. 20, p. 17–23.

Legget, R. F., and Shriever, W. R., 1960, Site investigations for Canada's first underground railway: Civil Engineering and Public Works Review, v. 55, no. 642, p. 73–79.

Liberty, B. A., 1969, Paleozoic geology of the Lake Simcoe area, Ontario: Geological Survey of Canada, Memoir 355, 201 p.

Lo, K. Y., and Morton, J. D., 1976, Tunnels in bedded rock with high horizontal stresses: Canadian Geotechnical Journal, v. 13, p. 216–230.

Palmer, J. H. L., and Lo, K. Y., 1976, In situ stress measurements in some near-surface rock formations—Thorold, Ontario: Canadian Geotechnical Journal, v. 13, no. 1, p. 1–7.

Robinsky, E. I., and Morton, J. D., 1973, Foundation investigation for CN Tower, Toronto: Preprints 26th Canadian Geotechnical Conference, p. 237–245.

Sharpe, D. R., 1980, Quaternary geology of Toronto and surrounding area: Ontario Geological Survey Preliminary Map P.2204, Geological Series, Scale 1:100,000.

Taylor, Griffith, 1936, Topographic control in the Toronto region: Canadian Journal of Economics and Political Science, v. 2, no. 4, Nov. 1936, p. 1–19.

Walker, B. P., 1978, Short caissons founded on a dewatered sand layer: Preprints 31st, Canadian Geotechnical Conference, p. 8.1.2–8.1.24.

White, O. L., 1961, The application of soil consolidation tests to the determination of Wisconsin ice thicknesses in the Toronto region: (M.A.Sc Thesis), University of Toronto, 95 p.

White, O. L., Karrow, P. F., and MacDonald, J. R., 1974, Residual stress relief phenomena in Southern Ontario: Proceedings, Canadian Symposium on Rock Mechanics, 9th, Montreal, December 1973, p. 323–348.

Manuscript Accepted by the Society May 24, 1982

Geological Society of America
Reviews in Engineering Geology, Volume V
1982

Engineering geology of the Twin Cities area, Minnesota

Matt Walton, Director
Minnesota Geological Survey
1633 Eustis St.
St. Paul, Minnesota 55108

ABSTRACT

Effective geologic and geotechnical mapping in cities requires abundant subsurface data. Large data resources exist in the records of public agencies in the Twin Cities in the form of engineering test boring logs. An efficient system for acquiring and compiling these data aided by computer was developed and used to compile a number of geotechnical maps and reports on the geology, hydrology, engineering characteristics, and construction materials resources of the area. Much new information was obtained on the subsurface continuity and stratigraphy of complex Quaternary deposits, on the buried rock surface topography, and on the geology of bedrock formations.

INTRODUCTION

The simplest geology becomes complex if examined in enough detail. Urban geology is always complex, because as cities evolve there is always need for increasing levels of detail. This is a need geologists have been slow to meet. Urban geology tends to be site-specific. The descriptions of geology most meaningful to geologists commonly do not translate directly into terms and categories meaningful to engineers and planners, and broader stratigraphic and tectonic questions, which are of interest to geologists, tend to seem irrelevant to engineers and planners. Because cities do not lend themselves to the conventional pursuits of field geology, it is probably fair to say that cities tend to lack interest as places to "do geology," and many cities, which are mapped adequately in earlier times on a regional level of detail, are poorly mapped in the terms and details needed for modern development. By and large, geologic institutions and agencies have not produced the hard-copy geologic products needed by urban planners at the point in the planning process when they are needed, which is early in the process as a foundation for planning.

That this state of affairs is now changing is in large part due to the inspiration and guiding genius of Robert Leggett (1973). His vision of the role of geology in cities, expressed with persistent and persuasive grace over the years, has awakened the geologic profession to the chal- lenge of cities and engaged the interest of many urban planners. His work has shown the way, and the work reported here was a deliberate attempt to follow the lead of Robert Legget with a program and methodology for urban geology.

TWIN CITIES PROJECT

In 1974 the Minnesota Geological Survey (MGS) began discussing an urban geology pilot project with the U.S. Geological Survey (USGS). At that time, the U.S. Department of Transportation (DOT) was interested in the feasibility of underground transportation systems in American cities. DOT was also aware of the scarcity of subsurface geotechnical data sufficient to evaluate in depth the applications of new tunneling technology to mass transit systems for most major U.S. cities. Thus, the ingredients of a pilot program of urban engineering geology oriented toward future underground transportation systems were brought together.

To simply intensify the application of conventional geologic mapping methods to the Twin Cities of St. Paul and Minneapolis promised to produce little new information relevant to the problem. As with most of Minnesota, the bedrock geology of the metropolitan area is buried under a pervasive mantle of glacial drift, as much as several hundred feet thick, with very few outcrops of bedrock beyond the bluffs along the Mississippi River. Only a massive infusion of subsurface data could improve existing mapping. The glacial drift itself is a major factor in all engineering and land-use considerations, and it comprises more than 30 lithostratigraphic units which cannot be elucidated without subsurface information. But even without the problem of deep, complex overburden, most cities probably have little to gain from simply putting more effort into surface mapping, because so much of the surface has been disturbed and obscured by the works of man, and so much of what concerns the engineer and planner is subsurface.

Large numbers of test borings are constantly being made in cities for public works, utilities and industry. Questions of access to these data, their usefulness, and their coverage needed to be resolved. With aid from the State Planning Agency, the MGS was already engaged in collecting logs provided voluntarily by water well drillers in the metropolitan area (at that time there was no law requiring well drillers in Minnesota to submit logs). Logs with significant geologic information were being copied from drillers' files by an MGS team with a portable copier, the addresses of the wells were plotted on maps, and the locations were field checked (a very necessary step) and digitized. The logs were then interpreted geologically and computer coded for machine processing. It was proposed to adapt this program to the collection of engineering test borings if enough were available on a voluntary basis from public agencies and private industry. MGS coding forms for wells and test borings are reproduced in Figure 1 (a, b, c, d, e, f). Codes are described by Holtzman and Wahl (1979).

Aided by a grant from the USGS, an inventory was made of the subsurface data base available in the Twin Cities urban area. The results of the inventory exceeded expectations (Olsen and others, 1975). There were 186,215 test boring logs found in the archives of more than 60 agencies involved in public works in various units of state, county, and municipal government in the metropolitan area. The plan was to inventory the data in the public domain first and then to investigate the availability of proprietary data in industry. When it became evident that enough data were available in the public domain to saturate the data-gathering capacity, no further effort to tap private sources was expended. No doubt additional data would be available if industry was willing to pool geotechnical data from completed projects. If such arrangements were set up in cities, the resulting data base would undoubtedly be of great practical value.

DOT identified a core area in the Twin Cities of primary interest for underground transportation systems, and MGS and USGS undertook a joint project of mapping and geotechnical and hydrogeological analysis based on logs of test borings supplemented by considerable test data on the engineering properties of samples of soils and rock that accompanied many of the logs. The project area, which was mapped at a scale of 1:24,000, is shown on Figure 2. The division of tasks between MGS and USGS was as follows. MGS collected, interpreted, and computer coded the logs of test borings and prepared geologic maps and sections. The St. Paul regional office of USGS compiled and interpreted hydrologic data and produced a series of hydrogeologic maps; it also compiled data on existing tunnels in the area. The results have been published by USGS as Map I-1157 (Norvitch and Walton, eds., 1979).

This publication consists of 7 sheets or plates:

1. *Introduction and data base,* 1:24,000, by Bruce A. Bloomgren, Bruce M. Olsen, and James R. Poppe, MGS. The locations and types of test borings and other data used in the project are shown, and a text describes the sources and methods of data collection and processing.

2. *Surficial geology,* 1:24,000, John H. Mossler and Matt S. Walton, MGS. The Quaternary deposits appearing on the surface are classified and mapped. Bedrock outcrops are shown. A text describes the Quaternary geologic history and the engineering characteristics of the Quaternary geologic units, and a table gives engineering soil classifications and test data for these units.

3. *Bedrock geology,* 1:24,000, by Bruce A. Bloomgren, Bruce M. Olsen, and Matt S. Walton, MGS. The bedrock geology is mapped, and the buried topography of the bedrock surface is shown by contours. A text describes the bedrock geology and its engineering characteristics, and tables give geotechnical test data.

4. *Thickness of drift,* 1:24,000, by Bruce A. Bloomgren and James R. Poppe, MGS. The thickness of unconsolidated Quaternary deposits overlying bedrock is shown by isopach contours.

5. *Geologic sections and engineering characteristics,* MGS. Five geologic sections are shown with a table describing the engineering and land-use characteristics of all Quaternary geologic units.

6. *Hydrogeologic setting,* by Eric L. Madsen and Ralph F. Norvitch, USGS. Four maps, scale 1:48,000, show configuration of the water table in surficial deposits, potentiometric surface of water in the St. Peter aquifer, structure contours on the top of the St. Peter Sandstone, and hydrostatic head in relation to the top of the St. Peter Sandstone. A generalized hydrogeologic section of the Twin Cities area is also shown.

7. *Hydraulic properties and tunneling constraints,* by Eric L. Madsen and Ralph F. Norvitch, USGS. Two maps, scale 1:48,000, show information on dewatering for tunnel construction in the St. Peter Sandstone, flood limits along the Mississippi River, and the locations of tunnels and caves in the St. Peter Sandstone. Tables show the

hydraulic characteristics of bedrock units, data on tunnels in the Twin Cities area, and factors relating to tunnel construction.

The computerized data base acquired to produce these products is in itself a valuable product, now in constant use and undergoing steady expansion. The target of the initial data acquisition campaign was to compile a network of 25 test boring logs per km^2 completed to bedrock throughout the 200 km^2 study area, for an average data point spacing of 200 m, and a total of 5,000 logs of good quality. This norm was readily achieved or exceeded in areas of industrial and commercial activity and along arterial streets and freeways. It was not fully attainable in older residential areas, but these areas have less construction activity. The data are thus most abundant where most needed. Considerable redundancy was allowed in the log acquisition process in order to cross check and select the most representative data. In all about 20,000 test boring logs were copied with related location documents, which are maintained in paper files. Of these about 4,000 logs were selected, located, classified, correlated, coded and entered into the computer, supplemented with about 500 water well logs. Considerable diversity was found among systems for storage and retrieval of site-exploration data. Logs may be filed by unique serial number, project title with serial numbers within the project, geographic coordinates, and field engineer's notebook numbers. Generally, the exact locations of logs are tied to project drawings or site plans, and in some cases, there were problems finding recoverable reference coordinates or bench marks into which to tie these documents. The primary field technique to be learned in order to do this kind of geology is how to use the archives of a variety of data sources.

Once the logs and location drawings are in hand, the most critical problem is the translation of engineering log descriptions, blow counts, sample analyses and other data reported in the logs into a geologic classification of coherent lithostratigraphic units. Without intimate direct field experience with the local geology as a basis for correlating and classifying test boring data, it is doubtful that successful geologic mapping could be accomplished over a complex area solely on the basis of logs obtained from others. The urban geologist will continue to need to do intensive field work on all available exposures, even if his major sources of data are buried in filing cabinets.

RESULTS

The results of the Twin Cities Project have been twofold. The successful development of a technique for mapping the geology of the metropolitan area rapidly with significantly greater accuracy, detail and an added subsurface dimension has produced products that are more useful

and has led to demands for further work. Secondly, substantial additions have been made to knowledge of the geology of the area. New projects which have followed from the initial effort include: the compilation of structure contour and isopach maps (1:100,000 scale) for the nine major hydrogeologic units in the Twin Cities metropolitan area (Jirsa, 1981) to be used by USGS for a hydrologic model of the area; expansion of engineering geologic mapping to cover all of the Twin Cities urban area within the outer belt interstate highway system at a scale of 1:48,000 (Figure 2) (Walton, ed., in preparation); a survey of the construction material resources of the metropolitan area for the Metropolitan Council (Meyer and Bloomgren, in preparation); and a detailed analysis of the geologic factors affecting the planning of a unique industrial-commercial development known as the St. Paul Energy Park (Figure 2) (Walton, Jirsa, and Kanivetsky, 1981). The latter project was mapped at a scale of 1:6,000, and special attention was given to the possibility of constructing an Aquifer Thermal Energy Storage (ATES) system as a major component of the advanced energy concepts embodied in the Park. The information gained from this work has also allowed us to deal confidently with a number of problems relating to waste management in the Twin Cities area.

Geologically, in its broad outlines, the Twin Cities area is relatively simple. An almost undeformed and completely unmetamorphosed sequence of Lower Paleozoic sedimentary formations forms a broad, shallow artesian basin centered beneath the Twin Cities. These almost horizontal, well-stratified formations are overlain by an almost unbroken blanket of glacial drift. With few exceptions, exposures of bedrock are confined to bluffs along the incised valleys of the Mississippi, Minnesota, and St. Croix Rivers. This simple stratigraphic and structural framework is greatly complicated from the geotechnical point of view by two factors. First, the bedrock surface beneath the drift and other Quaternary deposits is cut by an elaborate network of preglacial and englacial drainageways, many of which have little or no expression in present topography and drainage (Figure 3). The major buried valleys are several times larger than the present major river valleys, and the topographic relief of the bedrock surface is several times greater than present relief. Secondly, the glacial drift and other Quaternary deposits are highly complex. There are about 35 mapped lithostratigraphic units in the metropolitan area.

Systematic collection and processing of subsurface data has enabled us to map the interface between the bedrock geology and the Quaternary geology in far greater detail than hitherto was possible. As an example, in Figure 3, the axes of buried bedrock channels are shown in a connected network covering the entire metropolitan area for the first time. Interfluves in the area commonly reach altitudes of 900 ft. to 1,000 ft. above MSL. The major buried valleys are incised to altitudes of less than 550 ft. By com-

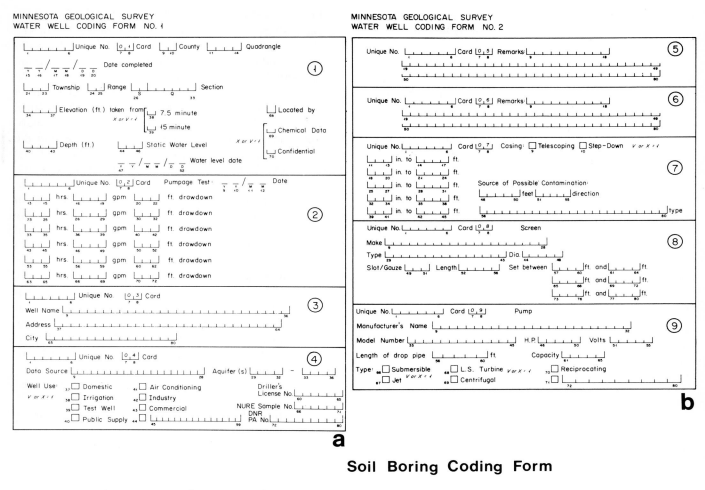

a

b

Soil Boring Coding Form

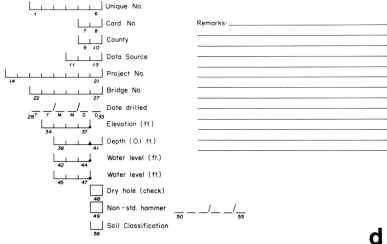

d

Figure 1. (This and facing page) Minnesota Geological Survey coding forms for subsurface data: a. Water well coding form No. 1. b. Water well coding form No. 2. c. Water well coding form No. 3. d. Soil boring coding form No. 1. e. Soil boring coding form No. 2. f. Water chemistry coding form.

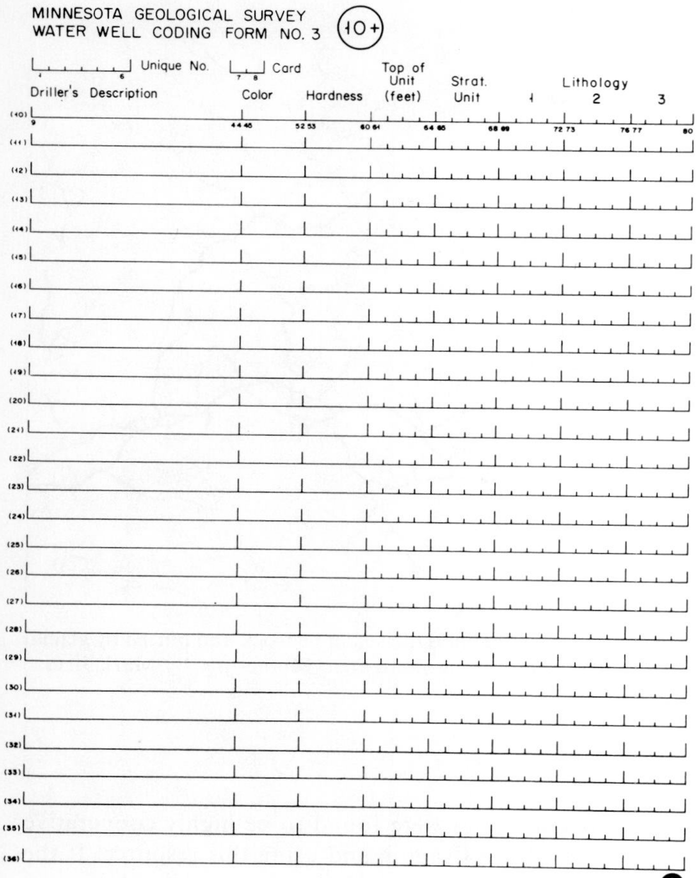

MINNESOTA GEOLOGICAL SURVEY
WATER WELL CODING FORM NO. 3 (10+)

Water - Chemistry Coding Form

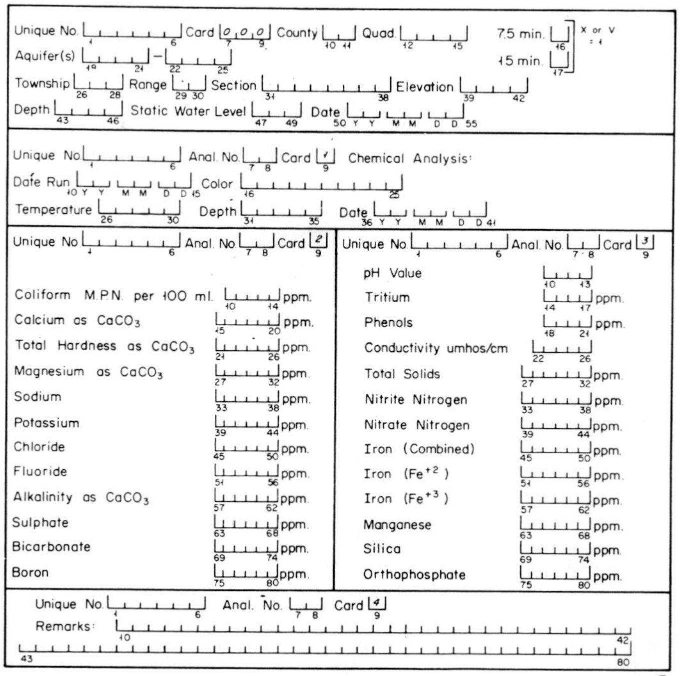

c

f

Soil Boring Coding Form

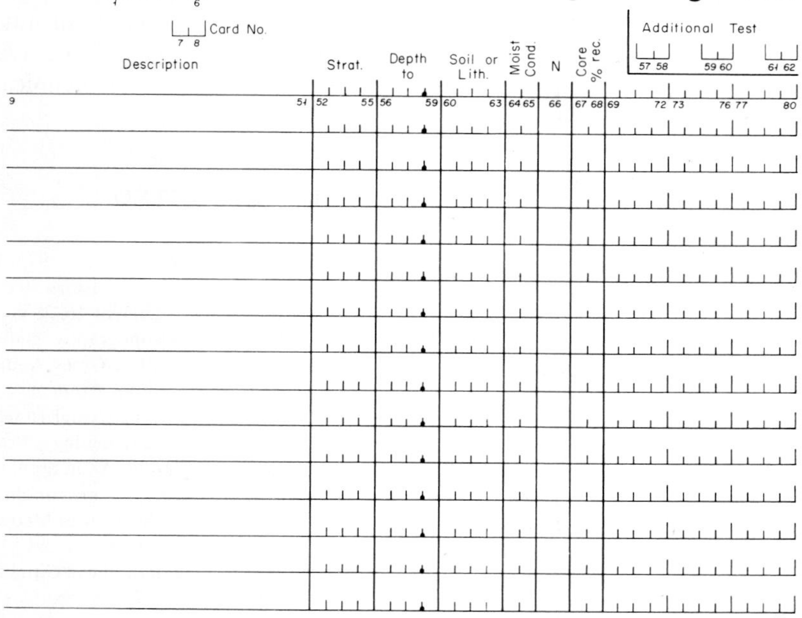

e

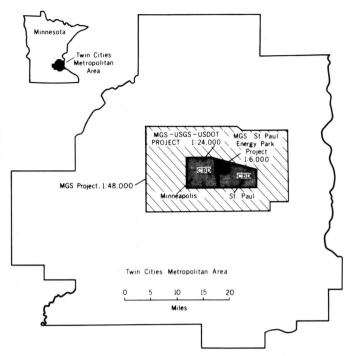

Figure 2. Geotechnical mapping projects based on engineering test borings in the Twin Cities metropolitan area, Minnesota.

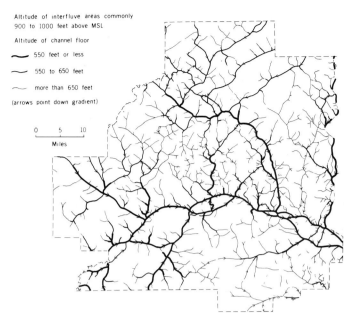

Figure 3. Stream channels incised in bedrock and buried by glacial drift, Twin Cities metropolitan area, Minnesota. By Mark Jirsa.

parison, the mean water level of the Mississippi River at St. Paul is 687 ft. above MSL.

A similar improvement has been made in mapping the unconsolidated materials in the metropolitan area. Repeated ice advances during the Pleistocene Epoch obliterated the bedrock topography and deposited drift commonly 100 to 200 ft. thick, and as much as 500 ft. thick in the deeper valleys. Deposits from the last two glacial advances during the late Wisconsinan dominate the area and are complexly intermingled. The systematic use of test boring logs for surficial geologic mapping has allowed the investigation of the subsurface continuity and superpositional relationships of the units. A striking result is that only a few limited areas have been found where a Quaternary lithostratigraphic unit mapped at the surface continues down to bedrock. Commonly, a succession of tills, outwash, and other deposits is present. Without the subsurface data, it is impossible to draw valid conclusions about unconsolidated materials at depth from a conventional surficial geologic map.

One other conclusion may be drawn. If the Twin Cities metropolitan area is representative of most large urban areas, a very large resource of geological and geotechnical information is buried in the files of a large number of agencies and organizations. Much of this is in the public domain and is accessible to systematic acquisition. Hundreds of thousands of test borings represent tens or hundreds of millions of dollars worth of effort. Almost without excep-

tion, public agencies were found to be highly cooperative and interested in salvaging and using this resource. If the resource is not salvaged, it will be lost because many agencies periodically purge their archives of inactive materials. Computer technology provides the means to manage geotechnical data bases for urban areas. Computer mapping techniques provide a ready means of updating subsurface mapping as new data become available. A national program to develop this geotechnical resource would be of lasting value.

REFERENCES CITED

Holtzman, R. C., and Wahl, T. E., 1979, Minnesota Geological Survey subsurface geology data base: water wells: Minnesota Geological Survey Information Circular 16, 28 p.

Jirsa, M., 1981, Bedrock topography, geology, structure contour and isopach maps for the Twin Cities Aquifer Model Project: Report to Twin Cities Metropolitan Council (to be published by Minnesota Geological Survey), 23 maps and 16 sections with text, 1:48,000.

Legget, R. F., 1973, Cities and geology: New York, McGraw-Hill, 624 p.

Meyer, G., and Bloomgren, B. A., in preparation, Construction materials resources in the Twin Cities metropolitan area: Minnesota Geological Survey report to the Twin Cities Metropolitan Council.

Norvitch, R. F., and Walton, M. S., eds., 1979, Geologic and hydrologic aspects of tunneling in the Twin Cities area, Minnesota: U.S. Geological Survey, Map I-1157, 7 plates.

Olsen, B. M., Bloomgren, B. A., and Holtzman, R. C., 1975, Engineering geology of the Twin Cities area, program development, inventory of public geoengineering data sources: Minnesota Geological Survey

Final Report of Investigation, June 30, 1975, for U.S. Geological Survey grant 14-08-001-G-168, 13 p.

Walton, M. S., ed., in preparation, Engineering geology of the Twin Cities urban area, Minnesota: Minnesota Geological Survey, 5 maps and sections with text, 1:48,000.

Walton, M., Jirsa, M., and Kanivetsky, R., 1981, Engineering geology of the St. Paul Energy Park and vicinity, *in* Honeywell Technology Strategy Center, Technical/economic feasibility study of central energy system alternatives for the St. Paul Energy Park, St. Paul Port Authority.

MANUSCRIPT RECEIVED BY THE SOCIETY MAY 11, 1982
MANUSCRIPT ACCEPTED JUNE 1, 1982